# Mammalian Anc
# The Cat

**Aurora M. Sebastiani**

Youngstown State University (Emerita)


**Dale W. Fishbeck**

Youngstown State University

**Morton Publishing Company**

925 W. Kenyon, Unit 12

Englewood, Colorado  80110

http://www.morton-pub.com

**Book Team**

Publisher: Douglas Morton
Managing Editor Chris Rogers
Production/Design: Ash Street Typecrafters, Inc.
Cover Design: Bob Schram
Illustrations: Michael Schenk
Photography: Dale Fishbeck

Printed in the United States of America

10  9  8  7  6  5  4  3  2

ISBN: 0-89582-364-0

# Contents

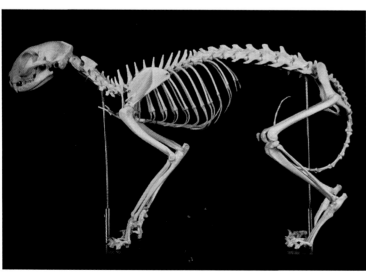

# Preface

This laboratory manual was designed for biology students who take a comprehensive course in mammalian anatomy, e.g., biology majors, pre-medical students, pre-dental students, pre-physical therapy students, pre-nursing students, anatomy and physiology students, etc. Available books for such a course are often heavily slanted toward ample illustration with little text or copious descriptive text with minimal illustration. The design of this manual is a text with adequate detail as well as superior photographic illustration to introduce students to the morphology of a mammal whose anatomy closely parallels that of the human. In many cases, the next step is a course in Human Gross Anatomy.

Color photographs are the main source of illustration in this manual. Many of the photographs are unique to this manual. All major systems are covered in depth and in a logical sequence. The format of the book will permit its use in courses ranging from lower to upper division. Differences between the cat and humans are routinely noted. Detailed dissection instructions are numerous with many hints for attaining superior results. This is quite unusual. Most manuals, if there is adequate illustration, show completed dissections with little instruction or advice on achieving usable dissections. Necessary anatomical terms are in **boldface** type. A glossary of definitions of many boldface terms and an index are available for further reference.

# Acknowledgments

The authors would like to express their sincere appreciation to Chris Rogers, Developmental Editor at Morton Publishing for his assistance and Joanne Saliger for page layout and format. For his illustrations we also thank Michael P. Schenk.

Technical aid provided by the Media Center at Youngstown State University was essential to the production of the photographic illustrations in this manual. Particularly, we want to thank Shirley Ann Rogers for her many hours of hard work, dedication, and often unique and insightful suggestions to solve difficult and perplexing problems involved in the photography of uncooperative preserved cats. We thank Mary Fishbeck for her help in proofreading the text.

To Ashton for putting up with hot lights and human shenanigans designed to induce him to strike a pose, we apologize. To Wendy Anderson, his owner and handler, we express great appreciation.

# Introduction

This book is written for Biology majors, nursing students, and pre-professional students whose curriculum requires a basic course in anatomy. An essential part of a course in mammalian anatomy is practical and should include a detailed dissection of a representative mammal. Perhaps a human would be the most interesting for most students. However, since cadavers are not readily available and most institutions do not have the facilities to handle them properly, we feel that the domestic cat, *Felis catus*, is an extremely good substitute.

Stephen O'Brien, a prominent scientist, involved in the Human Genome Project, recently pointed out that of the approximately 100 genes so far mapped in cats, each has its human counterpart. Furthermore, DNA base pair sequences are so similar that the genes and their arrangement can be determined when comparing the two. Even the gene position on the chromosomes are often very similar (O'Brien, 1997). Perhaps, with good reason, the anatomy of cats and humans is quite similar, with the exceptions largely related to differences in adaptations associated with food procurement and locomotion.

The differences between the cat and human provide interesting examples of adaptations among mammals. A number of systems in the cat exhibit adaptations for its predatory and carnivorous lifestyle — for example, the teeth are modified for feeding primarily on meat. The sharp canines pierce and hold struggling prey, the incisors nip small pieces from the meal, while a pair of lateral molariform teeth, called carnassial teeth, are designed to deal with tendons, ligaments, and shearing large chunks of meat. The cat's predatory habits are further emphasized by the general configuration of its head. The jaws are elongated to form a muzzle, which is an efficient shape for handling struggling prey. Another obvious suite of characteristics that exemplify both a predatory food habit and quadruped locomotion is illustrated in the structure of the fore- and hind-feet as well as the tail. The cat walks on its tiptoes, thereby lengthening the leg and enabling it to run swiftly and function as an agile hunter. Additionally, the toes are equipped with laterally compressed, hooked, and retractile claws to climb and hold on to struggling meals. The long tail is used as a balance organ during its daily maneuvers and also as an organ of communication. If you have any doubts about the function of the tail, watch a cat as it leaps from a high perch or as it meets another cat or lies in wait for a mouse.

Since humans are omnivorous and include a wide range of food in their diet they exhibit less specialization of teeth. In the human, although canines, incisors, and molariform teeth are present, they are shaped differently and are adapted to handle a greater variety of foods, e.g., hamburgers, french fries, and salads at the salad bar. In contrast to cats, human molars are designed to grind, not to slice and cut, and since we are not predatory mammals, our jaw structure is shorter than the cat.

Human locomotion is bipedal which means that we walk upright on our hindlimbs and also on the entire foot from heel to toe. This permits the human foot to function as a stable gripping surface for locomotion. However, this stability does not allow us to develop into swift runners. Remember, most of our food doesn't move too fast or require active capture! For this reason, in contrast to the cat, our finger and toe tips are protected by dorso-ventrally flattened "claws" called nails. Since human locomotion is normally bipedal and no longer requires the counterbalance of a rebounding rear end, the human tail has been greatly reduced in length and consists of a few vertebrae that are usually not externally obvious.

As the various systems are studied, major differences between the cat and the human will be noted.

★　★　★　★　★

In order to comprehend dissection directions and to become a literate anatomist, one needs to be able to understand and speak the language of anatomy. Students are expected to be able to communicate intelligently and precisely, both orally and in the written form. In other words, you are expected to pronounce and spell anatomical and directional terms correctly. Directions for dissection in this book include the proper terminology, therefore, it becomes imperative that the student recognizes these terms and becomes familiar with them. Our experience has indicated that students who read the text as well as consult the diagrams learn and understand mammalian anatomy far better than those who attempt to learn anatomy solely from diagrams. "Picturebook dissection" does not work!

The following discussion will provide you with necessary information to begin your study.

## Terms: Anatomical and Directional

Some general directional terms include: **Dorsal** (the back or toward the back of the cat); **Ventral** (the belly or toward the belly of the cat); **Cranial** (toward the head); **Caudal** (toward the tail) [Figure I–1]. Just as often, in quadrupeds, **Anterior** (meaning ahead or before) and **Posterior** (meaning after or behind) will be encountered in descriptive anatomy. Very commonly, students will be directed toward the **Medial** (toward the midline) or **Lateral** (toward the side) aspect of the cat. The **Midline** is an imaginary line that extends directly down the middle of the dorsal and ventral surfaces. Frequently, you may encounter the directional terms, **Proximal** (next to or nearest to the point of origin or attachment) and **Distal** (some distance from the point of origin or attachment) [Figure I–1].

Often, planes of reference are important in understanding relationships of the morphology of organs, relationships among organs of a system within a body cavity, or relationships of organs and systems in a given view. In Figure I–1, a section parallel to the midline of the cat is referred to as **Sagittal**. Therefore, there are an infinite number of sagittal sections, as long as you do not run out of cat. On the other hand, there is

only one **Mid-sagittal** section which passes exactly down the midline of the body. A **Transverse** or cross section is illustrated in Figure I–1. Just as there are an infinite number of sagittal sections, there are also an infinite number of transverse sections that may extend from the tip of the nose to the tip of the tail. Transverse sections are analogous to the slices of a loaf of bread, although usually much thinner. A **Frontal** section is made along the entire length of the cat parallel to the belly and back and illustrated in Figure I–1. Again, there can be numerous frontal sections.

## Suggested Equipment Check List

### Dissection Tools

- 1 pair of fine point dissection scissors
- 1 scalpel handle, preferably No. 4, with replaceable blades
- Replaceable blades, preferably those designated as 21–25
- 1 steel probe, preferably a Huber-Mall
- 2 pair of straight forceps, one with medium points and the second with fine points
- Dissecting pins

Often, these tools are available in a kit, however, you will probably be advised by your instructor as to their purchase.

### Other Equipment

Safety goggles — these are strongly recommended to prevent eye injury from preservative fluids, bone chips and possible injury from dissection equipment

- Gloves — optional
- Lab jackets or coats — optional
- Sewing needles — these should be large needles
- Coat and button or carpet thread — this is heavy thread and should be white to prevent color from bleeding into the muscle
- Small spray bottle — any empty, clean spray bottle will work to hold preservative fluid to keep your specimen pliable and relatively fresh

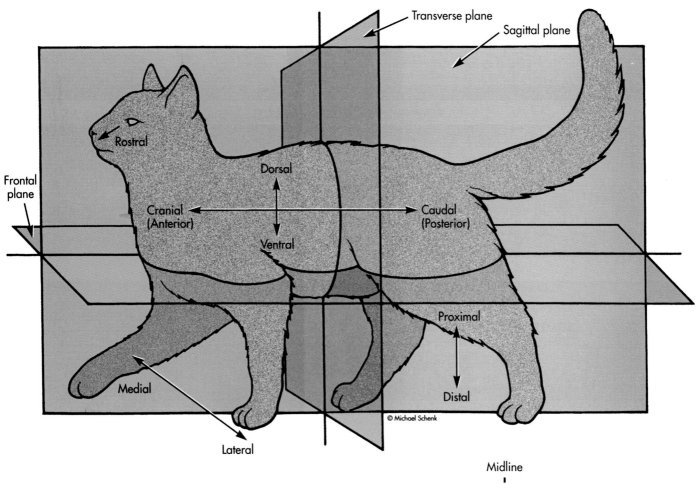

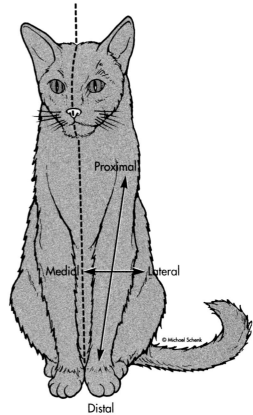

*Figure 1-1* Planes of the body.

# Skeletal System

This is a system consisting of individual organs often referred to as "bones." When these organs are viewed individually, it is often difficult to appreciate the interrelationships of their structure and function. Let us consider some of those functions. Articulation of the individual bones or organs of this system plays a central role in providing the supporting mechanism and shape of the animal. Without a skeletal system, a mammal would be shapeless. Perhaps we would resemble an earthworm with hair and mammary glands.

Body locomotion is another significant function of the skeleton. Bones, however, cannot move by themselves but serve as levers for lever systems producing what we commonly perceive as movement. The movement is produced by muscles that are attached to the bony levers whose fulcrums are the joints of the body [Figure 1–1].

Although there are various classifications of joints, a junction between two bones, the system used here is that based upon the functional nature of the joint. In this system, a **synarthrosis** is a joint in which there is little or no movement, e.g., sutures between the bones of the skull. An **amphiarthrosis**, on the other hand, permits slight movement, e.g., between individual vertebrae in the vertebral column. Free movement between bones occurs around joints called **diarthroses**, e.g., between the head of the humerus or upper arm bone and the glenoid cavity of the scapula or shoulder blade.

Certain bony complexes provide protection for some of the more vulnerable soft and vital organs: the cranium protects the brain, the vertebral column protects the spinal cord, and the rib cage and sternum shield the heart, lungs, and major blood vessels. In addition, bones serve several other functions such as sites for blood cell formation or hemopoiesis, fat deposition, and mineral deposits of essential ions such as calcium and phosphate.

Contrary to what you may conclude after studying this system, bones are living organs. The skeletal systems of all vertebrates are constantly subjected to remodeling activities, during which, part of a bone may be entirely remodeled in a very short period of time, e.g., in humans the distal epiphysis of the femur is replaced approximately every six months. Since bony tissue is a reservoir for minerals such as calcium and phosphates, it is normal for mineral recycling to occur between bones and the blood. Calcium is essential for such physiological activities as muscle contraction, coagulation of blood, and the dynamics of membrane permeability, while phosphates are necessary

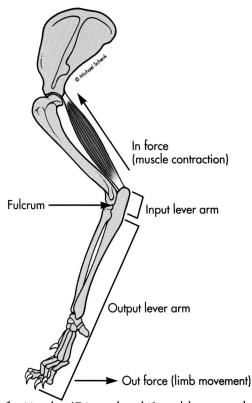

**Figure 1–1** Muscles (*Triceps brachii*) and bones as lever systems.

for synthesis of nucleic acids, production of ATP, and metabolic events involving activation or deactivation of enzymes. Injuries to this living bony tissue require active repair processes.

During the study of the skeletal system, you will become familiar with distinctive processes and their positions, markings, foramina, and other features specific for each bone. These will allow you to distinguish left and right members of paired bones. It is important to identify the position of the bone in the articulated skeleton in order to appreciate the relationship of regional skeletal elements.

The skeleton consists of two parts known as the **axial** and **appendicular** divisions. The functions of these subdivisions are really very different from each other. The components of the axial division surround and protect soft body tissues and include the bones of the skull, the mandible, the hyoid, the vertebral column, the ribs, and the sternum. In contrast, the appendicular division is surrounded by soft tissues and can be further subdivided into the pectoral girdle with its forelimb and the pelvic girdle with its hindlimb [Figure 1–2].

## Axial Division

### The Skull

The skull consists of the cranium whose bones surround the brain and permit the cranial nerves to enter or exit through a number of openings known as

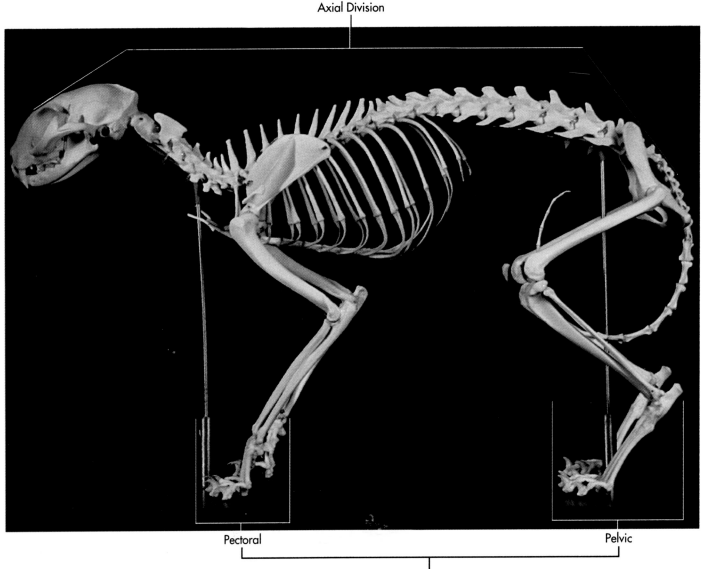

Axial Division

Pectoral

Pelvic

*Figure 1-2*    Cat skeleton.

Appendicular Division

foramina, fissures, and canals.* Closely associated with the cranium are a number of facial bones that give the face its shape. This essential complex (cranial and facial bones) contains a number of cavities that surround and protect the major sense organs such as the eyes, portions of the auditory apparatus, olfactory organs, and with the articulated mandible, the gustatory organs, all of which have evolved as specialized organs closely associated with the central nervous system [Figure 1–3a, Figure 1–3b, and Figure 1–3c].

As you examine the individual bones of the skull, refer to the above figures for positions of the bones relative to one another.

---

* In the discussion of the skull, there will be numerous references to branches of cranial nerves (C.N.) as follows: C.N. I — Olfactory, C.N. II — Optic, C.N. III — Oculomotor, C.N. IV — Trochlear, C.N. V — Trigeminal, C.N. VI — Abducens, C.N. VII — Facial, C.N. VIII — Vestibulocochlear, C.N. IX — Glossopharyngeal, C.N. X — Vagus, C.N. XI — Spinal Accessory and C.N. XII — Hypoglossal. In the text, reference will be made in the following manner, e.g., C.N. V, C.N. XII, etc.

## The Premaxilla

The paired **premaxillae** [Figure 1–4a and Figure 1–4b] occur at the most anterior margin of the upper jaw, forming approximately one-sixth of the hard palate through the contribution of paired **palatine processes** at its cranial end. Three **incisors** are rooted in each premaxilla, while only two are found in humans, one central and one lateral. In humans, the premaxilla is fused with the maxilla and is not identifiable as a separate bone, however, the incisors are located in the central portion of the human maxilla where the premaxilla can be identified in many other mammals. A pair of openings, the **anterior palatine foramina** (incisive ducts), can be seen just posterior to the incisors in the ventral view, while in the human a single incisive foramen occurs in a comparable position in the maxilla. The premaxillae are bordered by the nasal bones dorsally, and laterally and caudally by the maxillae. With the nasals the premaxillae form the anterior edge of the nasal cavity.

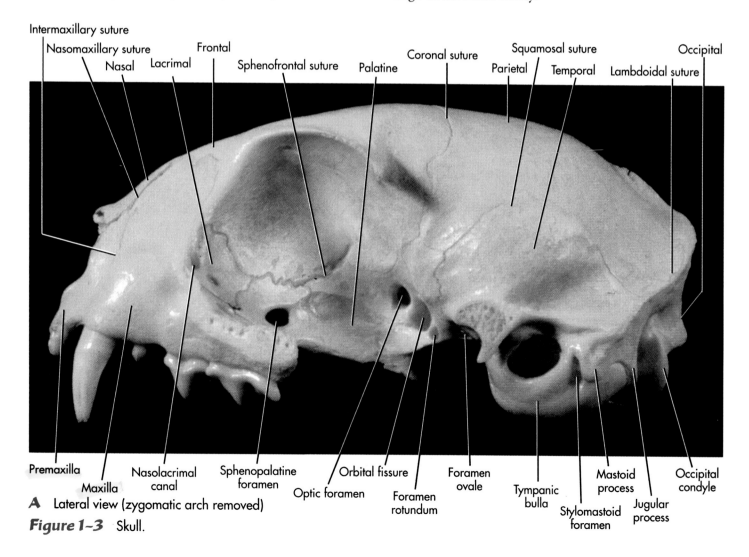

**A**   Lateral view (zygomatic arch removed)

***Figure 1–3***   Skull.

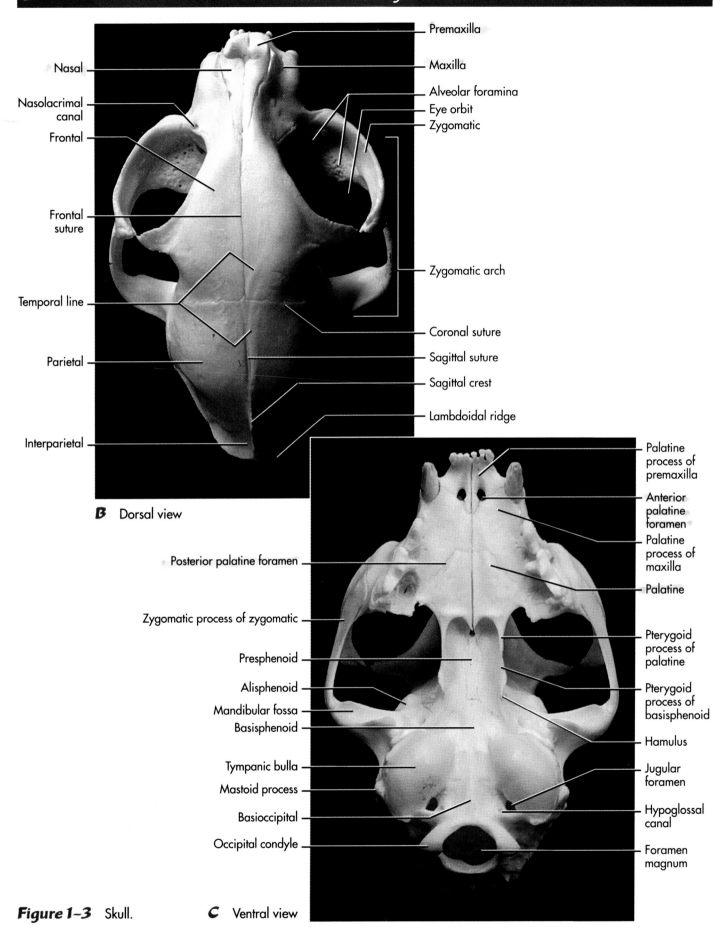

Nasal

Nasolacrimal canal

Frontal

Frontal suture

Temporal line

Parietal

Interparietal

Premaxilla

Maxilla

Alveolar foramina

Eye orbit

Zygomatic

Zygomatic arch

Coronal suture

Sagittal suture

Sagittal crest

Lambdoidal ridge

**B** Dorsal view

Posterior palatine foramen

Zygomatic process of zygomatic

Presphenoid

Alisphenoid

Mandibular fossa

Basisphenoid

Tympanic bulla

Mastoid process

Basioccipital

Occipital condyle

Palatine process of premaxilla

Anterior palatine foramen

Palatine process of maxilla

Palatine

Pterygoid process of palatine

Pterygoid process of basisphenoid

Hamulus

Jugular foramen

Hypoglossal canal

Foramen magnum

***Figure 1-3*** Skull.     **C** Ventral view

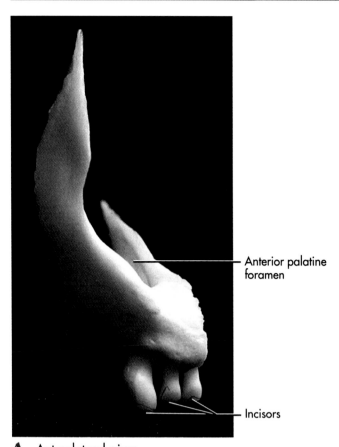

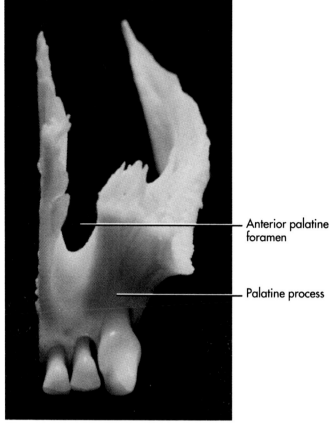

**A** Anterolateral view

**B** Ventral view

***Figure 1-4*** Right premaxilla.

## The Maxilla

Lateral to the premaxillae are the paired **maxillae** [Figure 1–5a and Figure 1–5b] that complete the upper jaw and contribute to the hard palate ventrally as shelves of bone known as the **palatine processes of the maxillae**. These processes extend back to the posterior border of the hard palate laterally but are joined medially by paired palatine bones to complete the complex that we call the hard palate. In contrast, the contribution by the palatine bones in the human is greatly reduced. Each maxilla articulates with the zygomatic or malar, the premaxilla, nasal, lacrimal, frontal, and palatine bones and extends into the eye orbit as the anterior floor.

At the anterior border of the maxilla is a perceptible bulge in the **alveolar process** that accomodates the extremely long root of the **canine** tooth. Posterior to the canine is the smallest of three **premolar** teeth. Postero-medial to the third premolar is a vestigial **molar**. The roots of all of these teeth are embedded within the alveolar process of the maxilla.

Dorsal to the canine and first premolar tooth is the elongated, flat, thin **frontal process** that is wing-shaped. The **infraorbital foramen** pierces the maxilla at the junction of the **body** and frontal process. Through this foramen pass the infraorbital blood vessels and infraorbital nerve (C.N. V). Take note of the many small openings, the **alveolar foramina**, in the floor of the orbit through which small branches of the infraorbital nerve (C.N. V) pass to the teeth in the upper jaw [Figure 1–3b]. At the posterior end of the body is the **zygomatic process**. On the medial aspect of the canine alveolar elevation exists a small lateral contribution to the nasal conchae, the **maxilloturbinate**. In humans, it appears that the maxilloturbinate is a separate bone and is identified as the inferior nasal concha. No maxillary sinuses occur in the cat, however, each human maxilla contains one.

## The Nasal

Medial to the premaxilla and maxilla and cranial to the frontals are the paired **nasal** [Figure 1–6] bones

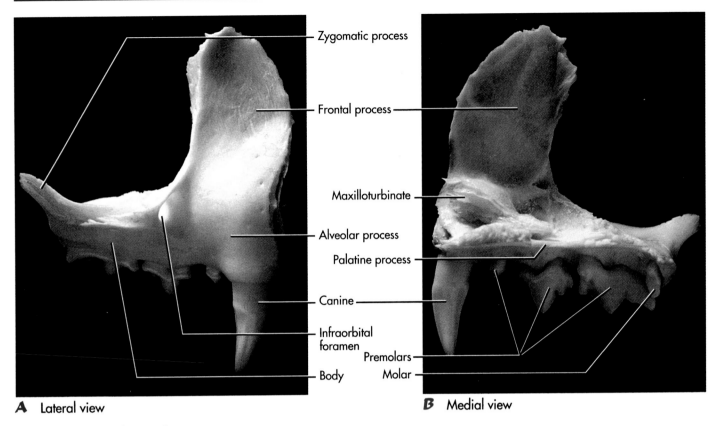

Zygomatic process

Frontal process

Maxilloturbinate

Alveolar process

Palatine process

Canine

Infraorbital foramen

Premolars

Body    Molar

**A**   Lateral view                    **B**   Medial view

***Figure 1–5***   Right maxilla.

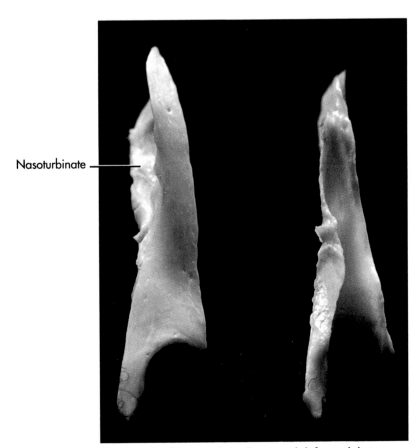

Nasoturbinate

***Figure 1–6***   Nasal: right cranial, left caudal views.

that form the dorsal wall of the nasal cavity. Another small dorsal contribution to the nasal conchae, the **nasoturbinate**, is present on the ventromedial aspect of the nasals. Humans do not have a homologous contribution to the turbinates from the nasals.

## The Ethmoid

The **ethmoid**, an unpaired cranial bone [Figure 1–7], is entirely associated with the nasal cavity. The major bulk of the ethmoid, the **ethmoturbinates**, composed of elaborately scrolled, thin laminate plates of bone, comprise most of the nasal conchae and fill most of the nasal cavity. In humans, the superior and middle nasal conchae are homologous with the ethmoturbinates in the cat. The thin **perpendicular plate of the ethmoid** separates the two lateral ethmoturbinates and with the vomer forms the bony portion of the nasal septum. Caudal to the perpendicular plate is the thin, concave, perforated **cribriform plate**. Through these foramina pass fibers of the Olfactory Nerve (C.N. I) that synapse

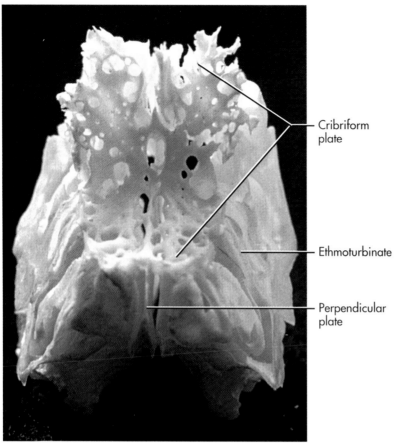

Cribriform plate

Ethmoturbinate

Perpendicular plate

**Figure 1–7** Ethmoid: caudal view.

## The Vomer

Ventral to the ethmoid and dorsal to the hard palate is the single **vomer** [Figure 1–8] that completes the bony nasal septum. The dorsal, V-shaped, groove of the vomer cradles the perpendicular plate of the ethmoid while the lateral wings articulate with the ethmoturbinates. Its cranial end articulates with the palatal processes of the premaxilla, the ventral region with the palatine processes of the maxilla while the caudal end articulates with the presphenoid.

## The Palatine

Posterior to the palatine processes of the maxillae are the paired **palatine** bones [Figure 1–9a and Figure 1–9b]. The palatine bone consists of a horizontal plate and a curved irregularly shaped vertical plate. The paired **horizontal plates of the palatines** meet in the mid-ventral line and form the caudal end of the hard palate. Two small foramina, the cranial openings of the **posterior palatine canals** through which the greater palatine nerve of the maxillary division of the Trigeminal Nerve (C.N. V) pass, are found within the lateral portion of the horizontal plates. The entire antero-lateral surface of these plates articulates with the palatine processes of the maxilla and terminates posteriorly with the **maxillary spine**. The narrow postero-lateral extensions of the vertical plates form the **pterygoid processes of the palatine** that articulate with the pterygoid processes of the basisphenoid. These palatine processes continue

with neurons that lie in the olfactory bulbs situated directly above the cribriform plate. In humans, a triangular, dorsal projection from the cribriform plate, the crista galli, serves as an anterior point of attachment of the meninges (protective brain membranes). Additionally, in contrast to the cat, there are extensive sinuses in the ethmoid of humans.

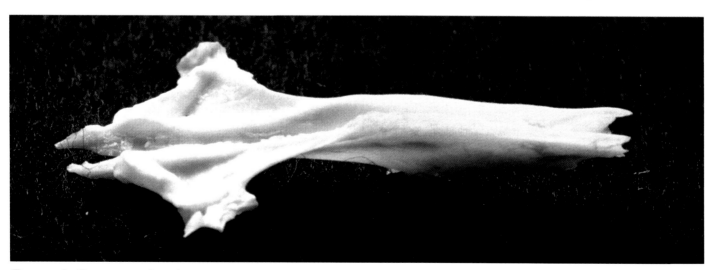

**Figure 1–8** Vomer: dorsal view.

Pterygoid process          Horizontal plate
   Maxillary spine          Posterior palatine canal

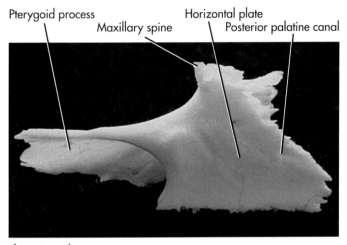

**A**   Ventral view

Posterior palatine canal          Sphenopalatine foramen

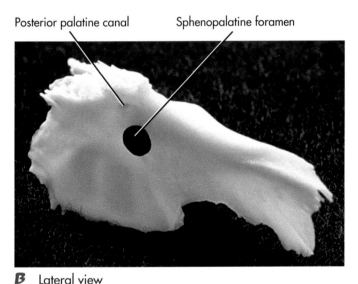

**B**   Lateral view

***Figure 1-9***   Right palatine.

dorso-medially as thin, curved, laminar plates that articulate with the presphenoid. The pterygoid processes in the human have been abbreviated into the vertical palatine plates that are intimately associated with the greater wing of the sphenoid. The larger anterior third of these vertical plates is pierced by the **sphenopalatine foramen** carrying the sphenopalatine nerve (C.N. V) and corresponding blood vessels. A smaller opening, the **posterior palatine canal**, occurs slightly cranial and lateral to the sphenopalatine foramen. Through it passes the greater palatine nerve (C.N. V) and corresponding artery. These plates articulate dorsally with the frontal bone and cranially with the lacrimal bone.

## The Lacrimal

The small wafer-like bone that is roughly shaped like a rhombus and located in the antero-medial portion of the eye orbit, is the **lacrimal** [Figure 1–10]. The **nasolacrimal canal** is a prominent landmark of the anterior portion of the eye orbit. The canal includes an anterior notch in the lacrimal and is completed by a groove in the frontal process of the maxilla with which it articulates. In addition, the lacrimal articulates with the frontal and palatine.

## The Frontal

The cranial portion of the skull roof consists of the paired **frontals** [Figure 1–11a and Figure 1–11b]. Dorsally, the articulated frontals form a smooth surface

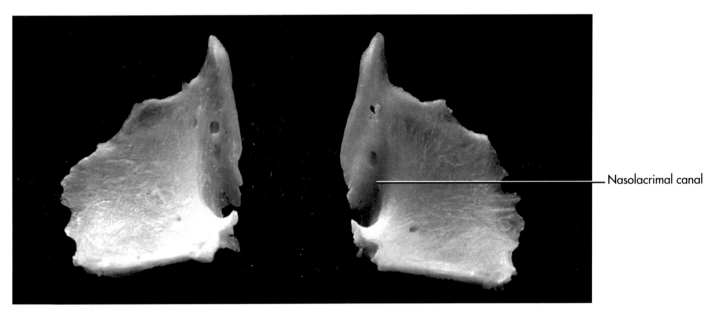

Nasolacrimal canal

***Figure 1-10***   Right and left lacrimal: lateral view.

that resembles a short Chinese pagoda. The anterior **frontal spines** form the roof-peak of the pagoda that articulate with the nasals and maxillae while the **postorbital processes** complete the lower edge of the roof.

The caudal surface that articulates with the parietals, forms the lower part of the building. The lateral surface, prominently concave, shapes the dorsomedial and posterior aspect of the orbit. Articulation of the frontal with the lacrimal, ethmoid, maxilla, presphenoid, and palatine bones completes the medial and ventral part of the eye orbit.

The medial view reveals a number of distinctive features. The obvious vertical plate abuts its partner

at the site of the external sagittal suture and together they join the perpendicular plate of the ethmoid located ventrally. By peering into the anterior ends of the articulated frontal bones one can observe a recessed oval foramen leading into the extensive **frontal sinus**. The furrowed ethmoid surface on the craniomedial wall of the eye orbit mirrors the surface of the nasal conchae, since it is in this area that the ethmoid and the frontal closely approach one another. Along the posterior border of this area is a curved ridge, extending from the ventral edge of the frontal sinus opening to the ventral border of the frontal bone, that matches the curvature of the cribriform plate with which it articulates. A number of minute, inconspicuous foramina in the medial orbital surface of the frontal are often difficult to see. These openings allow the passage of small blood vessels and nerves. In the human, a supraorbital notch or foramen transmitting corresponding nerves and veins occurs along the supraorbital margin. Note the **olfactory fossa** which houses the olfactory lobes and the anterior portion of the **cerebral fossa** containing the anterior part of the cerebrum.

### The Zygomatic

The gently curved surface of the **zygomatic** or malar bone [Figure 1–12] forms the lateral boundary of the eye orbit. Two projections occur posteriorly. A dorsal **orbital process** curves up toward the postorbital process of the frontal to surround the orbit with an incomplete bony ring. In the human, the bony ring is complete. The temporal fenestra (opening) inherited by mammals (e.g., the cat) from their "reptilian" ancestors has been enclosed largely by the greater wing of the sphenoid. A ventral **zygomatic process** articulates with the zygomatic process of the temporal, forming the cheek prominence or zygomatic arch. A distinct ridge along the lateral surface marks the position of the origin of the masseter muscle. The curved anterior end is irregularly serrated and fits into a trough in the maxilla.

### The Parietal

Caudal to the frontal and forming the posterior portion of the cranial vault are the paired **parietals** [Figure 1–13a, Figure 1–13b, and Figure 1–14]. Each bone is roughly rectangular in shape with a

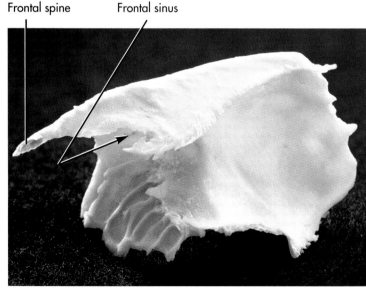

Postorbital process             Frontal spine

**A**   Lateral view

Frontal spine      Frontal sinus

**B**   Medial view

***Figure 1–11***    Right frontal.

Zygomatic process      Orbital process

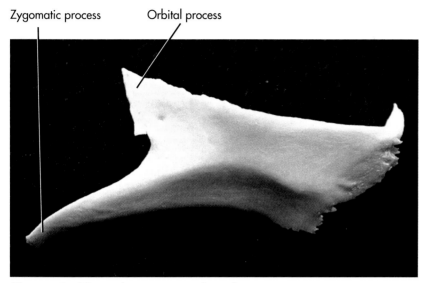

*Figure 1-12*   Right zygomatic: lateral view.

The concave anterior two-thirds of the medial surface reflects the gyri (elevations) and sulci (furrows) of the parietal lobe of the cerebral hemisphere of the brain and constitutes the posterior portion of the **cerebral fossa**. The **tentorium** projects anteriorly as a curved shelf with a prominent medial notch that together with its partner forms a large opening that is shaped like the upper part of a valentine. Through this large foramen passes the brainstem of the central nervous system. Caudal to the tentorium is the anterior portion of the **cerebellar fossa**. The irregular surface of this fossa also reflects the gyri and sulci of the cerebellum.

smooth, curved outer surface. The articulation between the paired parietals completes the sagittal suture (also described in the discussion of the frontal bone). The parietals at their caudal ends diverge to accomodate the articulation with the dorso-medially located interparietal (in a disarticulated skull the interparietal may be a separate bone or may remain attached to one of the parietals). The occipital articulates with the parietal-interprietal complex. The lateral edge articulates with the squamosal portion of the temporal.

## The Interparietal

A single, triangular bone located between the parietals and the occipital is the **interparietal** [Figure 1-15]. The dorsal surface is distinguished by a medial projection called the sagittal crest that in some cats extends anteriorly onto the surface of the parietals. Posteriorly, this crest is continuous with the lambdoidal crest of the occipital. The interparietal is quite conspicuous in young cats, however, in older cats is generally fused with the parietals. In the human, the interparietal may have been lost or at least cannot be distinguished.

Cerebral fossa (posterior)     Tentorium     Cerebellar fossa (anterior)

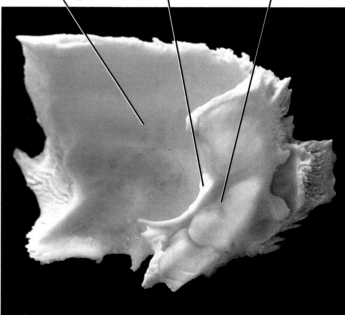

**A**   Lateral view                **B**   Medial view

*Figure 1-13*   Right parietal.

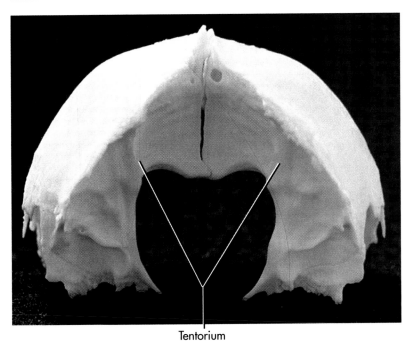

**Figure 1–14**   Paired parietals: caudal view.

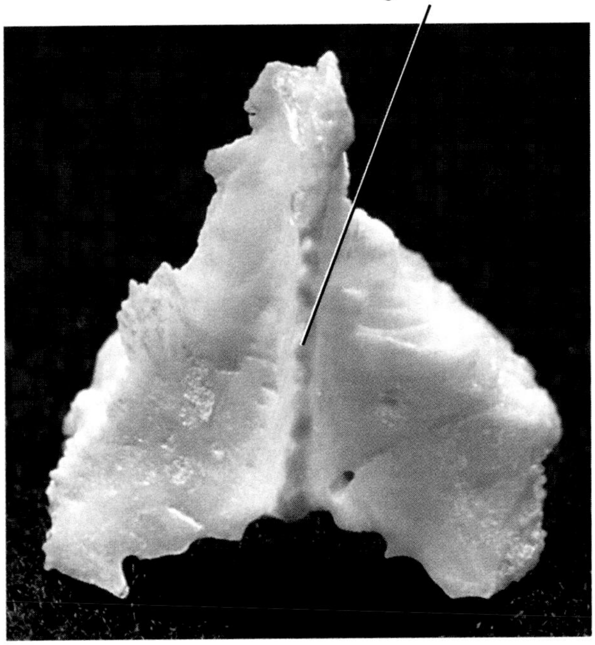

Sagittal crest

**Figure 1–15**   Interparietal: caudal view.

Tentorium

## The Occipital

The **occipital** bone [Figure 1–16a and Figure 1–16b] completes the posterior portion and base of the skull. From the posterior aspect, this skull bone resembles an equilateral triangle that has curved sides, breaking the rules of geometry. A large opening, the **foramen magnum**, is situated in the ventral part of the occipital. The foramen magnum marks the site of transition of the brain into the spinal cord as that portion of the central nervous system enters the vertebral canal.

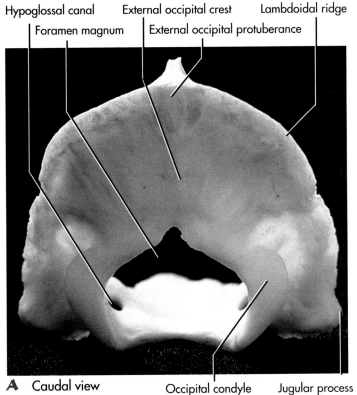

Hypoglossal canal    External occipital crest    Lambdoidal ridge

Foramen magnum    External occipital protuberance

Basioccipital    Hypoglossal canal    Occipital condyle    Jugular process

**A**   Caudal view    Occipital condyle    Jugular process    **B**   Ventral view

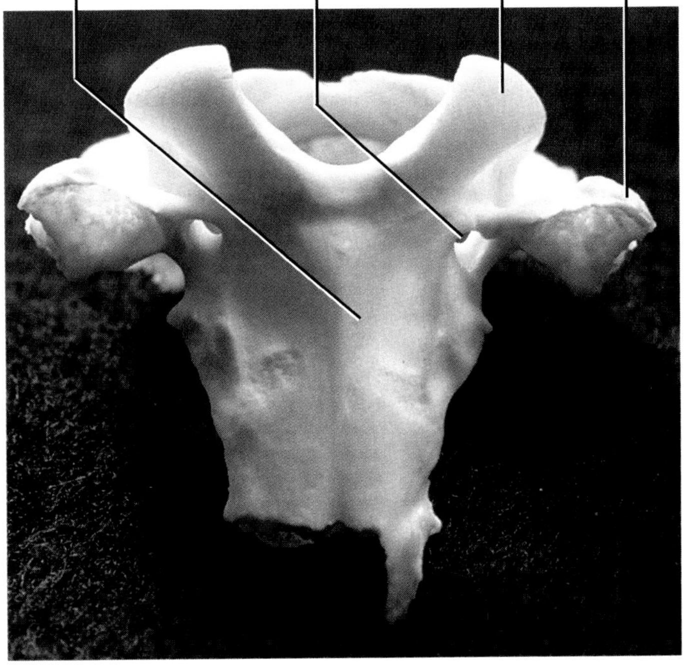

**Figure 1–16**   Occipital.

The basal part, the **basioccipital**, is flat and elongated, and articulates with the basisphenoid portion of the sphenoid anteriorly and the petrous part of the temporal bone laterally. The lateral portions, the **exoccipitals**, articulate with the petrous and mastoid portions of temporal. Notice the prominent **occipital condyles** with which the atlas or first cervical vertebra articulates. Lateral to each condyle and separated by a deep depression is a short, blunt projection, the **jugular process**, at the vertices of the triangle base. This projection overlaps the tympanic bulla of the temporal, with which it articulates. At the site of this articulation is an opening, the **jugular foramen**, through which pass the Glossopharyngeal (C.N. IX), the Vagus (C.N. X) and the Spinal Accessory (C.N. XI) cranial nerves along with the internal jugular vein. Medial to the jugular foramen and located in a notch associated with the wall of the foramen is the **hypoglossal canal** through which the Hypoglossal Nerve (C.N. XII) passes. As one looks through the foramen magnum, the extremely variable **condyloid canal**, through which passes a small vein or veins, can be identified dorsal to the hypoglossal canal.

The **supraoccipital** or squamous portion forms an arch over the foramen magnum and articulates with the parietals and interparietals. The sharp edge of the arch that extends from one jugular process to the other is known as the **lambdoidal ridge** (nuchal crest). An inconspicuous median crest, the **external occipital crest**, extends from the lambdoidal ridge to the upper rim of the foramen magnum. The **external occipital protuberance** is located at the junction of this crest with the lambdoidal ridge.

## The Sphenoid

Anterior to the occipital sits the unpaired **sphenoid** [Figure 1–17a, Figure 1–17b, and Figure 1–17c] whose shape has often been described as resembling a butterfly. The body of the "butterfly" is known as the **basisphenoid** whereas the wings are referred

- Pterygoid process
- Hamulus
- Alisphenoid
- Foramen ovale
- Basisphenoid

**A**   Ventral view

- Hamulus
- Pterygoid process
- Orbital fissure
- Foramen rotundum
- Foramen ovale
- Alisphenoid

**B**   Lateral view

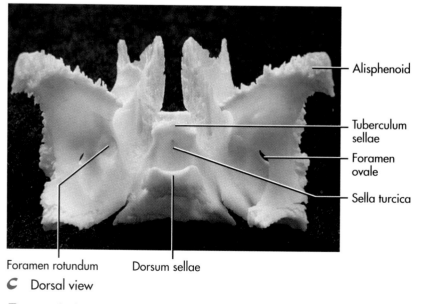

- Alisphenoid
- Tuberculum sellae
- Foramen ovale
- Sella turcica

Foramen rotundum        Dorsum sellae

**C**   Dorsal view

**Figure 1–17**   Sphenoid.

to as the **alisphenoids**. Two anteriorly oriented projections termed the **pterygoid processes** have fused with the alisphenoids. In mammalian ancestors these processes were separate pterygoid bones. The **hamulus,** a thin rod, extends posteriorly from the body of the pterygoid process. As previously mentioned, these processes articulate with the pterygoid processes of the palatine. Dorsal to the pterygoid process are three foramina. The cranial margin of the first of these openings, the **orbital fissure,** is incomplete. The articulation of the presphenoid with the sphenoid at this site completes the cranial margin of the fissure [Figure 1-18]. Through this opening passes the Oculomotor Nerve (C.N. III), the Trochlear Nerve (C.N. IV), the Ophthalmic division of the Trigeminal Nerve (C.N. V) and the Abducens Nerve (C.N. VI). The single orbital fissure of the cat is represented in the human by a superior orbital fissure that is continuous with an inferior orbital fissure located in a comparable position.

Like the orbital fissure in the cat, similar nerves and blood vessels are transmitted through these openings. The middle opening of this trio of foramina in the cat is the **foramen rotundum,** through which passes the Maxillary branch of the Trigeminal Nerve (C.N. V). The third opening is the **foramen ovale,** through which exits the Mandibular division of the Trigeminal Nerve (C.N. V). In the human there is an additional small foramen, the foramen spinosum, that is located posterolateral to the foramen ovale. Through this foramen passes a branch of the mandibular nerve and some blood vessels. Laterally, the dorsally curved portion of the "butterfly" wing, the alisphenoid, articulates with the squamous portion of the temporal, while the caudal portion of the wing articulates with the tympanic bulla. The inner surface of the alisphenoid is smoothly concave.

Ventrally, the body of the basisphenoid is rather smooth and has a slight medial ridge, a continuation

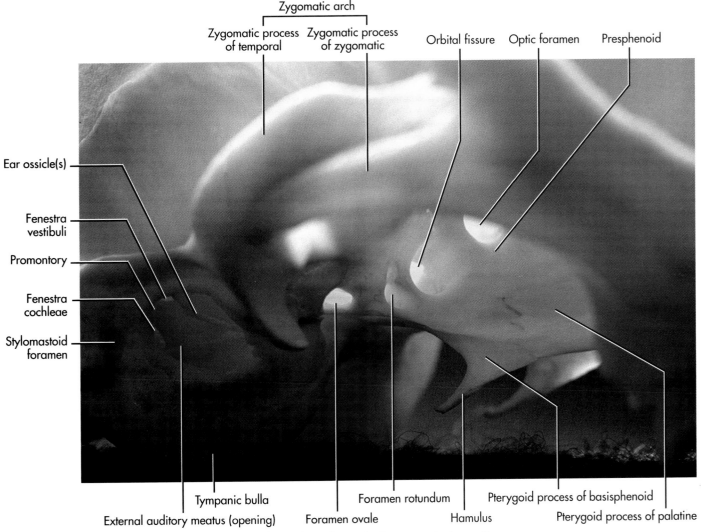

*Figure 1-18*   Sphenoid, presphenoid, tymbanic bulla region (enlarged).

of the ridge present on the ventral surface of the basi-occipital with which it articulates, posteriorly. The anterior end of the basisphenoid articulates with the body of the presphenoid. The dorsal or inner surface of the basisphenoid is distinctly saddle-shaped. The anterior elevation of the saddle is the **tuberculum sellae** whereas the more prominent and rounded posterior elevation is the **dorsum sellae**. Between the two elevations is a conspicuous depression known as the **sella turcica** in which the hypophysis (pituitary gland) rests. A nutrient foramen occurs posterior to the tuberculum sellae and a pair of similar foramina are present posterior to the dorsum sellae.

## The Presphenoid

The singular **presphenoid** [Figure 1–19a and Figure 1–19b] consists of a body and two wings. The ventral surface of the body resembles an hourglass with a deep anterior notch and a rounded posterior base. A median ridge, fairly prominent posteriorly, is continuous with the ridge of the basisphenoid. Two articulating facets lateral to the ridge accomodate the pterygoid processes of the sphenoid. As one peers into the notched anterior end of this bone two conspicuous **sphenoidal sinuses**, separated by a median longitudinal bony partition, are evident. These sinuses end blindly at the posterior end of the body of the presphenoid. The wings project postero-laterally and resemble small triangles. Lateral to the body and piercing the base of the triangle is the **optic foramen** through which the Optic Nerve (C.N. II) and opthalmic artery pass. On the dorsal or inner aspect, the presphenoid is smooth and distinguished posteriorly by the transverse **chiasmatic groove** that extends between the optic foramina. The chiasmatic groove is the site of the optic chiasma. The human sphenoid consists of a complex resulting from the fusion of the presphenoid and sphenoid and although the individual bones are not distinct, structures, processes, and foramina identifiable in the cat are found in comparable positions.

## The Temporal

When turned upside down, the **temporal bone** [Figure 1–20a and Figure 1–20b] resembles a young nestling bird stretching its wing. This is a complex bone that consists of the **squamous**, the **petrous**, and the **tympanic** portions. The squamous part represents the breast of the "nestling," and is thin and smooth laterally while

the medial surface reflects the contours of the cerebellum that rest against it. The **zygomatic process**, a distinctly curved, anteriorly oriented projection representing the "wing" of the bird, extends from its

Sphenoidal sinus    Optic foramen

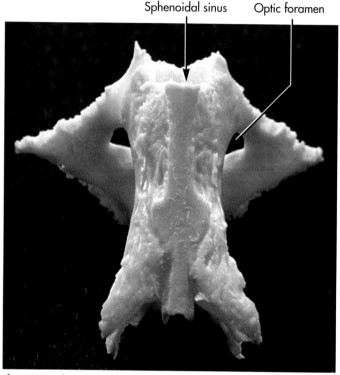

**A**  Ventral view

Chiasmatic groove    Optic foramen

**B**  Dorsal view

***Figure 1–19***   Presphenoid.

ventrolateral surface. The anterior half of this process is beveled along the ventral border to accomodate the zygomatic process of the zygomatic (malar) bone. A groove, the **mandibular fossa**, in the posterior part of the process provides the articulating surface for the condyloid process of the mandible. The small **postmandibular process**, projecting from the proximal basal portion of the zygomatic process, functions as a posterior brace for the condyloid process of the mandible.

The tympanic portion (head of the bird) is roughly ovoid and hollow. This portion is the **tympanic** or **auditory bulla** [Figure 1–18]. An irregular oval opening on the lateral surface, the **external auditory meatus** (eye of the bird), leads into the tympanic cavity. Often the **malleus** and **incus**, two of the three middle ear ossicles can be identified within the **tympanic cavity**. The third ossicle or **stapes** is not visible since it is not only small, but is oriented more medially and fits into the oval window of the inner ear. However, if the ossicles are not present, it is possible to see several openings, the **fenestra cochleae** (round window), the **fenestra vestibuli** (oval window) and the foramen leading to the facial canal. The opening of the round window is located below and passes under an elevated rim, the **promontory**, in a fashion similar to a tunnel entering a mountain. The oval window is located dorsal to the promontory and is oriented at approximately a right angle to the tunnel mentioned above. Caudal to the fenestra ovalis and dorsal to the tunnel rim is a small groove leading into the facial canal permitting passage of the Facial Nerve (C. N. VII) through the petrous portion of the temporal. Notice the distinct thin ridge in the floor of the auditory canal extending along a more-or-less anterior to posterior line. This is the dorsal edge of the typmanic bulla where it articulates with the petrous portion of the temporal.

The mastoid portion of the petrous region (beak of the bird) is elongated posteriorly and articulates with the lateral portion of the occipital. A prominent, angular, nipple-shaped projection, the **mastoid process**, overlaps the bulla posterior to the external auditory meatus. The **stylomastoid foramen**, occurring anterior to the

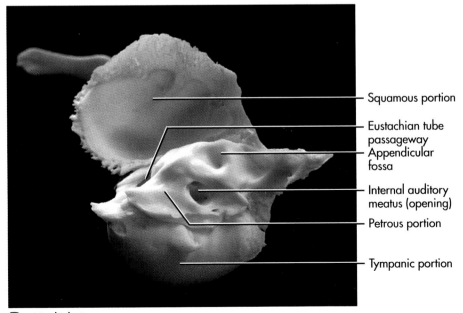

Squamous portion

Zygomatic process

Mandibular fossa

Postmandibular process

External auditory meatus (opening)

Fenestra vestibuli

Tympanic portion

Stylomastoid foramen

Mastoid process

**A**   Lateral view

Squamous portion

Eustachian tube passageway

Appendicular fossa

Internal auditory meatus (opening)

Petrous portion

Tympanic portion

**B**   Medial view

*Figure 1–20*    Right temporal.

mastoid process permits passage of the Facial Nerve (C.N. VII). A distinct opening, the **internal auditory meatus,** occurs in the medial surface. A bony partition divides the meatus into a dorsal canal through which passes the Facial Nerve (C.N. VII) and several ventral foramina for the passage of the Vestibulocochlear Nerve (C.N. VIII). Within the petrous bone the membranous acoustic and equilibrium apparatus resides in the bony labyrinth that is slightly larger but of a similar shape. Dorsal to the meatus is a small, deep fossa, the **appendicular fossa,** that reflects the postion of the small appendicular lobe of the cerebellum. A conspicuous elongated slit between the petrous portion and the tympanic bulla admits the eustachian tube into the middle ear cavity.

The temporal bone in the human, with some minor modifications, is quite similar to the cat. Perhaps one of the most obvious differences is the absence of a tympanic bulla, however, the tympanic or middle ear cavity of the bulla that houses the ear ossicles is certainly present and the outer covering of the region is represented by the much elaborated mastoid process that in the cat could be overlooked by the careless student. A pointed, downward directed styloid process, not present in cats, is evident just anterior to the stylomastoid foramen.

## Surface Features

Although the overall skull topography is fairly smooth, there are some conspicuous features such as sutures, lines and ridges, and openings [Figure 1–3a, Figure 1–3b, and Figure 1–3c]. Sutures, synarthrotic joints, are immovable articulations found between adjacent skull bones and are generally identified using the names of the bones between which they occur.

**Intermaxillary:** between the premaxillary and maxillary bones

**Nasomaxillary:** between the nasal and maxillary bones

**Sphenofrontal:** between the sphenoid and frontal bones

**Frontal:** between the frontal bones

**Coronal:** between the parietal and frontal bones

**Sagittal:** between the parietal bones

**Squamosal:** between the parietal and squamous portion of the temporal bone

**Lambdoidal:** caudad of the parietals, separating them from the occipital and interparietal

A *faint* dorsal feature is the **temporal line** that demarcates the origin of the temporalis muscle. It extends from the caudal margin of the postorbital process as a gentle curve over the frontal bone onto the parietal bone meeting its opposite partner in a V-shaped pattern terminating at the cranial end of the sagittal crest. Some variability in the extent of the temporal line is seen dependent upon the age-related development of the temporalis muscle in individual cats. Older cats often have more prominent temporal lines. The extent of the sagittal crest also varies with the age of the cat. In older, more mature animals, it extends from the lambdoidal ridge onto the the posterior surface of the parietals. Its height and rugosity, likewise, varies with age.

Note the prominent, lateral curved bar or cheekbone, the **zygomotic arch,** composed of a posterior zygomatic process of the temporal that overlaps an anterior zygomatic process of the malar or zygomatic.

## Cavities and Sinuses

Mammal skulls possess a number of spaces, cavities, and sinuses which reduce the weight of the skull and protect and house sense organs [Figure 1–21]. The **nasal cavity,** the most anterior of these spaces, houses the highly convoluted turbinates of the ethmoid, maxilla, and nasal bones whose mucous membrane plays an essential role in humidifying, warming, and filtering of respiratory air. It is also within this membrane that olfactory receptors associated with the sense of smell occur. A nasal septum, consisting of the dorsal bony perpendicular plate of the ethmoid with a rostral cartilaginous portion along with the ventrally located vomer, divides the nasal cavity into right and left halves. The **external nares** (nostrils) open anteriorly into these cavities. The caudal cribriform plate of the ethmoid through which pass the olfactory fibers, separates the nasal cavity from the cranial cavity.

The **cranial cavity** is organized into four distinct areas. The **olfactory fossa** occurs just caudal to the cribriform plate and houses the olfactory bulbs where the olfactory fibers synapse. Posterior and continuous with the olfactory fossa is the **cerebral fossa** that houses the cerebrum, the diencephalon, and the mesencephalon (midbrain). In the floor of the cranial cavity is the **sella turcica** in which the hypophysis (pituitary) sits. The **tentorium** marks the caudal end of the cerebral fossa. Posterior to the tentorium lies the **cerebellar fossa** which surrounds the pons, cerebellum, and the

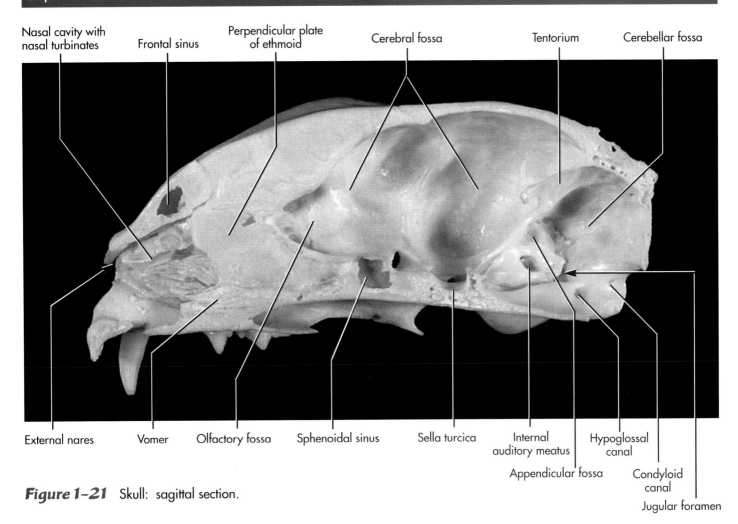

Nasal cavity with nasal turbinates | Frontal sinus | Perpendicular plate of ethmoid | Cerebral fossa | Tentorium | Cerebellar fossa

External nares | Vomer | Olfactory fossa | Sphenoidal sinus | Sella turcica | Internal auditory meatus | Hypoglossal canal | Appendicular fossa | Condyloid canal | Jugular foramen

***Figure 1–21*** Skull: sagittal section.

medulla oblongata. A small deep depression, the **appendicular fossa**, lies dorsal to the **internal auditory meatus** in the petrous portion of the temporal bone. The **foramen magnum** opens at the caudal end of the cerebellar fossa. Notice the considerable topography of the surface of the cranial cavities which mirrors the contours of the external brain surface and also the blood vessels associated with the brain.

Two air-filled spaces, the **frontal sinus** in the frontal bone and the **sphenoidal sinus** enclosed in the presphenoid bone of the skull probably function in weight reduction. In addition, in the human, sinuses are also present in the ethmoid and maxillary bones.

In comparison, the cranial cavity of humans can be subdivided into three distinct cavities, the anterior, middle, and posterior areas. Since humans are not nearly as keen "smellers" that most other mammals are, there are no distinct olfactory bulbs, hence no olfactory fossa is present. Further, the bony tentorium of the cat is represented by a fold of the dura mater, the tentorium cerebelli in humans.

## The Mandible

The lower jaw or **mandible** [Figure 1–22a, Figure 1–22b, and Figure 1–22c] completes the bones of the head. The mandible consists of a pair of **dentary** bones that articulate cranially at the **intermandibular symphysis**. Within the first two years of human life the two dentary bones fuse to produce a single bone, the mandible, and unlike the cat, cannot be separated. At the caudal end of the mandible are a pair of **condyloid processes**, each of which articulates with an elongate groove, the mandibular fossa, in the zygomatic process of the temporal. Notice that these processes are bar-shaped in the cat, a typical design in carnivores allowing them to hold struggling prey but also reducing rotary and lateral grinding movements. The condyloid process of the human is not designed as an elongate bar but is more ovate since this shape is an adaptation of an omnivore, one who eats a wide variety of foods. Humans rarely need to subdue struggling prey!

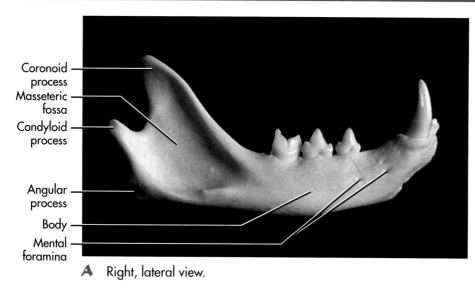

Coronoid process
Masseteric fossa
Condyloid process
Angular process
Body
Mental foramina

**A** Right, lateral view.

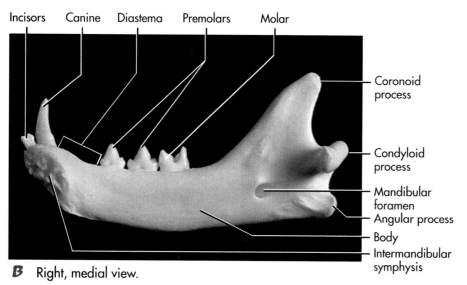

Incisors    Canine    Diastema    Premolars    Molar

Coronoid process
Condyloid process
Mandibular foramen
Angular process
Body
Intermandibular symphysis

**B** Right, medial view.

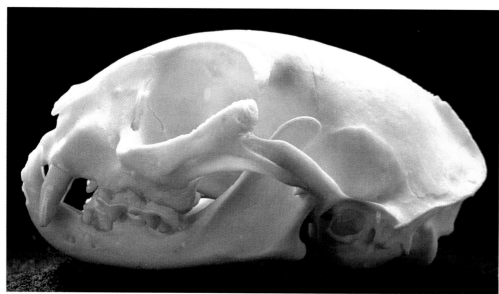

**C** Skull with mandible

*Figure 1–22* Dentary.

In lateral view, the cranial end consists of a relatively smooth, rounded bar, the **body**, that contains two or three **mental foramina** through which pass branches of the mandibular division of the Trigeminal Nerve (C.N. V). The caudal end of the mandible expands into the **ramus**. The dorsal part of the ramus, the **coronoid process**, is the site of insertion of the temporalis muscle, the largest and most powerful of the jaw muscles of carnivores. The well defined triangular-shaped depression, the **coronoid** or **masseteric fossa**, accomodates the insertion of part of the masseter muscle, another of the powerful jaw adductors. Notice the small rounded projection, the **angular process**, at the extreme caudal end of the mandible. Another portion of the masseter and pterygoid muscles insert there.

The medial surface of the mandible is relatively smooth with an exception anteriorly at the symphysis where several rugosities occur to facilitate a strong interlocking joint between the dentaries, and is unevenly sculptured posteriorly where the pterygoid and other jaw muscles insert. The prominent **mandibular foramen** faces caudally and admits the Mandibular division of the Trigeminal Nerve (C.N. V).

Teeth, anchored in sockets, are found along the dorsal, **alveolar border**. In each half of the mandible three small **incisors** are located anteriorly, followed by a single sharp **canine**. A wide space, the **diastema**, separates the canine from the two caudal **premolars** and a single **molar**. For further discussion and comparison of the teeth with the human see page 98 of the digestive system.

# The Vertebral Column

Among terrestrial vertebrates, since body weight is no longer supported by water, mechanical stress caused by the weight of complex organ systems must be transferred to the longitudinal bony beam known as the vertebral column and therefore it has evolved into an important, specialized supporting and locomotory unit. The vertebral column consists of a series of articulated bones called the vertebrae that are separable into five regions: cervical, thoracic, lumbar, sacral, and caudal. The vertebrae provide the main axial support of the body. Support of both appendicular girdles is an essential part of this integrated locomotory and weightbearing unit; the pelvic girdle directly articulates

with the sacral region of the vertebral column while the pectoral girdle is associated and held in place by muscles in the thoracic region. The thoracic vertebrae play a secondary and equally important role as the rib-bearing region. Notice in the mounted specimen that the articulated vertebral column has two curvatures, concave in the cervical-thoracic region and convex in the posterior thoracic lumbar region that impart bowlike actions to the vertebral column during locomotion. In addition, cushioning fibrocartilaginous **intervertebral discs** occur between each of the individual vertebrae. If it were not for a concave lumbar curve in the human, the vertebral columns of the cat and human would look very similar [Figure 1–23a and Figure 1–23b].

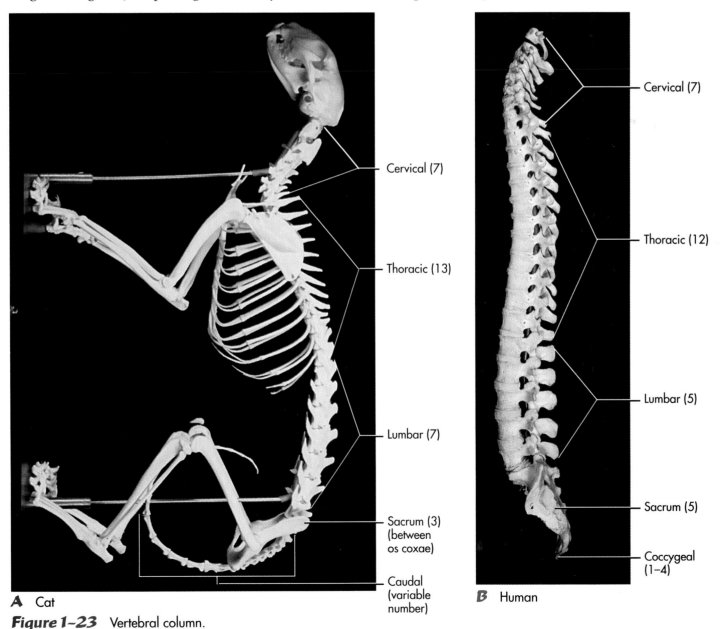

Cervical (7)

Thoracic (13)

Lumbar (7)

Sacrum (3)
(between
os coxae)

Caudal
(variable
number)

Cervical (7)

Thoracic (12)

Lumbar (5)

Sacrum (5)

Coccygeal
(1–4)

**A**   Cat

**B**   Human

**Figure 1–23**   Vertebral column.

## Cervical Vertebrae

The **cervical vertebrae** are the most cranial. Almost all mammals — including cats, humans, and giraffes — possess seven cervical vertebrae. Although specializations exist in all regions of the vertebral column, certain features are common to all.

A vertebra is constructed with a solid **centrum** or **body** that forms the main ventral support for the spinal cord that rests in the obvious opening, the **vertebral canal**. The vertebral canal is completed by a dorsal pair of **laminae** whose dorsocaudal extensions form the **spinous process** and a pair of **pedicles** between the laterally projecting **transverse processes** or **diaphyses** and the centrum. At the cranial end of each vertebra are two processes; the **prezygopophyses**, whose articulating facets face dorsally or dorsomedially and articulate with two caudal processes, the **postzygapophyses** on the posterior end of the vertebra just preceding it. The articular surface of the postzygapophysis faces ventrally or ventromedially. Notice that each vertebra possesses both a pre- and postzygapophsis to facilitate articulation with adjacent vertebrae [Figure 1–24a, Figure 1–24b, and Figure 1–24c].

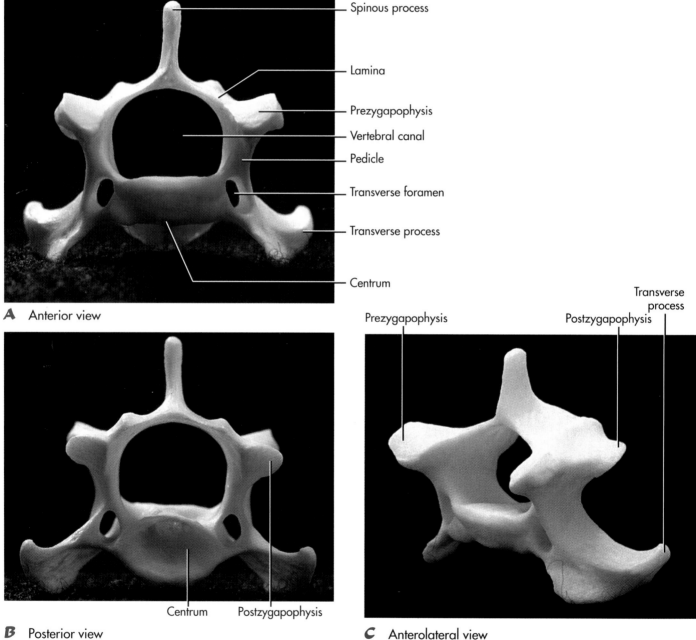

Spinous process

Lamina

Prezygapophysis

Vertebral canal

Pedicle

Transverse foramen

Transverse process

Centrum

**A**   Anterior view

Centrum    Postzygapophysis

**B**   Posterior view

Prezygapophysis        Postzygapophysis      Transverse process

**C**   Anterolateral view

*Figure 1–24*   Cervical vertebra.

The first and second cervical vertebrae, the atlas and axis, respectively, are very distinctly structured. The ringlike **atlas** [Figure 1–25a and Figure 1–25b] lacks a centrum and a distinct spine and has broad, winglike **transverse processes**. The inner articular facets of the expanded **prezygapophyses** accomodate the rounded surfaces of the occipital condyles of the skull. Notice that the **postzygapophyses** do not project as distinctly from the atlas as the prezygapophyses but, nevertheless, bear well defined facets for articulation with the prezygapophyses of the axis.

The **atlantal foramen**, the first intervertebral foramen, through which the first spinal nerve and vertebral vein exit and the vertebral artery enters is located dorsal to the prezygapophysis. Typical of the first six cervical vertebrae is the **transverse foramen** that passes through the transverse process. The vertebral arteries and veins, the blood supply of the brain, pass through these foramina. Look inside the **vertebral canal** and identify the foramen that allows passage of a small branch of the vertebral artery to form a small artery that extends caudally along the ventral surface of the spinal cord. The human atlas, very similar to that of the cat, possesses only the transverse foramen.

The axis [Figure 1–26], in lateral view, resembles a blacksmith's anvil with its pronounced **spinous process** overhanging the **arch of the atlas**. A second distinctive feature is the cranially projecting **odontoid process** or **dens**, laterally flanked by a pair of **prezygapophyses** with smooth articulating surfaces to articulate with the atlas. The odontoid process represents the centrum of the atlas that has fused with the centrum of the axis and provides an "axle" around which the atlas can pivot to allow rotation of the head on the neck. Take note of the rather typical **centrum** of the axis in posterior view. Thin caudally projecting **transverse processes** are present with their characteristic **transverse foramina**. Find the **postzygapophyses** with their ventrally directed articulating facets on the dorsal aspect of the arch.

Except for a strong reduction of the cranial and caudal portions of the spinous process, the human axis is quite similar to the cat. The human spinous process is bifurcated and strongly grooved posteriorly.

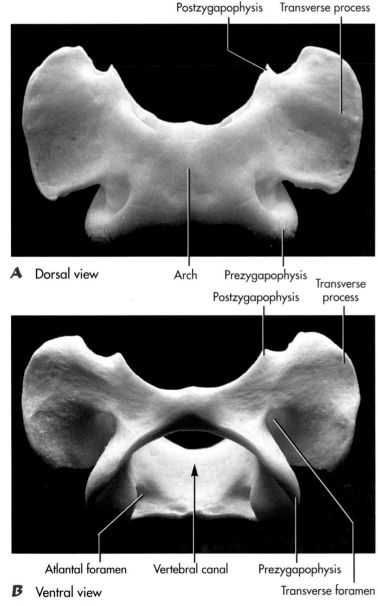

Postzygapophysis    Transverse process

**A**   Dorsal view     Arch     Prezygapophysis

Prezygapophysis
Postzygapophysis     Transverse process

Atlantal foramen    Vertebral canal    Prezygapophysis

Transverse foramen

**B**   Ventral view

**Figure 1–25**   Atlas.

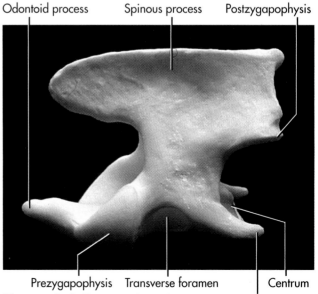

Odontoid process     Spinous process     Postzygapophysis

Prezygapophysis    Transverse foramen     Centrum

Transverse process

**Figure 1–26**   Axis: lateral view.

The remaining cervical vertebrae, in many respects, are similar to one another and possess typical vertebral characteristics, with some notable exceptions. The spinous process of the third is very abbreviated, while those of the fourth through the seventh acquire increasing prominence. Note the absence of the transverse foramen in the seventh. The transverse process of the sixth is bifurcated.

In humans, cervical vertebrae 2–6 possess short, bifurcated spinous processes, while in the seventh it is single and elongated. All seven cervical vertebrae have transverse foramina.

## Thoracic Vertebrae

Among vertebrates, the **thoracic vertebrae** tend to be the least specialized. Typically, cats have 13 thoracic vertebrae [Figure 1–27]. Identify features that are similar to the cervical vertebrae.

Take note of the **articular facet** on the ventral surface of the transverse process with which the tuberculum of the rib articulates and also the **demifacets** occurring on the centrum of two adjacent vertebrae with which the capitulum of the ribs articulates. These facets are unique landmarks found only on thoracic vertebrae.

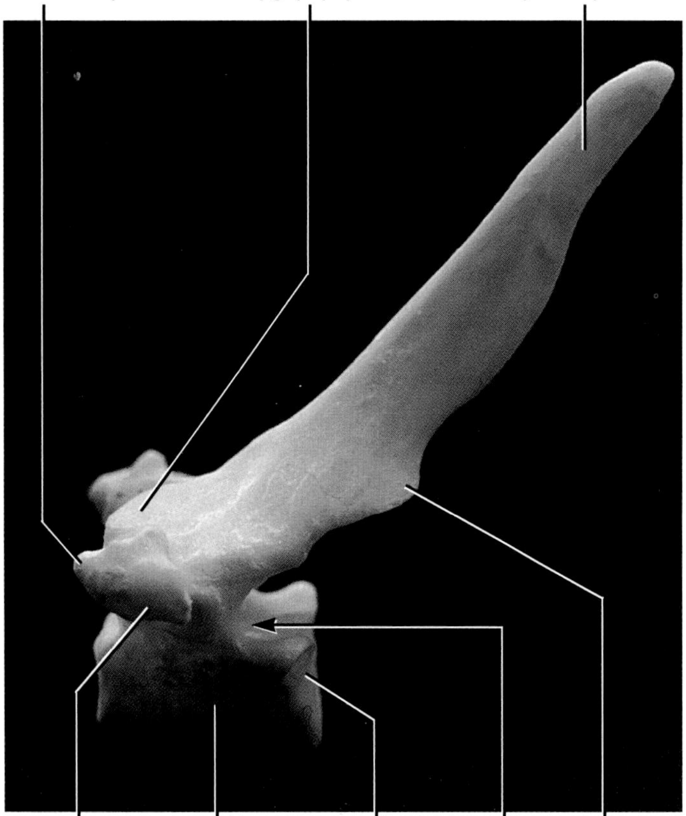

Neural spines of the first nine or ten thoracic vertebrae are very distinct and elongated, and point caudally whereas the spine of the eleventh or twelfth, the **anticlinal vertebra**, makes an abrupt change in direction and points cranially. The spines of the rest of the vertebrae posterior to the anticlinal vertebra continue with this orientation. With the anticlinal vertebra there is also a noticable change in the length of the spinous process. It is in this same area of the vertebral column that **accessory processes** pointing caudally, appear on the lateral aspects of the pedicles. Note that the eleventh thoracic vertebra has a much reduced transverse process that is absent from the last two vertebrae. The loss of the tuberculum on the last few ribs undoubtedly correlates with the loss of the transverse processes.

Among humans there are 12 thoracic vertebrae and all spines project in the same direction and an accessory process, per se, is not present, although it is probably represented by a tubercle on the transverse process.

## Lumbar Vertebrae

The seven **lumbar vertebrae** are characterized as the largest of the vertebrae, increasing in size toward the caudal end [Figure 1–28]. Identify portions of this vertebra that are similar to those of the cervical vertebrae. Perhaps the most obvious landmark on lumbar

Transverse process     Prezygapophysis          Spinous process

Articular facet   Centrum   Demifacet   Vertebral canal
                                         Postzygapophysis

***Figure 1–27*** Thoracic vertebra: lateral view.

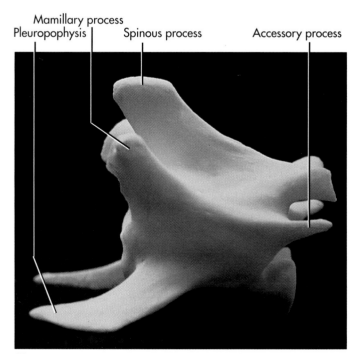

Mamillary process
Pleuropophysis      Spinous process          Accessory process

***Figure 1–28*** Lumar vertebra: lateral view.

vertebrae is the cranially projecting **pleuropophysis**, representing the transverse process with an embryonic rib fused to it. Additionally, **accessory processes**, tooth-like projections, located ventral to the postzyga-pophyses, are generally evident on all but the last two, while **mammillary processes** can be seen on all of the lumbar vertebrae.

In the human, there are five lumbar vertebrae that are structurally similar to those of the cat except for the absence of the pleuropophysis.

## The Sacrum

This complex consists of three fused vertebrae in the adult, but separate in the kitten, that act as a brace for the pelvic girdle [Figure 1–29a and Figure 1–29b]. Notice that the three vertebrae decrease in size caudally, while each retains most of the characteristics of the preceding lumbar vertebra. Note, also, the fusion of the pleuropophyses into a single lateral structure as well as dorsal and ventral foramina to accommodate the passage of spinal nerves between each of the adjacent fused vertebrae.

The human sacrum is composed of five fused vertebrae and no pleuropophyses.

## Caudal Vertebrae

Vertebrae of the tail are the smallest and most variable in number [Figure 1–30]. The more cranial of

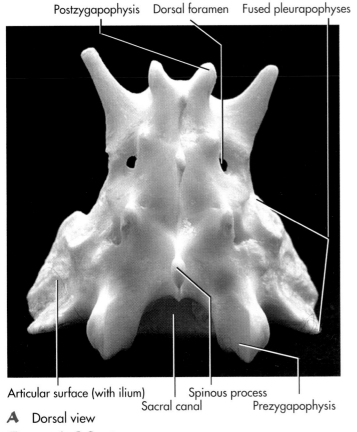

Postzygapophysis    Dorsal foramen    Fused pleurapophyses

Articular surface (with ilium)     Spinous process     Prezygapophysis     Sacral canal

**A**   Dorsal view

***Figure 1–29***   Sacrum.

Ventral foramina

**B**   Ventral view

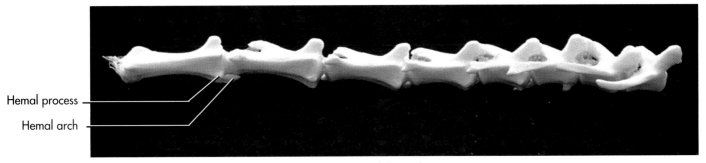

Hemal process

Hemal arch

***Figure 1–30***   Caudal vertebrate, anterior toward the right.

these exhibit rather typical vertebral characteristcs whereas the more caudal vertebrae rapidly lose them and come to resemble simple cylinders representing the centra. Take note of the two small **hemal processes** on the ventral surface of the centra with which V-shaped **hemal arches** or chevron bones, housing caudal blood vessels, articulate. Hemal arches identifiable in the intact cat, are often lost during skeletal preparation, but one is present in Figure 1–30.

Human caudal vertebrae are much less numerous (3–5), often rudimentary and sometimes fused. These vertebrae are called the coccyx in the human. Usually the only time that we appreciate the fact that we have a tail is when we damage it and are unable to sit comfortably for some time.

## The Hyoid

This is actually a complex of derivatives of several former ancestral gill supports [Figure 1–31]. In mammals, this apparatus, located ventral to the larynx and at the root of the tongue, serves as a site of origin of tongue and larynx muscles. It is H-shaped and consists of a **body** forming the bar of the H and two **cranial** or **lesser** and two **caudal**

or **greater horns** or **cornua**, forming the upper and lower uprights of the H. Notice that each cranial horn consists of four small bones, while each caudal horn possesses a single fused bone. In the human, this apparatus is a single fused bone and possesses a body and a pair of greater cornua (caudal horns) and a pair of lesser cornua (cranial horns), similar to the cat.

## The Sternum

In the cat, the **sternum** is slim and elongate and is composed of a series of articulated **sternebrae** [Figure 1–32]. It lies ventrally in the midline of the thorax and its posterior end lies just posterior to the diaphragm. It consists of three regions, an anterior slightly keeled **manubrium** that resembles the tip of a spear, the **body** consisting of six similar, articulated sternebrae, and a

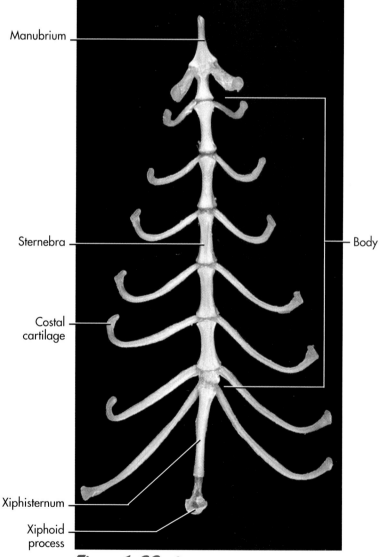

**Figure 1–31**  Hyoid.

**Figure 1–32**  Sternum.

posterior elongated **xiphisternum** with a distal cartilaginous end known as the **xiphoid process**.

**Costal cartilages** associated with the vertebrosternal ribs are generally attached at intervals to the sternum. The first of these is associated with the manubrium at about its midpoint. In some cats, a fusion line indicates the possibility of two individual sternebrae having been united to form the single manubrium. The other eight ribs articulate with the sternum at analogous points between adjacent sternebrae along its length. The eighth and ninth sternal articulations are closely associated with one another.

The human sternum is flat and consists of an anterior manubrium, the body representing a fusion of four sternebrae, and the terminal xiphoid process whose proximal end may ossify in adulthood. Seven costal cartilages associated with vertebrosternal ribs appear to articulate at positions approximately analogous to those of the cat.

### The Ribs

There are thirteen pairs of **ribs**, the first nine pairs, identified as the **vertebrosternal** ribs, are considered to be true ribs since their distal ends attach individually to the sternum by means of costal cartilages. There is a great deal of variability in the last four pairs. Generally, the next three pairs or the **vertebrochondral** ribs, are attached by means of cartilage to each other or to the costal cartilage of the ninth. The final pair has no sternal attachment and therefore is referred to as the **vertebral** or "floating" ribs.

Although the ribs may be of varying lengths, their morphology is quite similar [Figure 1–33]. The basic shape is a curved, flattened rod, whose proximal end bears a **head** or **capitulum** that articulates with demifacets occurring on the centrum of two adjacent thoracic vertebrae. A second projection, the **tuberculum**, bearing a smooth facet, articulates with the transverse process of a vertebra. Notice that the tuberculum progressively decreases in prominence antero-posteriorly and is absent from the last two or three pairs of ribs. The slightly constricted area between the capitulum and the tuberclum is known as the **neck**. The proximal curved portion or **angle** of the rib blends into the distal part known as the **body**. A small, pointed projection, the **angular process**, can be located on the angle of the rib.

Perhaps one of the most confusing aspects of rib morphology is determination of whether it is right or

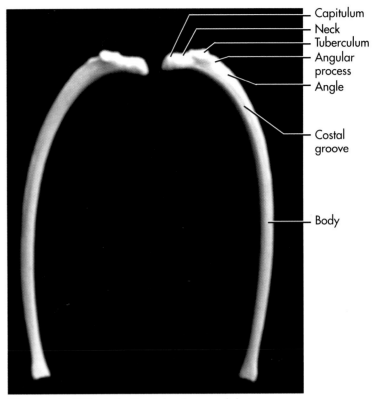

**Figure 1–33** Left rib, right rib: caudal view.

Capitulum
Neck
Tuberculum
Angular process
Angle
Costal groove
Body

left. One clue is that the articulating surfaces of the capitulum and tuberculum are angled posteriorly, i.e., when examined from the caudal view, the surfaces of the capitulum and tuberculum slant toward you, whereas the opposite is true of a rib looked at from the cranial view. Additionally, a **costal groove** found along the angle of the rib is oriented caudally.

In contrast to the cat, humans possess twelve pairs of ribs, seven of which are vertebrosternal, three vertebrochondral and two vertebral.

## Appendicular Division

### Pectoral Girdle and Appendage
#### The Clavicle

The **clavicle** in cursorial (running) mammals is drastically reduced and often embedded in the muscle of the shoulder. This is typical of vertebrates adapted for running. In the cat, it is a slender, rodlike, curved bone with the sternal end slightly enlarged [Figure 1–34]. The human clavicle is much more robustly constructed with a slight sigmoid curve and its articulation reflects a more primitive mammalian condition. It articulates medially with the manubrium of the sternum and laterally with the acromion process of the scapula.

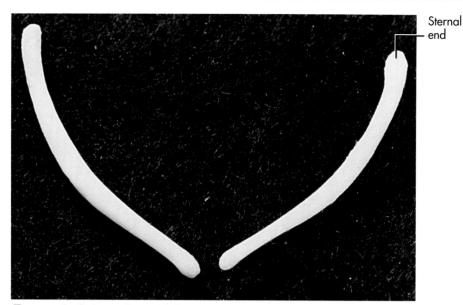

Sternal end

**Figure 1–34**   Right and left clavicle: cranial view.

### The Scapula

The **scapula** is a flat triangular bone that articulates with the humerus [Figure 1–35a and Figure 1–35b]. The curved **dorsal** or **vertebral border** continues anteriorly as the **cranial border** and posteriorly as the **caudal** or **axillary border**. At the vertex of the triangle is a concave surface known as the **glenoid fossa** with which the head of the humerus articulates. A small beak-like projection, the **coracoid process**, extends medially from the anterior border of the glenoid fossa. Lateral to it is the **supraglenoid tubercle**. A prominent lateral ridge, the **scapular spine** begins at about the midpoint of the vertebral border and extends just dorsally to the glenoid fossa and terminates in a free, pointed **acromion process**. The upper curved, thicker portion of the free edge is identified as the **tuberosity of the spine** while the caudally projecting, sharp-angled **metacromion** occurs just dorsal to the acromion. The spine divides the lateral surface into an anterior **supraspinous fossa** and a posterior **infraspinous fossa**.

On the medial surface, the **subscapular fossa**, is somewhat flat with a narrow elevation marking the medial line of the spine overlying it on the lateral surface. Two oblique ridges are obvious landmarks indicating points of muscle attachment on the anterior surface of the fossa, while a single prominent ridge occurs along the posterior margin of the fossa again indicating the point of muscle attachment. A somewhat concave surface is present between this ridge and the posterior margin for muscle attachment. A variable number of nutrient foramina are present on both surfaces.

Other than the disproportionate surface area of the infraspinous portion of the scapula in the human, the cat and human scapulae are quite similar.

### The Humerus

The proximal or upper long bone of the anterior limb is known as the **humerus** [Figure 1–36]. It articulates proximally with the scapula and distally with the radius and ulna. It consists of a slightly curved diaphysis and two prominent epiphyses. The proximal epiphysis consists of a smooth, rounded medial **head** that articulates with the glenoid cavity of the scapula. Medial to the head is the smaller **lesser tuberosity** and lateral to the head is the larger **greater tuberosity** for muscle attachment. The **bicipital groove**, that accomodates the tendon of the biceps brachii muscle, separates these two tuberosities. At the distal end are a pair of prominent condyles, a larger medial **trochlea**, and a smaller lateral **capitulum**, with which the ulna and radius articulate, respectively.

Proximal to the trochlea is the **coronoid fossa** and proximal to the capitulum is the **radial fossa**. Medial and proximal to the trochlea is the prominent **medial epicondyle** and lateral and proximal to the capitulum is the less obvious **lateral epicondyle**. The very conspicuous ovoid slit occurring proximal to the medial epicondyle is the **supracondyloid foramen**. Through the foramen passes the median nerve and the brachial blood vessels. On the posterior side proximal to the trochlea and capitulum is the deep, prominent **olecranon fossa** with which the olecranon of the ulna articulates.

Posteriorly, a sharp **supracondyloid ridge** extends from the lateral epicondyle to about the midpoint of the diaphysis. A prominent rugosity, the medial **pectoral ridge**, and the sharp, crestlike, lateral **deltoid ridge** converge anteriorly at about midshaft. These surface irregularities mark the positions of muscle attachments. Numerous nutrient foramina occur in both diaphysis and epiphyses of the humerus.

Other than the presence of the anatomical neck and the absence of the supracondyloid foramen, the human humerus is similar to the cat.

### The Radius

The natural position of the **radius** [Figure 1–37] in the forearm of the cat extends from the lateral proximal humeral end to the medial distal carpal end, therefore this long bone crosses over the ulna in the lower arm. As is typical of a long bone, it consists of a central diaphysis and proximal and distal epiphyses. The proximal epiphysis or **head** is slightly concave to accomodate its articulation with the capitulum of the humerus. Cicumscribing the head is the narrow, smooth **articular circumference** for articulation with a notch in the ulna. Below the head is the **neck**. Just distal to the neck on the postero-lateral surface of the diaphysis is the **bicipital tuberosity** for the insertion of the tendon of the biceps brachii muscle. An obvious roughened surface, the **interosseous crest**, is present

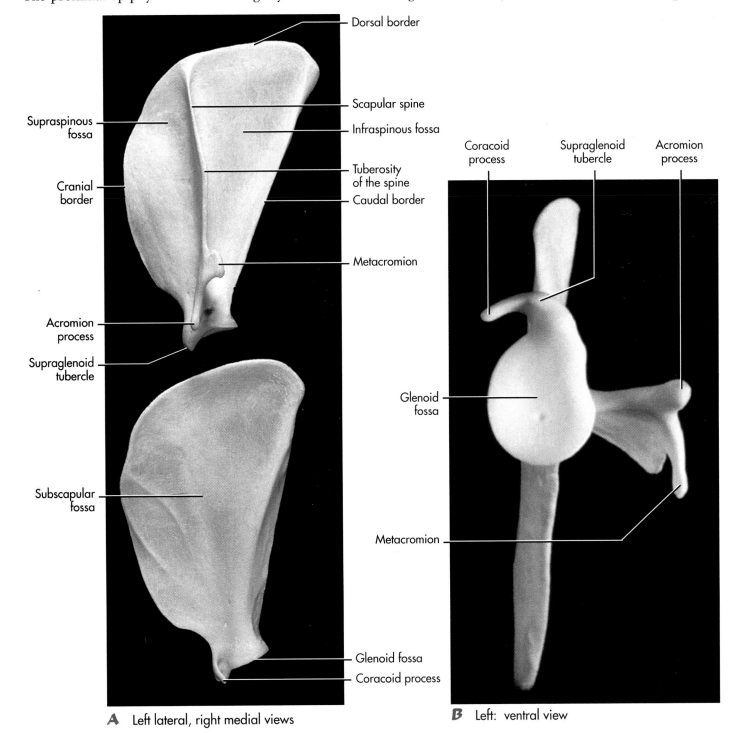

**A**   Left lateral, right medial views

*Figure 1–35*   Scapula.

**B**   Left: ventral view

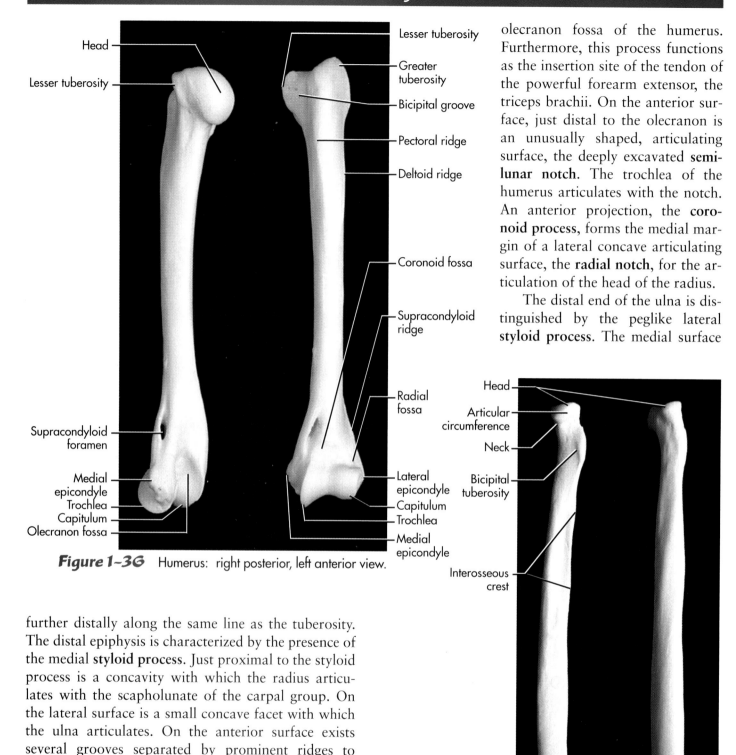

**Figure 1-36**　Humerus: right posterior, left anterior view.

**Figure 1-37**　Radius: right posterior, left anterior view.

olecranon fossa of the humerus. Furthermore, this process functions as the insertion site of the tendon of the powerful forearm extensor, the triceps brachii. On the anterior surface, just distal to the olecranon is an unusually shaped, articulating surface, the deeply excavated **semilunar notch**. The trochlea of the humerus articulates with the notch. An anterior projection, the **coronoid process**, forms the medial margin of a lateral concave articulating surface, the **radial notch**, for the articulation of the head of the radius.

The distal end of the ulna is distinguished by the peglike lateral **styloid process**. The medial surface

further distally along the same line as the tuberosity. The distal epiphysis is characterized by the presence of the medial **styloid process**. Just proximal to the styloid process is a concavity with which the radius articulates with the scapholunate of the carpal group. On the lateral surface is a small concave facet with which the ulna articulates. On the anterior surface exists several grooves separated by prominent ridges to allow passage of tendons. Its human counterpart is very similar.

### The Ulna

The second bone of the forelimb is the **ulna**, another long bone consisting of a diaphysis and a pair of epiphyses [Figure 1–38]. The proximal end is better known as the **olecranon** which articulates with the articulates with the cuneiform and pisiform of the carpals. On the medial surface of the ulna, just proximal to the styloid process, observe the small articulating surface with which its radial counterpart articulates. Along the antero-lateral aspect of the ulnar diaphysis, notice the usually prominent **interosseous crest** that approximates the crest on the corresponding area of the radius. A tough sheet of connective tissue extends from the crest of the radius to the crest of the ulna, stabilizing the lower foreleg by preventing major torsion or twisting movement between the radius and ulna. The human ulna is very similar in structure to the cat.

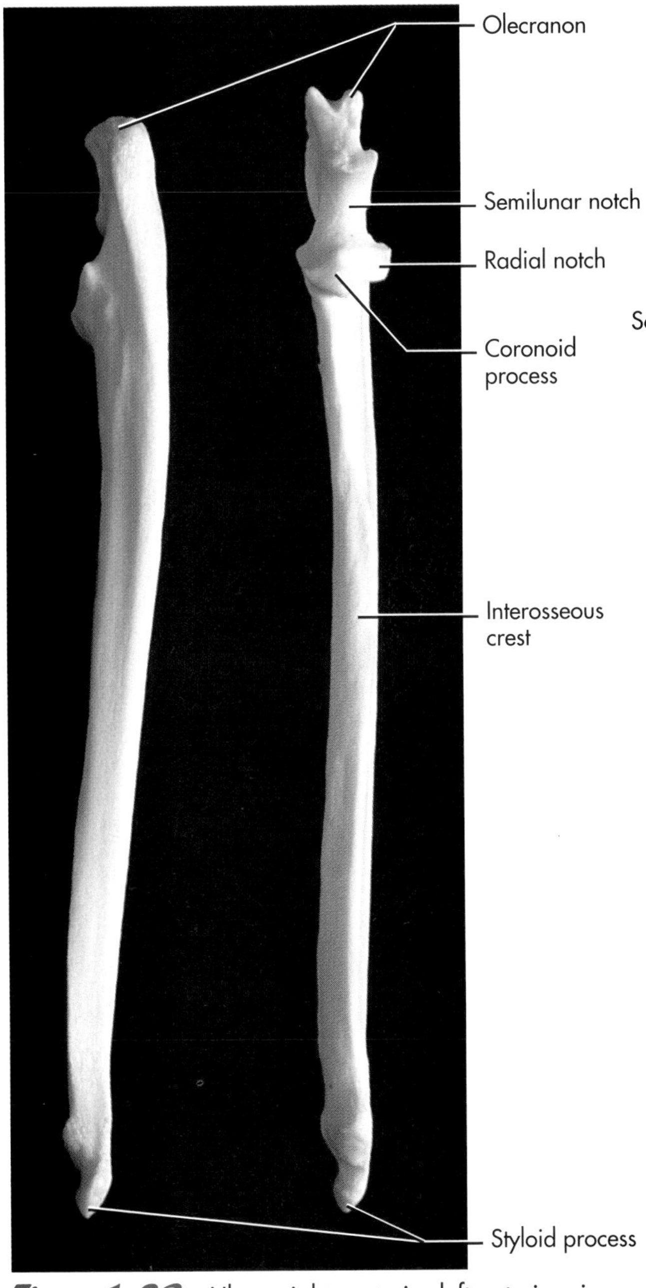

### The Carpals and the Manus

A series of seven, small, irregularly shaped bones, the **carpals**, organized into two rows, a proximal set of three and a distal set of four, separate the forefoot or manus from the foreleg and are known as the wrist bones [Figure 1–39].

The most medial and largest of the proximal row is the fused scaphoid and lunate called the **scapholunate**, which, in the human, occur as separate carpals. In the middle of this row is the **cuneiform**, known as the triquetral in the human. The most lateral of the proximal set is called the **pisiform**. Although from the anterior view the pisiform appears as a small bone, a considerable portion projects posteriorly, therefore, it is substantially larger than it first appears. This row articulates proximally with the radius and ulna and distally with the second row of carpals.

In the distal row, from medial to lateral, are the **trapezium, trapezoid, capitate,** and **hamate**. Distally, these bones articulate with the metacarpals of the hand.

Olecranon

Semilunar notch

Radial notch

Coronoid process

Interosseous crest

Styloid process

*Figure 1–38*    Ulna: right posterior left anterior view.

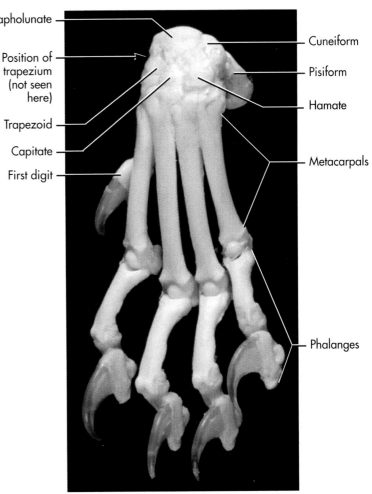

Scapholunate

Position of trapezium (not seen here)

Trapezoid

Capitate

First digit

Cuneiform

Pisiform

Hamate

Metacarpals

Phalanges

*Figure 1–39*    Left manus and carpals.

The **manus** consists of five **metacarpals** with which the proximal **phalanges** of the five digits articulate [Figure 1–39]. There are two phalanges in the thumb and three in each of the other four toes. Sesamoid bones occur at the junctions of the metacarpals and the phalanges. Contrary to the human digit condition, the cat, typical of most feline carnivores, has well-developed retractile claws, an obvious adaptation among these predators to aid in capturing and holding frisky prey.

## Pelvic Girdle and Appendage

### The Os Coxa or Innominate

This irregularly shaped, elongated, complex consists of three individual bones, the **ilium**, the **ischium**, and the **pubis** [Figure 1–40a and Figure 1–40b]. In the

juvenile cat, these bones can be distinguished because they are separated by sutures. In the adult cat they become fused and the sutures become less obvious. The pelvic girdle of the cat is comprised of the paired innominate bones that articulate ventrally along the medial surfaces of the pubic and ischial portions forming

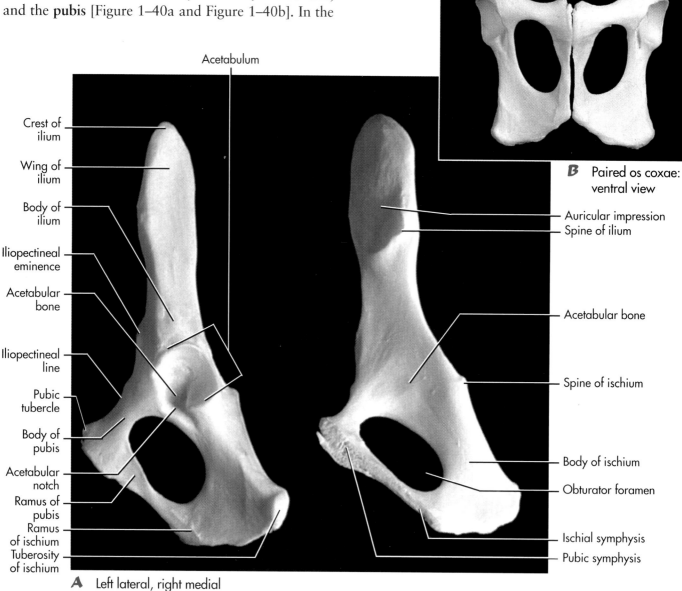

**B** Paired os coxae: ventral view

Auricular impression
Spine of ilium

Acetabular bone

Spine of ischium

Body of ischium

Obturator foramen

Ischial symphysis
Pubic symphysis

Acetabulum

Crest of ilium
Wing of ilium
Body of ilium
Iliopectineal eminence
Acetabular bone
Iliopectineal line
Pubic tubercle
Body of pubis
Acetabular notch
Ramus of pubis
Ramus of ischium
Tuberosity of ischium

**A** Left lateral, right medial

**Figure 1–40** Os coxa.

the **pubic** and **ischial symphysis**, respectively [Figure 1-40b]. The ilial portion of the innominates is rather firmly articulated medially with the sacrum, a specialized region of the vertebral column.

The cranially projecting ilium is wing-shaped with a concave lateral surface and is called the **wing of the ilium**. The dorsal portion of the wing is roughly thickened and is called the **crest**. The thickest portion of the ilium proximal to the wing is the **body** and its base contributes to the formation of the deeply concave **acetabulum**. The anterio-ventral margin of the ilium is known as the **ileopectineal line**. This pelvic landmark continues onto the pubic surface to the symphysis. At about the level of the acetabulum lies the **ileopectineal eminence** along the ileopectineal line. Along the posterior border below the crest is the **spine of the ilium**.

The posterior part of the ischium consists of the heavy, broad **body** and the more lightly constructed, **ramus**. The roughened, thickened posterior end of the body is known as the **tuberosity of the ischium**. Very near the cranial end of the ischium and along the posterior border is the fairly prominent **spine of the ischium**.

The third bone that contributes to the formation of the innominate is the pubis. That portion of the pubis that is continuous with the ramus of the ischium is logically called the **ramus of the pubis** which terminates as the **pubic tubercle**. The more robust **body** forms a more-or-less right angle with the ramus and joins the body of the ilium to complete the os coxa.

The very prominent opening, the **obturator foramen**, is surrounded by the ischium and pubis. Through this foramen passes the obturator nerve. The incomplete cup-shaped acetabulum, permitting the articulation of the head of the femur, lies above the obturator foramen. Notice the gap in the acetabulum created by the **acetabular notch**. The thin shell-like medial wall of the socket is formed by the **acetabular bone**, a minor component of the innominate.

With the exception of the rough, earlike **auricular impression** by which the os coxa articulates with the sacrum, the medial surface of the innominate is smooth. This association between the sacrum and the os coxae stabilizes the postion of the pelvic girdle and its appendages and provides the posterior weightbearing surface.

The most significant difference in the human is observed in the upright position of the innominate and in the breadth of the ilium, therefore the ilium becomes the major weightbearing portion of the bone.

Both of these characteristics are related to our upright posture. In humans, the innominates are sexually dimorphic. In females, the ilium flares laterally while in males the ilium is more upright. Additionally, the angle between the pubes in females is obtuse while in males it is acute. These differences are related to child bearing in females.

### The Femur

The proximal bone of the posterior limb is the **femur** [Figure 1-41]. It is a typical long bone consisting of a central shaft or diaphysis and a proximal and

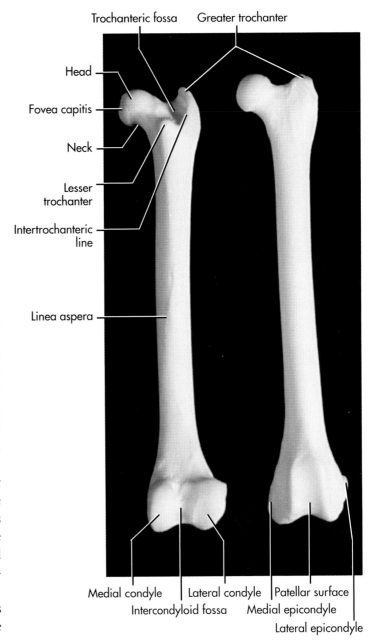

*Figure 1-41*  Femur: right posterior, left anterior.

distal epiphysis. A prominent ball-like projection, the **head,** with an irregular depression, the **fovea capitis,** is located on the medial aspect of the proximal epiphysis. The head articulates with the acetabulum of the innominate and the fovea capitis is the site of attachment of a ligament that helps anchor the femur to the ventral portion of the acetabulum. The constricted **neck** connects the head to the epiphysis. Equally as prominent on the lateral aspect of the femur is the **greater trochanter** where hip muscles attach. Medial to the greater trochanter is a conspicuous depression, the **trochanteric fossa.** Extending from the greater trochanter and running along its rim and terminating in a small triangular projection, the **lesser trochanter,** is the **intertrochanteric line.** Several ridgelike lines extend around the neck and lesser trochanter. Notice the prominent ridge extending from the greater trochanter and along the postero-lateral aspect of the femur, crossing from lateral to medial at midshaft. This ridge is joined by a much less conspicuous line extending from the lesser trochanter to form the **linea aspera.** These ridges provide sites of muscle attachment.

The distal end of the femur is distinguished by two prominent projections, the **medial** and **lateral condyles** whose smooth, rounded surfaces articulate with the proximal end of the tibia. A deep posterior notch, the **intercondyloid fossa,** separates the condyles. Take note of the two irregularly shaped prominences, the **medial** and **lateral epicondyles,** located above the condyles and providing sites for muscle attachment. The anterior tongue-shaped, smooth surface, the **patellar surface,** is joined by the patella ("kneecap") to form a smooth surface over which major extensor muscle tendons ride. Several very conspicuous openings, nutrient foramina, for the passage of blood vessels and nerves are found in the diaphysis and both epiphyses. Generally, the human femur is very similar.

### The Patella

The kneecap or **patella** [Figure 1–42] is a major member of that group of bones known as sesamoid bones that are associated with muscle tendons, in this case the tendon of the quadriceps femoris muscle, the major extensor of the leg. Its shape resembles a smooth pumpkin seed and its posterior surface articulates with the condylar articular surfaces of the femur and therefore appears as a negative mirror image of the patellar surface of the femur. The human patella is very similar to the cat patella.

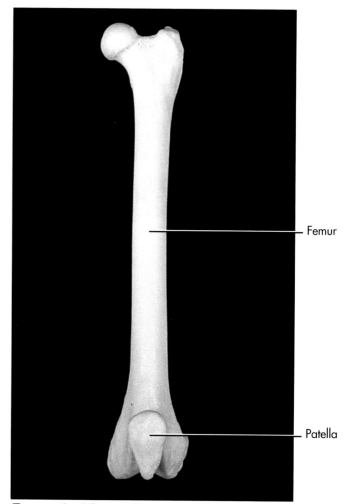

**Figure 1–42**  Patella *in situ:*  left anterior.

### The Tibia

The **tibia** [Figure 1–43] is the longer and more robust of the two lower leg bones and is the primary weightbearing bone of the hindlimb. It consists of a triangular diaphysis and two irregular epiphyses. The proximal epiphysis is roughly triangular, when viewed from above. The base of the triangle includes a **medial** and **lateral condyle** whose surfaces exhibit articular facets that accomodate the articular surfaces of the femoral condyles. The **popliteal notch** on the posterior surface delineates the two condyles. On either side of the condyles are a **medial** and **lateral tuberosity.** A double pointed projection, the **spine** separates the articular facets. A triangle, whose base is formed by the medial and lateral tuberosities, has its vertex marked by the **tibial tuberosity.** Continuous with the tuberosity is the tibial crest extending along the anterior surface of the femur. Beneath the lateral condyle is the **articular facet** for the head of the fibula.

The distal epiphysis has two prominent projections, the longer being the **medial malleolus** and the shorter the **dorsal projection**. Notice the two grooves on the medial surface of the malleolus over which tendons of lower leg muscles ride. Take note of the **articular facet** on the postero-lateral surface of the dorsal projection for articulation with the fibula. The lower surface of this epiphysis consists of two concave articular facets with which the talus (astragalus) of the ankle articulates.

Several ridges identifiable as muscle attachment regions can be observed on the posterior surface of the diaphysis. Morphologically, the human tibia is very similar to that of the cat.

### The Fibula

The slender long bone of the hind limb, lateral to the tibia is the **fibula** [Figure 1–43]. Similar to other long bones it consists of a diaphysis and two epiphyses. The proximal epiphysis is comprised of an irregularly shaped **head** whose medial surface bears a smooth facet for articulation with the lateral surface of the tibia. The medial surface of the diaphysis is flattened, while the lateral surface is gently curved. The

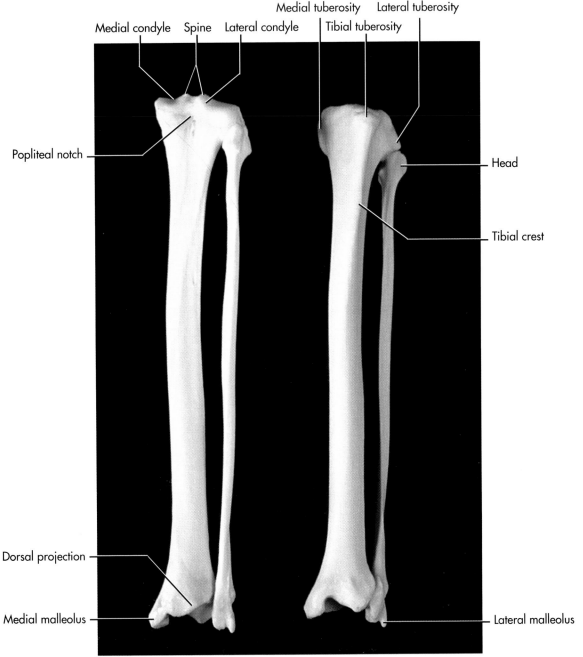

*Figure 1–43*   Articulated tibia and fibula: right posterior, left anterior.

distal epiphysis is distinguished by the **lateral malleolus.** Facets for articulation with the tibia and talus can be found on its medial surface. Grooves to accomodate lower leg muscle tendons are visible laterally and ventrally. The human fibula is very similar.

### The Tarsals and the Pes

The number of **tarsal bones** (7) is identical to the number of carpals, however, in contrast to the carpals, they vary in size [Figure 1–44]. This is particularly true of the medially located **talus** whose size and shape probably relate to the fact that it is the bone with which the tibia and fibula articulate and therefore represents the weightbearing bone of the ankle set. The **calcaneus,** laterally located, is the longest bone of the ankle and forms the heel. The groove on the exposed surface of the calcaneus accomodates the tendon of Achilles. Distal to the talus lies the **navicular.** A row of four tarsal bones, identified from medial to lateral, consist of the **medial cuneiform, intermediate cuneiform, lateral cuneiform,** and **cuboid.**

The pes consists of five **metatarsals** that articulate with the distal row of four tarsal bones. With the exception of the first, which has been greatly reduced, the other four are very elongated and each articulates with a series of three **phalanges,** and similar to the manus terminate in a well developed retractile claw [Figure 1–44]. Note the sesamoid bones at the junction of the metatarsals and phalanges.

There are two major differences in the human. One of these is the presence of the first digit or "big toe" and the second is the way in which the human walks on its foot, since the entire foot from heel to toe is placed on the substrate. In walking on its toes, the cat has increased its leg length, reduced the amount of friction between the foot and substratum and therefore can attain greater speed.

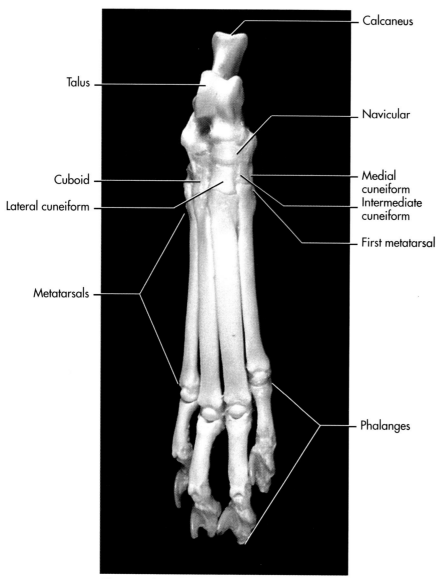

**Figure 1–44**   Right pes and tarsals.

# Muscular System

2

Now we are ready to examine the second of two complementary systems comprising what we recognize as the locomotory complex and call the muscular system. We will be concentrating on what most of us recognize as "muscle," in ourselves and other vertebrates, i.e., the bulk of our body mass that gives our bodies shape and definition.

The function of muscle is contraction. In vertebrates, there are three types of muscle, smooth or involuntary, associated with systems not involved in body locomotion, e.g., the digestive system, cardiac occurring only in the heart and involuntary in function, and skeletal or striated which is voluntary in function and generally associated with visible body movements and also aids in such activities as returning venous blood and lymphatic fluid, especially from the posterior limbs, toward the heart.

The tissues of the muscular system bring about not only externally visible locomotory movements, but also some important subtle, sophisticated, internal movements, such as food propulsion through the digestive tract, adjustment of blood vessel diameters to control blood volumes in various body regions, regulation of respiratory tube diameter, erection of hair follicles, and intrinsic eye functions such as dilation and constriction of the pupil.

The gross anatomy of a whole muscle includes the swollen middle region called the **belly**, the less movable end known as the **origin**, and the more movable end called the **insertion** [Figure 2–1]. In some muscles that are capable of several actions, the origin and insertion may be reversed during contraction. The points of origin and insertion are marked by the presence of dense connective tissue which anchor each muscle to a bone, straplike tendons, or to other muscles, by means of flat sheetlike aponeuroses.

Macroscopically, the structure of a muscle consists of a variable number of muscle cells (fibers) each encased in connective tissue, the endomysium, occurring in bundles called fasciculi and wrapped in connective tissue, the perimysium. Finally, groups of fasciculi surrounded by connective tissue, the epimysium, make up the whole muscle, e.g., the *Biceps brachii*. Microscopically, each of the muscle fibers contains two types of contractile proteins, actin and myosin, which are organized into very regular and serially repetitive arrangements. This repetitive banding pattern is a prominent characteristic of striated muscle.

As you will learn during your study of muscles, muscle shapes vary, dependent primarily upon the

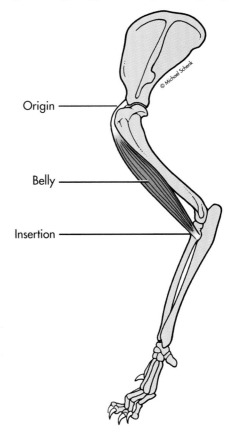

Origin

Belly

Insertion

© Michael Schenk

***Figure 2-1*** Gross anatomy of a muscle (*Biceps brachii*).

arrangement of fibers within each muscle and its relationship with the tendon of insertion. Perhaps an arrangement, with which you are most familiar, is known as **convergent** [Figure 2–2a]. The fibers in this arrangement are basically parallel, however, converge at either end of the muscle. The fibers are arranged in parallel throughout the length of **strap** muscles [Figure 2–2b]. Muscles whose architecture includes a straight blunt origin and a convergent insertion are called **fan-shaped** [Figure 2–2c]. An oblique arrangement of fibers inserting into a tendon or tendons constitutes the pennate class of muscle architecture. Within this group are **unipennate** [Figure 2–2d], where the fibers insert into one side of a tendinous insertion, **bipennate** [Figure 2–2e], where the muscle fibers insert into both sides of a centrally located tendon, and **multipennate** [Figure 2–2f], where the muscle fibers insert into several tendons whose orientation may vary and may appear as combinations of the unipennate and bipennate subgroups.

Muscles are capable of producing a variety of movements called actions. Actions of muscles associated with hinge joints, e.g., the elbow, produce actions known as **flexion**, causing reduction of the angle at the joint and **extension**, causing an increase in the angle of the joint. When appendages or portions of appendages, e.g., the digits, are moved away from a midline reference point or spread, the action is referred to as **abduction**. In contrast, movement toward the midline reference is called **adduction**. Movement of an appendage parallel to the longitudinal axis, producing an anterior action, e.g., swinging a leg forward, is known as **protraction** and the opposite action is known as **retraction**. **Rotation** involves the movement of a portion of the body, around a central axis, e.g., the head on the neck. A specialized action involving rotation of the radial head in the ulnar notch produces actions known as **pronation** and **supination**. When the cat is standing, the manus is pronated or palm down, however, when grooming itself, the manus is supinated or palm up.

Individual muscles generally do not bring about actions by themselves. Most actions are the result of the combined effort of several muscles. Those muscles that affect the action directly are called **prime movers**. Prime movers, however, usually are assisted by others known as **synergists**. These muscles not only aid in bringing about the main action, but also may stabilize the joint or portions of the skeleton involved in the action and are known as **fixators**. Muscles whose actions oppose one another are called **antagonists**.

## Skinning the Cat

In spite of what you may have heard, there is only one way to skin a cat. Since cat specimens are usually packed individually in plastic bags, containing both the cat and some preservative fluid to aid in maintaining a moist environment, carefully remove the specimen from the bag, retaining the fluid to keep the cat moist when it is returned to the bag for storage.

Lay the cat on its dorsal surface on a large dissecting tray. Now is the time for you to make a number of observations concerning your specimen and also plans for dissection. Note that the body is divided into several

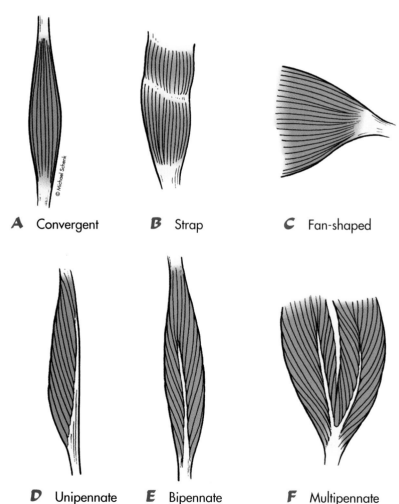

**A** Convergent    **B** Strap    **C** Fan-shaped

**D** Unipennate    **E** Bipennate    **F** Multipennate

*Figure 2-2* Muscle architecture.

regions: a **head, neck, trunk,** and **tail.** A number of distinguishing features of the head, all associated with the concentration of special senses in this region, can be seen. Among them are the paired **external ears** or **pinnae,** the paired **eyes** with an **upper eyelid** or **superior palpebra,** and a **lower eyelid** known as the **inferior palpebra,** paired **nostrils** or **external nares,** and tufts of coarse hairs known as **whiskers** or **vibrissae** on either side of the face. Note the **nictitating membrane** in the lower, medial corner of the eye [Figure 2–3].

The trunk can be divided into an anterior **thoracic** region delineated by the rib cage, a middle **abdominal** region, and a posterior **pelvic** region. Along the ventral surface of the trunk, or the belly, are two rows of paired **nipples,** associated with the mammary glands. They tend to be more prominent in females than in males, especially if the female is either pregnant or has been recently pregnant. Dorsal to the genital region in both sexes and located directly below the tail is the **anus,** the external terminal opening of the digestive system.

There are two sets of paired appendages, **forelimbs,** including the **manus** associated with the cranial portion of the trunk and **hindlimbs,** including the **pes** associated with the caudal end of the trunk [Figure 2–3]. Palpate the genital area to ascertain the sex of the cat. If it is a male, you will feel the testes enclosed within the scrotum; if it is a female, note the urogenital aperture.

The cat will be skinned on *one side only* and the skin should be kept in a *single piece* so that it can be wrapped around the skinned surface when the cat is not being actively worked on. Before attempting to remove the skin, observe several possible areas on the body where skin may have been removed to facilitate the injection of blood vessels with latex, e.g., the neck region, the forearm, and the hindleg. Of all the injection sites, the muscles and the blood vessels of the neck region are most likely to be damaged. Another area that may influence your decision occurs in cats whose hepatic portal system has been injected since the incision in the abdominal area is usually stapled or sutured shut. In this case, you may want to skin the specimen on the opposite side. If the staples occur in the midventral line, simply choose either side for your incision and cut a flap around the stapled area. Before selection of the side that you wish to skin, observe the position of the injection sites discussed above and choose the pathway that allows you to avoid the majority of problem areas.

Since the success of the skinning process is closely correlated with your ability to complete clean, precise cuts, a new blade in your scalpel is essential. Make a careful, shallow incision, just deep enough to break the skin, beginning at the base of the neck 1/2 inch left or right of the midventral line to avoid any muscles whose origin or insertion is on the midline. Determine whether it is possible to pull the skin away from the underlying tissue. Use your fingers, a pair of forceps or a scalpel with the blade held parallel to the underlying muscle or toward the skin and sever the connective tissue from the skin. If your specimen is a

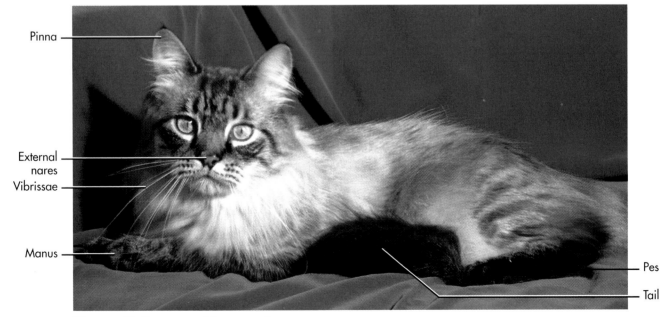

*Figure 2-3*    External features of a cat.

female that has been pregnant recently, as you skin the thoracic and abdominal regions you may encounter the mammary glands that will appear as flattened, tannish masses that you might mistake for muscle. It is preferable to remove these glands with the skin. Continue caudally to a level approximately two inches anterior to the cranial edge of the hindlimb. Now angle your incision along the midline of the hindlimb continuing to a point just proximal to the digits where you will make an encircling incision around the pes. If your specimen is a male, exercise extreme caution at this juncture since the spermatic cord is imbedded within the fat and connective tissue of the groin area and directly beneath the skin. Another reason for this care is that the leg skin is very thin and a major superficial vein, the saphenous, lies directly under the skin. Therefore, carefully sever the fascia from the skin in this area.

Return to the thoracic region and begin an incision opposite the forelimb, continuing down the medial aspect, and encircling the manus just proximal to the digits. Be exceptionally cautious when skinning the radial side of the lower forelimb since a thin, narrow muscle band, the brachioradialis m., a nerve, and blood vessels, adhere closely to the skin and may be mistakenly severed. In addition, along the lateral aspect of the forelimb, from the wrist to the shoulder, courses the cephalic vein, that can again, very easily, be removed along with the skin. It should not be, however! Carefully skin the body, hindlimb and forelimb. As the trunk is skinned, an extensive dermal muscle, the **cutaneous maximus** m., especially prominent in the axillary, pectoral, and abdominal regions, will be encountered. This is the muscle in horses that allows them to twitch and get rid of flies, dogs to shake water out of their coats, etc. It is best to remove this muscle with the skin, exerting great care in the axillary region. In the dorsal shoulder region, take care not to cut through a heavy white connective tissue (aponeurosis) between the paired acromiotrapezius muscles.

Concentrate now on the neck and head regions. Be careful of superficial blood vessels in the ventrolateral position in the neck. During your dissection of this area, note another dermal muscle, the **platysma** m., that adheres closely to the neck and head muscles. Again, it is desirable to remove the platysma with the skin. Notice that the skin in the head region is much thicker than other areas of the body. Extend the ventral incision to the base of the mandible, outlining the

mouth, the nose, and the eye, continuing the incision to the midline of the forehead. As you loosen the skin from the underlying tissues, make a circular incision around the ear and reflect the skin. Continue the skinning process to approximately 1/2 inch past the middorsal line along the entire length of the cat [Figure 2–4a, Figure 2–4b, and Figure 2–4c].

Humans lack a cutaneous maximus and, for this reason, they do not have the ability to twitch their skin, and scar much more easily than other mammals. The platysma, however, is well developed in humans. As you look in a mirror, grimace and note the tendinous, stringy appearance of your neck, the action of the platysma.

## Preparing the Cat for Muscle Dissection

To properly dissect and appreciate muscle relationships, it is necessary to remove extraneous tissues that tend to adhere to the surface of the superficial muscles [Figure 2–5a and Figure 2–5b]. Carefully remove fatty tissue lying on external muscle surfaces. Usually there is a very heavy deposit of fat in the groin area. If your specimen is a male, exercise extreme caution during the removal of fat in this region since the spermatic cord, a thin, small diameter tube lies in close proximity to this fat deposit. Another area where fat accumulations may occur is the region between the scapulae on the surface of the aponeurosis connecting the two acromiotrapezius muscles. Exert caution while removing this fatty tissue here so that the aponeurosis is not destroyed. There will be other areas on the body surface where heavy sheets of dense connective tissue covered by fatty tissue may occur (lumbosacral region, the insertion end of the tensor fascia latae muscle, biceps femoris muscle, etc.). Caution should always be exerted to avoid damaging these important areas of fascia and any other underlying structures. Fascia associated with muscle insertions should not be removed.

After skinning the cat, there may be pieces of the dermal muscles (platysma and cutaneus maximus) left adhering to the muscle surfaces. These should be carefully removed. The epitrochlearis appears very much like a piece of cutaneus maximus on the medial surface of the brachium. Do not remove this muscle or the thin aponeurosis by which it inserts in the vicinity of the elbow.

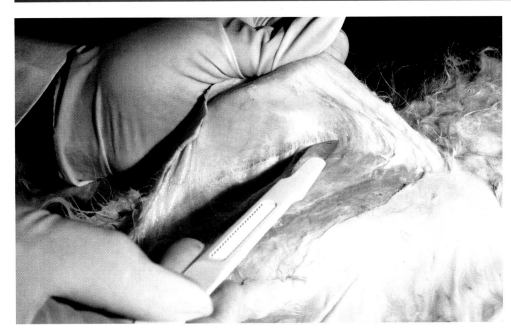

**A** Proper skinning technique. The edge of the scalpel blade is held next to the skin.

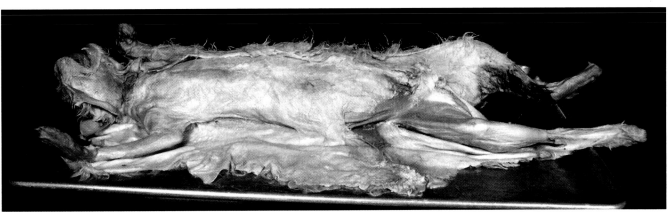

**B** Cat properly skinned.

Cutaneous maximus (trunk)

Platysma (neck and head region)

**C** Dermal muscles.

*Figure 2-4*　Skinning the cat.

**A** Before removal of overlying connective tissue.

***Figure 2-5*** Chest muscles.

**B** After removal of overlying connective tissue showing an example of differences in muscle fiber direction in contiguous or overlying muscles.

## Direction of Muscle Fibers

During the dissection of your specimen, it is very advantageous to be able to distinguish where one muscle ends and an adjacent or overlapping muscle begins. In order to identify individual muscles, look for the direction of muscle fiber orientation. For example, in muscles such as the abdominals, consisting of three sheetlike layers superimposed one on the other, it becomes essential to detect changes in fiber direction. Furthermore, most muscles are individually wrapped in layers of connective tissue called fascia and the areas where these layers abut one another can often be observed as distinct lines between muscles [Figure 2–5b]. Your ability to distinguish and separate contiguous muscles will be greatly enhanced by training yourself to appreciate these relationships and will be greatly appreciated by your instructor.

## Sewing and Cutting Muscles

Sewing a muscle may sound strange to you, but contending with the cut ends of several chest or leg muscles might change your mind. Since you will be identifying superficial and deep muscles, our solution is to first sew and cut the more superficial muscles and then dissect the underlying muscles.

Before attempting to sew and cut any muscle, dissect and separate the muscle from the point of origin to the point of insertion and free it from contiguous muscles. You are now ready to sew the muscle:

1. With approximately 18 inches of thread, thread the needle leaving one end longer than the other.

2. Make a knot only in the longer of the two free ends.

3. Insert the needle approximately 1/2 inch from the midline between the origin and insertion of the

muscle, pull it through and make a couple of over-cast stitches to thoroughly anchor the thread [Figure 2–6a]. Since the muscle will always be cut perpendicular to the muscle fibers, orient your sewing points accordingly.

4. Insert the needle approximately 1/2 inch from the midline of the muscle on the other side. Notice that there will be about an inch of space between the two anchor points [Figure 2–6b].

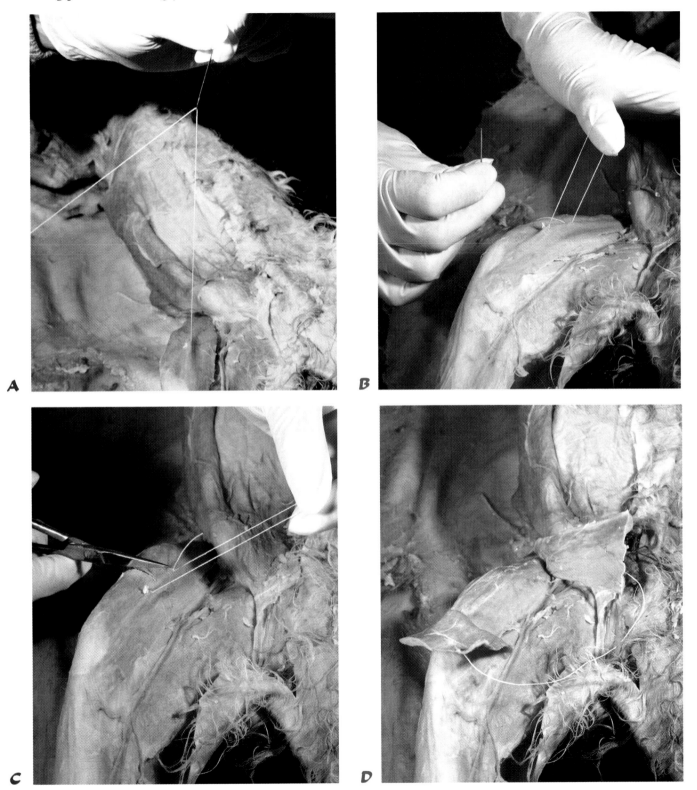

A

B

C

D

**Figure 2-6** How to sew and cut a designated muscle.

5. Pull the thread through, leaving a loop approximately three inches in length [Figure 2–6b].

6. Similar to the other side, make two to three overcast stitches to securely anchor the thread.

7. Cut the thread off at the second anchoring site, leaving the loop attached to the muscle.

8. Lift the muscle and carefully cut through the midline of the muscle only, leaving the loop of thread connecting the two ends [Figure 2–6c and Figure 2–6d]. **Remember to cut each muscle perpendicular to the muscle fibers.**

# Superficial Thoracic Muscles —

This group of muscles has a tendency to adhere tightly to one another, therefore, care should be exercised when separating them. Watch for the changes in muscle fiber orientation and the subtle white lines created by the connective tissue surrounding each muscle that indicate the extent of individual muscles.

## Pectoantebrachialis m.

This is the most superficial of the chest or pectoral muscles. It is a narrow, *thin* band that extends from the midline of the body to the upper portion of the forelimb [Figure 2–7]. This muscle does not occur in man.

**Origin:** Manubrium of the sternum

**Insertion:** Flat tendon into the superficial fascia of the antebrachium above the elbow

**Action:** Draws the forelimb toward the midline

**★★Sew and cut this muscle.**

## Pectoralis major m.

A superficial and deep portion of this muscle can be distinguished [Figure 2–7].

**SUPERFICIAL PORTION:** Flat, thin band, approximately the same width as the pectoantebrachialis and partially hidden by that muscle [Figure 2–8a].

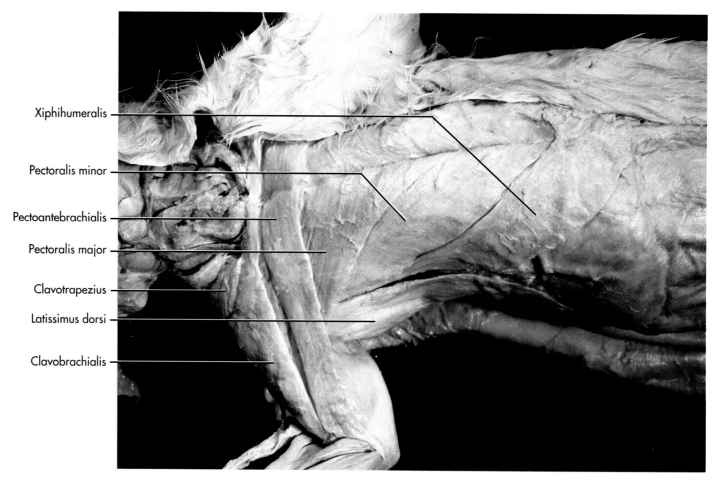

Xiphihumeralis

Pectoralis minor

Pectoantebrachialis

Pectoralis major

Clavotrapezius

Latissimus dorsi

Clavobrachialis

*Figure 2-7* Superficial chest muscles.

**Origin:** Midventral raphe and cranial half of the manubrium

**Insertion:** Middle third of the shaft of the humerus

**DEEP PORTION:** Flat band, approximately three times the width of the superficial part [Figure 2–8b]. In order to see the entire extent of this portion, the clavotrapezius and the clavobrachialis should now be dissected (see page 46). Exercise care while separating the clavotrapezius to avoid damaging the underlying pectoralis major. Furthermore, use care in separating this portion of the pectoralis major to avoid damaging the underlying pectoralis minor.

**Origin:** Cranial half of the sternum and midventral raphe

**Insertion:** Proximal third of the shaft of the humerus

**Common Action of Both Portions:** Draws the forelimb toward the midline and turns the manus forward

**★★Sew together and cut both portions of this muscle following careful separation of the two portions.**

### Pectoralis minor m.

A thick, fan shaped muscle extending caudally to and beneath the deep portion of the pectoralis major [Figure 2–7 and Figure 2–9]. Exert care to preserve the xiphihumeralis that passes dorsal to the pectoralis minor. Additionally, with great care, separate the latissimus dorsi from the lateral border of the pectoralis minor.

**Origin:** From the six sternebrae and sometimes the xiphoid process, resulting in the appearance

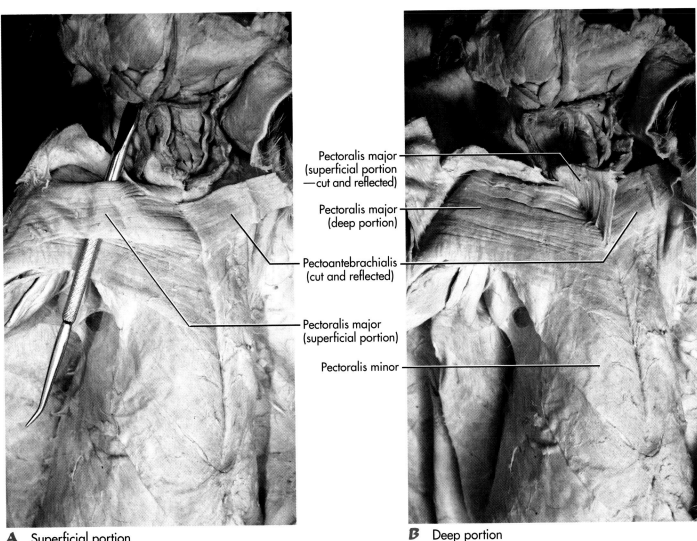

Pectoralis major
(superficial portion
—cut and reflected)

Pectoralis major
(deep portion)

Pectoantebrachialis
(cut and reflected)

Pectoralis major
(superficial portion)

Pectoralis minor

**A** Superficial portion

**B** Deep portion

*Figure 2-8* Pectoralis major.

of several slips that appear to be separate muscles

**Insertion:** Ventral border of the humerus from the bicipital groove to the middle of the humerus

**Action:** Draws the forelimb toward the midline

★★**Sew and cut this muscle.**

### Xiphihumeralis m.

A long, very thin, narrow band of muscle, lying along the posterior border of the pectoralis minor and,

according to some anatomists, actually a part of that muscle [Figure 2–7]. The xiphihumeralis muscle is absent in humans.

**Origin:** Median raphe in the vicinity of the xiphoid process

**Insertion:** Along the ventral border of the bicipital groove of the humerus

**Action:** Synergistic with the pectoralis minor in drawing the forelimb toward the midline

★★**Sew and cut this muscle.**

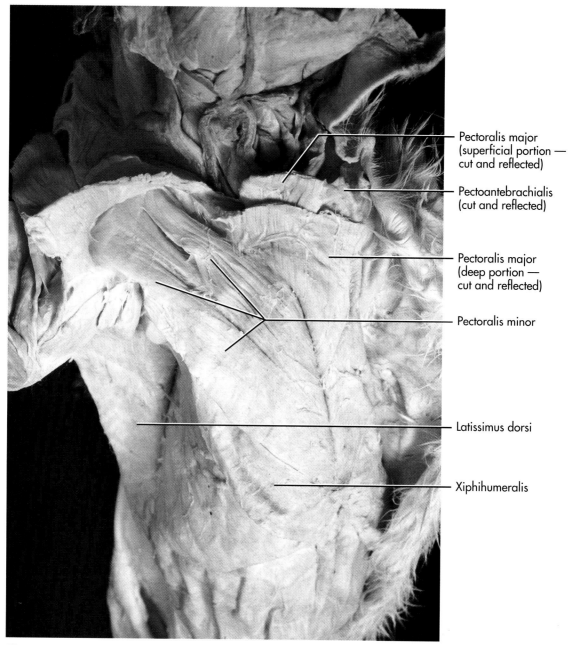

Pectoralis major (superficial portion — cut and reflected)

Pectoantebrachialis (cut and reflected)

Pectoralis major (deep portion — cut and reflected)

Pectoralis minor

Latissimus dorsi

Xiphihumeralis

*Figure 2-9* Pectoralis minor.

# Abdominal Muscles

Three sheetlike muscles and a longitudinal, bandlike muscle make up this group. Note that the left and right portions of the abdominal muscles are separated by a longitudinal white line of connective tissue known as the **linea alba**. The sheetlike muscles are thin and quite extensive, supporting the entire abdominal area and a portion of the ventral thoracic region. These muscles are layered and adhere closely to one another by means of fascia. Direction of fibers within each sheet are distinctive and this feature is used as a tool to identify the individual muscles. To facilitate dissection of these sheets, a three sided opening, one inch on each side should be made in the flank [Figure 2–10]. Carefully separate and identify the sheets of muscle.

## External oblique m.

The direction of the fibers of this muscle extend craniodorsally [Figure 2–10]. This is the most superficial of the three sheetlike abdominal muscles.

  **Origin:** Lumbodorsal fascia and the last 9 or 10 ribs

**Insertion:** Median raphe of distal portion of sternum, linea alba from sternum to pubis

  **Action:** Compresses the abdominal region

## Internal oblique m.

The direction of the fibers of this muscle extend caudodorsally [Figure 2–10]. This sheetlike muscle lies directly beneath the external oblique.

  **Origin:** Lumbodorsal fascia in common with the external oblique and iliac crest

**Insertion:** Linea alba by a thin aponeurosis in common with the external oblique and transversus abdominis

  **Action:** Compresses the abdominal region

## Transversus abdominis m.

Fibers of this muscle sheet extend nearly transversely between the origin and insertion [Figure 2–10]. This muscle sheet lies directly beneath the internal oblique.

  **Origin:** Aponeurosis from the costal cartilages of the vertebrochondral and vertebral ribs, transverse processes of lumbar vertebrae and ventral border of the ilium

**Insertion:** Linea alba in common with the two obliques

  **Action:** Compresses the abdomen

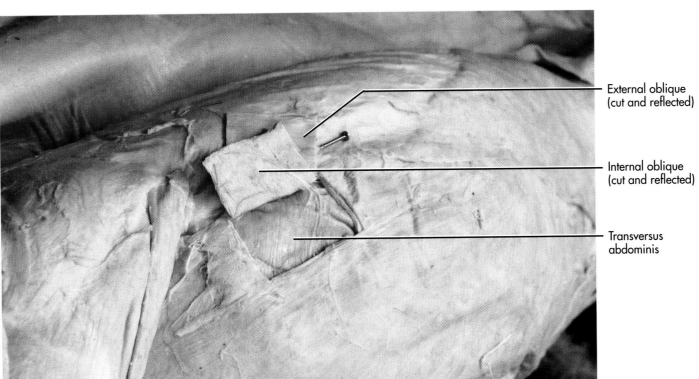

External oblique
(cut and reflected)

Internal oblique
(cut and reflected)

Transversus
abdominis

*Figure 2-10*    Abdominal window: abdominal muscles.

## Rectus abdominis m.

This muscle occurs as a longitudinally directed band of muscle on either side of the linea alba [Figure 2–11]. This muscle is encased in a sheath formed by the aponeuroses of the other three abdominal muscles. In humans, this muscle is reduced at its anterior end.

**Origin:** Tubercle of pubis

**Insertion:** First and second costal cartilage, proximal end of sternum by a tendon passing dorsal to the transversus costarum

**Action:** Compresses the abdominal region, pulls sternum and ribs caudally causing flexion of the trunk.

# Deep Thoracic Muscles ———

## Serratus ventralis m.

This is a large fan-shaped muscle, made up of obvious individual slips, extending between the thorax and the scapula [Figure 2–11]. Notice that these individual slips are more conspicuous at the caudal end of this muscle. In the human, this muscle is represented by two separate muscles, a cranial Levator scapulae originating from the cervical vertebrae and the caudal Serratus anterior originating from the ribs.

**Origin:** From the surface of the first nine or ten ribs and the transverse processes of the last five cervical vertebrae

**Insertion:** Vertebral border of the scapula

**Action:** Draws the scapula toward the thoracic wall and helps to support the scapula

## Scalenus anterior, posterior, and medius m.

These three bandlike muscles, Scalenus anterior, the most ventral, Scalenus posterior, the most dorsal, and Scalenus medius, situated between the two, lie at an oblique angle along the lateral aspect of the thorax [Figure 2–11 and Figure 2–20a]. Cranially, these three muscles unite into a single band or bundle.

**Origin:** S. anterior m. — from the second and third ribs, S. posterior m. — from the third or fourth ribs, S. medius m. — from the sixth through the ninth ribs

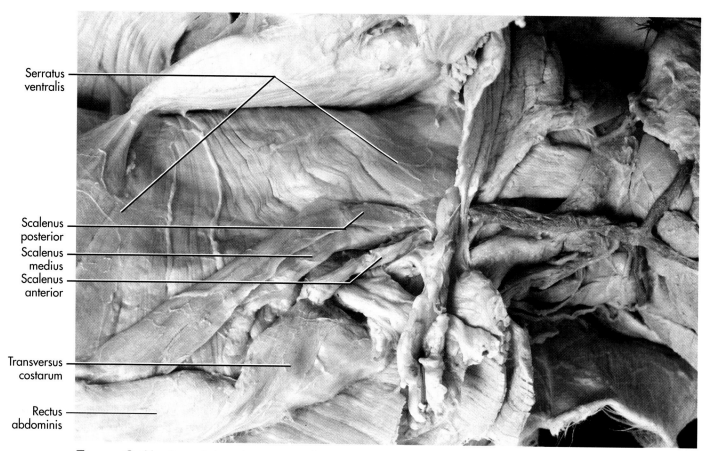

**Figure 2-11** Cranial deep thoracic muscles. **Note:** This cat had an unusually long scalenus posterior.

**Insertion:** Transverse processes of all cervical vertebrae

**Action:** Bends the neck and pulls ribs cranially

**★★This is an example of a muscle, whose origin and insertion may be reversed, thereby producing contrasting actions depending upon the fixed end.**

## *Transversus costarum m.*

This is a thin, bandlike muscle extending from the sternum and covering the cranial portion of the rectus abdominus muscle [Figure 2–11 and Figure 2–20a].

**Origin:** From the side of the sternum

**Insertion:** First rib and costal cartilage

**Action:** Pulls the ribs cranially

## *Intercostalis externus m.*

Note that the fibers of this outer layer of muscles lying in the intercostal spaces between adjacent ribs are oriented craniodorsally, similar to the external oblique layer, from which they were derived [Figure 2–12]. These muscles are absent from the costal cartilages of the first through the seventh ribs.

**Origin:** From a cranial rib

**Insertion:** To an adjacent caudal rib

**Action:** Protracts the ribs

## *Intercostalis internus m.*

This layer lies directly below the external intercostals [Figure 2–12]. Note that the fibers of these muscles are oriented caudodorsally, similar to the internal oblique layer, from which they were derived.

**Origin:** From a caudal rib

**Insertion:** To an adjacent cranial rib

**Action:** Retracts the ribs

## *Transversus thoracis m.*

This incomplete third layer lies beneath part of the internal intercostals and represents the thoracic portion of the transversus abdominis. It can best be seen later during the dissection of the thoracic cavity.

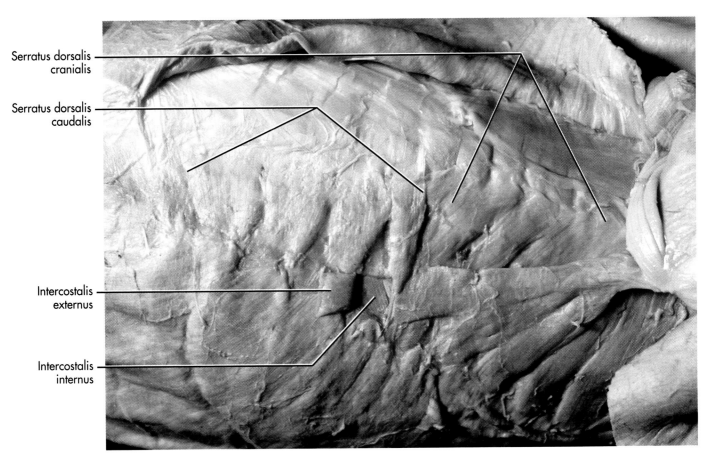

Serratus dorsalis cranialis

Serratus dorsalis caudalis

Intercostalis externus

Intercostalis internus

***Figure 2-12*** Caudal deep thoracic muscles.

Origin: Dorsolateral border of the sternum between the third to the eighth rib

Insertion: Costal cartilages near the junction of the ribs

Action: Moves ribs

### Serratus dorsalis cranialis m.

This thin layer of muscle appearing as slips extends along the dorsal part of the thorax and neck beneath the latissimus dorsi [Figure 2–12].

Origin: From the cervicothoracic middorsal fascia

Insertion: On the outer surface of the first nine ribs

Action: Draws the ribs cranially

### Serratus dorsalis caudalis m.

This thin layer of muscles, also appearing as slips, extends from the caudal end of serratus dorsalis cranialis to the lumbar region [Figure 2–12]. Note that, although appearing continuous, serratus dorsalis cranialis and serratus dorsalis caudalis possess fibers that are oriented in directions opposite one another.

Origin: From the lumbar middorsal fascia

Insertion: Last four or five ribs

Action: Draws the ribs caudally

## Superficial Back Muscles

### Clavotrapezius m.

This is a wide, flat muscle that covers most of the lateral portion of the neck [Figure 2–13 and Figure 2–14]. Take note that the levator scapulae ventralis passes below the clavotrapezius and must be separated from the clavotrapezius before it is cut.

Origin: Lambdoidal ridge, middorsal raphe over spine of the axis

Insertion: Clavicle and raphe between clavotrapezius and clavobrachialis

Action: Forward extension of the humerus

**★★Sew and cut this muscle.**

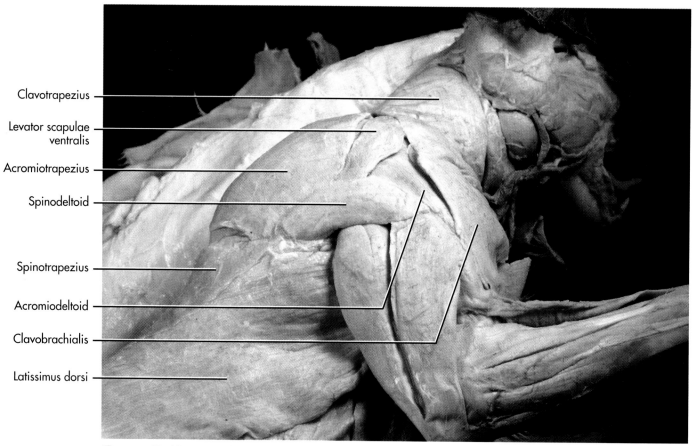

*Figure 2-13*  Superficial back muscles I.

## Clavobrachialis m.

This muscle is a continuation of the clavotrapezius onto the forelimb and is considered by some anatomists to be the cranial portion of the deltoid and is called the clavodeltoid [Figure 2–13 and Figure 2–14].

**Origin:** Clavicle and raphe between clavotrapezius and clavobrachialis

**Insertion:** Commonly inserted with the brachialis through a tendon on the medial surface of the ulna distal to the semilunar notch

**Action:** Flexes the forearm

**★★Sew and cut this muscle.**

## Acromiotrapezius m.

This is a *thin* trapezoidal muscle lying over the scapulae [Figure 2–13 and Figure 2–14]. Extreme care must be exercised while dissecting this muscle to prevent damage to the whitish middorsal tendon and fascia that hold the left and right acromiotrapezius muscles together over the vertebral column.

**Origin:** Middorsal line from the spine of the axis to the spinous process of the fourth thoracic vertebra

**Insertion:** Metacromion process and spine of the scapula

**Action:** Adduct and stabilize the position of the scapulae

**★★Sew and cut this muscle, *not* the aponeurosis!**

## Spinotrapezius m.

This is a triangular muscle and the most posterior of the trapezius group [Figure 2–13 and Figure 2–14]. With great care, dissect this muscle from the craniodorsal surface of the latissimus dorsi.

**Origin:** May originate from the spinous processes of most of the thoracic vertebrae

**Insertion:** Fascia of supraspinatus and infraspinatus muscles on either side of the spine

**Action:** Pulls the scapula dorsally and caudally

In the human, the trapezius is represented by a fusion of the three muscles in the cat.

**★★Sew and cut this muscle.**

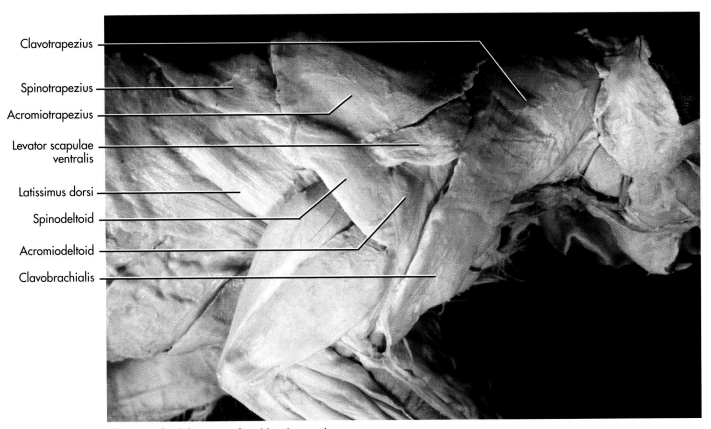

Clavotrapezius
Spinotrapezius
Acromiotrapezius
Levator scapulae ventralis
Latissimus dorsi
Spinodeltoid
Acromiodeltoid
Clavobrachialis

*Figure 2-14*  Superficial back muscles II.

## Latissimus dorsi m.

This is a large, thick, flat, triangular muscle just posterior to the trapezius group and covered craniodorsally by the spinotrapezius [Figure 2–13 and Figure 2–14]. The reason that the axillary region often appears to be so ragged is that the cutaneus maximus has its cranial origin in the axilla and has probably been cut off and left attached to the skin. As previously mentioned, in the dissection of the pectoralis minor, exercise care while separating the lateral edges of the latissimus dorsi and pectoralis minor.

Origin: Neural spines of the fourth or fifth thoracic to the sixth lumbar vertebrae

Insertion: Medial surface of shaft of humerus at the proximal end

Action: Pulls forelimb dorsocaudally

**★★Sew and cut this muscle.**

## Lower Back Muscles

To begin the dissection of the lower back and thoracic muscles use a pair of forceps to hold up the lumbodorsal fascia, make a small hole in the double layered fascia and then cut a three-sided window approximately two inches on a side [Figure 2–15]. Depending upon the size of the cat, the dimensions of the window may vary.

## Lumbar and Thoracic

### Multifidus spinae m.

This is an extensive muscle consisting of many bundles of fibers that can best be distinguished abutting the vertebral column in the lumbar region [Figure 2–15].

Origin: Primarily transverse processes of vertebrae

Insertion: Neural spines of more anterior vertebrae

Action: When both sides contract simultaneously, extends the vertebral column; when contracted unilaterally, bends the vertebral column toward that side

### Longissimus dorsi m.

This is another extensive muscle occupying the space between the neural spines and transverse processes and extending from the prominent lumbar region to the much less bulky thoracic and cervical regions

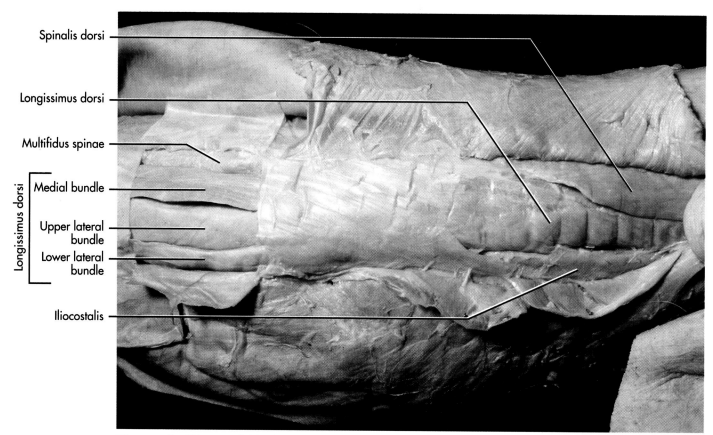

*Figure 2-15* Caudal back window: lumbar and thoracic back muscle complex.

[Figure 2–15]. There are a number of distinguishable bundles in the lumbar region, a medial and a lateral that is further subdivided by fascia into upper and lower lateral portions. Note that the longissimus capitis is the cervical extension of the longissimus dorsi.

**Origin:** Medial bundle — From neural spines of vertebrae in the vertebral column; Lateral bundle — From the ilium and neural spines of the vertebrae in the vertebral column

**Insertion:** Onto various processes of more anterior vertebrae of the vertebral vertebrae

**Action:** Extends the vertebral column

### Spinalis dorsi m.

This muscle is formed as a medial separation of the longissimus dorsi in the thoracic region [Figure 2–15].

**Origin:** From the neural spines of more posterior thoracic vertebrae

**Insertion:** Transverse processes of more cranial vertebrae

**Action:** Extends the vertebral column

### Iliocostalis m.

This is a thin muscle confined to the thoracic region consisting of a number of bundles lying lateral to the longissimus dorsi over the dorsal aspect of the ribs [Figure 2–15].

**Origin:** Lateral surface of the ribs

**Insertion:** Onto the lateral surface of more cranial ribs

**Action:** Pulls the ribs together

## Muscles of the Neck
### Sternomastoid m.

The origin of this paired bandlike muscle forms the apex of a V just cranial to the anterior end of the sternum while the arms of the V continue toward the base of the ear [Figure 2–16a and Figure 2–16b].

**Origin:** Cranial end of the manubrium

**Insertion:** Lambdoidal ridge and mastoid portion of the temporal bone

**Action:** **As a pair** — flexion of the head
**Individually** — turns the head

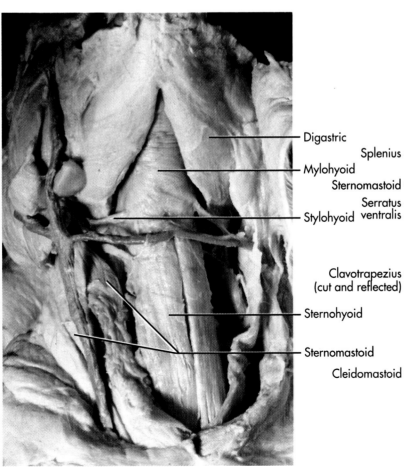

Digastric
Mylohyoid
Stylohyoid
Sternohyoid
Sternomastoid

**A**  Superficial neck muscles

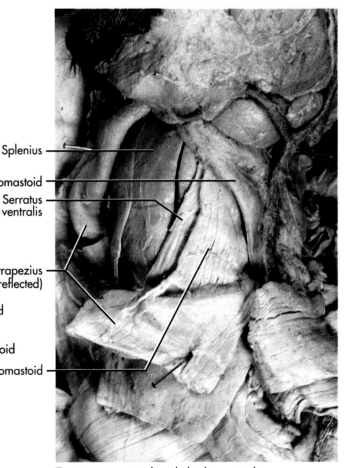

Splenius
Sternomastoid
Serratus ventralis
Clavotrapezius (cut and reflected)
Cleidomastoid

**B**  Sternomastoid and cleidomastoid

**Figure 2-16**  Muscles of the neck.

## Cleidomastoid m.

A flat bandlike muscle that extends between the clavicle and the temporal region of the skull lies dorsolateral to the sternomastoid [Figure 2–16b].

Origin: Mastoid process of the temporal bone

Insertion: Clavicle

Action: When clavicle is stationary — turns the head; When head is stationary — moves the clavicle anteriorly

**★★In the human, the sternomastoid and the cleidomastoid muscles are united into a single muscle, the sternocleidomastoid with similar actions.**

## Sternohyoid m.

A slender bandlike muscle lying along either side of the midventral line of the neck [Figure 2–17].

Origin: First costal cartilage

Insertion: Hyoid bone

Action: Retracts the hyoid

## Sternothyroid m.

This slender bandlike muscle lies somewhat dorsal to the sternohyoid and lateral to the trachea [Figure 2–18].

Origin: First costal cartilage

Insertion: Thyroid cartilage of the larynx

Action: Retracts the larynx

## Thyrohyoid m.

This is a small bandlike muscle lying along the lateral aspect of the larynx [Figure 2–18].

Origin: Lateral portion of the thyroid cartilage of the larynx

Insertion: Hyoid bone

Action: Protracts the larynx

## Cricothyroid m.

This broad, flat muscle band lies on the ventral surface of the cricoid cartilage of the larynx [Figure 2–18].

Origin: Surface of the cricoid cartilage

Insertion: Thyroid cartilage

Action: Regulates tension of the vocal cords

## Stylohyoid m.

This is a very slender band stretching across the posterior surface of the digastric m. [Figure 2–16a]. **Great care must exercised in dissecting this muscle because it is overlain with connective tissue and this, combined with its minute size, makes it especially vulnerable to removal.**

Origin: Stylohyal, a segment of the lesser cornua of the hyoid

Insertion: Body of the hyoid

Action: Elevates the hyoid

## Digastric m.

This thick muscle lies along the medial ventral border of the mandible [Figure 2–16a].

Origin: From the mastoid and jugular processes

Insertion: Medial ventral border of the mandible

Action: Depresses the mandible

## Mylohyoid m.

This thin, roughly triangular muscle with distinct transverse fibers, lying between the two dentary bones of the mandible, consists of a pair of muscles connected by a thin, tendinous median raphe [Figure 2–16a]. The raphe extends from the mandibular symphysis to the hyoid. **With a sharp scalpel make an incision through the median raphe. Carefully reflect one of these thin muscles toward the mandible, taking care not to shred its fibers.**

Origin: Medial surface of the mandibular body

Insertion: Median raphe

Action: Elevates the floor of the mouth

## Geniohyoid m.

A narrow, elongated muscle that lies along the median raphe dorsal to the mylohyoid [Figure 2–17].

Origin: Ventral surface of the mandible just lateral to the symphysis

Insertion: Body of the hyoid

Action: Protracts the hyoid

## Genioglossus m.

This is another narrow, elongated muscle that lies dorsolateral to the geniohyoid [Figure 2–17].

Origin: Ventral surface of the mandible, near the symphysis, and dorsal to the geniohyoid

Insertion: Tongue

Action: Draws tip of the tongue backward and the root forward

## Hyoglossus m.

Lateral to the geniohyoid lies this roughly rhomboidal muscle [Figure 2–17]. It can be readily identified since the hypoglossal nerve (C.N. XII) lies over its surface.

Origin: Body of the hyoid

Insertion: Tongue

Action: Retracts and depresses the tongue

## Styloglossus m.

This is a bandlike muscle lying lateral to the hyoglossus and parallel to the digastric m. [Figure 2–17]. To observe the styloglossus, carefully pull the digastric muscle laterally.

Origin: Mastoid process

Insertion: Tongue

Action: Retracts and elevates the tongue

Intrinsic muscles of the tongue are entirely contained within the body of the tongue and are known as the **lingualis proprius**. They make up the bulk of the tongue and assist in tongue movement.

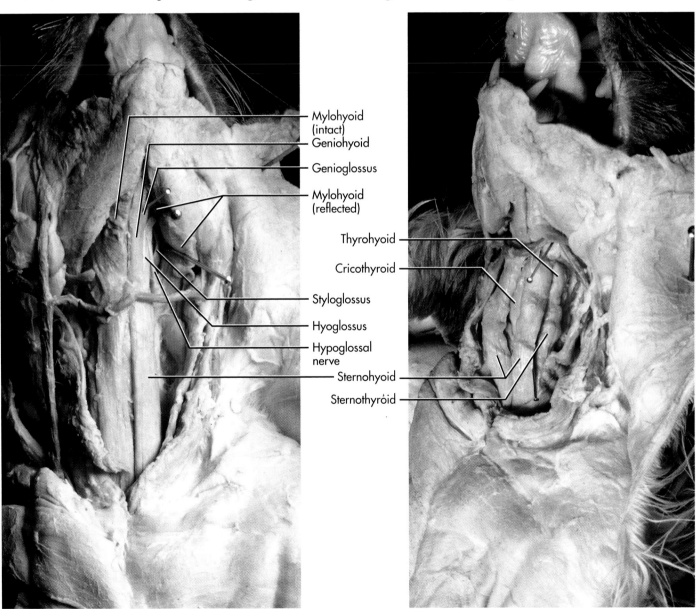

**Figure 2-17** Deep neck muscles.

**Figure 2-18** Ventral neck muscles.

# Deep Neck and Back Muscles —

## Rhomboideus capitis m.

This is the cranial portion of the rhomboideus complex that consists of a narrow, thin flat lateral band [Figure 2–19].

**Origin:** The mediolateral half of the lambdoidal ridge

**Insertion:** Along the dorsal border of the scapula

**Action:** Rotates and pulls scapula cranially

## Rhomboideus cervicis and thoracis m.

This portion of the complex is a thick trapezoidal muscle separated into an anterior cervical and posterior thoracic part [Figure 2–19].

**Origin:** Caudal portion of the cervical supraspinous ligament and vertebral spines of the first four thoracic vertebrae

**Insertion:** Vertebral border and outer surface of the scapula

**Action:** Adducts scapulae

## Splenius m.

This large, flat muscle on the dorsolateral aspect of the neck lies beneath the rhomboideus capitis [Figure 2–20a].

**Origin:** Midorsal line of neck and adjacent fascia

**Insertion:** Along the lambdoidal ridge of the occipital bone

**Action:** The joint action of the left and right splenius muscles elevate or extend the head, individually, each muscle flexes the head laterally

## Longissimus capitis m.

This narrow, straplike muscle, a cranial continuation of the longissimus dorsi, lies along the ventral edge of the spenius and may have a tendency to fuse with it [Figure 2–20a].

**Origin:** By several tendons from the prezygapophyses of cervical vertebrae 4–7

**Insertion:** Mastoid process of the temporal bone

**Action:** Lateral flexion of the head

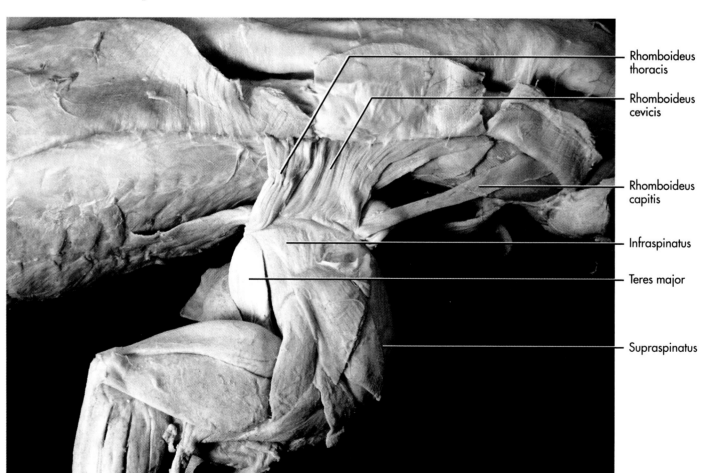

Rhomboideus
thoracis

Rhomboideus
cevicis

Rhomboideus
capitis

Infraspinatus

Teres major

Supraspinatus

*Figure 2–19*   Deep lateral neck and shoulder muscles I.

The next two muscles are sometimes identified as the semispinalis cervicis and capitis. These are flat muscles lying beneath the splenius [Figure 2–20b]. In order to identify these muscles, it will be necessary to bisect the splenius at right angles to its fibers and reflect the halves.

### Semispinalis cervicis m.

**Origin:** Spinous processes of cervical vertebra 7 and the first three thoracic vertebrae

**Insertion:** Median third of the lambdoidal crest

**Action:** Elevates the head

### Semispinalis capitis m.

**Origin:** Prezygapophyses of cervical vertebrae 3–7 and first three thoracic vertebrae

**Insertion:** Median third of the lambdoidal crest

**Action:** Elevates the head

### Longus colli m.

This is a narrow band of muscle that lies along the lateral aspect of the neck ventral to the scalene bundle [Figure 2–20a].

**Origin:** From the ventral surfaces of the first six thoracic vertebrae, and ventral surfaces of bodies and transverse processes of the cervical vertebrae

**Insertion:** Slips from the thoracic vertebrae unite and insert commonly onto the ventral portion of the sixth cervical transverse process, while slips from the cervicals extend cranially to insert on the midline of the centra of more anterior cervical vertebrae

**Action:** Bends the neck both ventrally and laterally

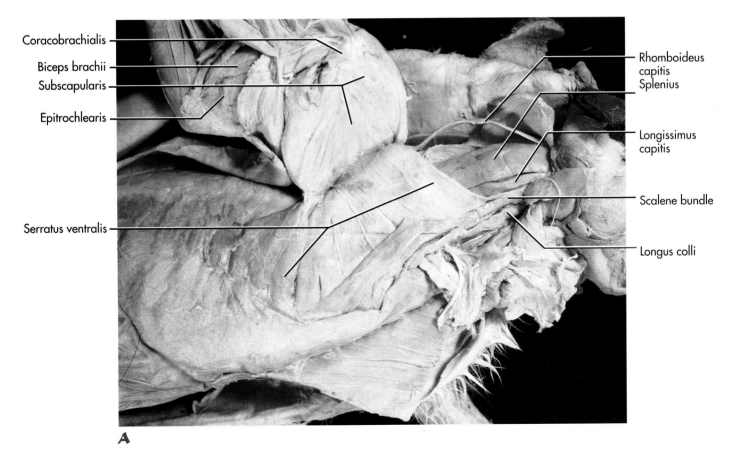

**A**

***Figure 2-20***   Deep lateral neck and shoulder muscles II.

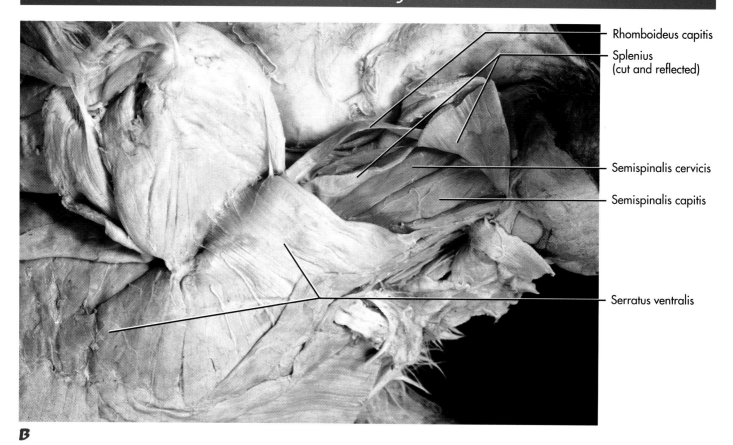

Rhomboideus capitis

Splenius
(cut and reflected)

Semispinalis cervicis

Semispinalis capitis

Serratus ventralis

**B**

Biceps brachii

Coracobrachialis

Subscapularis

Teres major

**C**

*Figure 2–20 (continued)*

# Muscles of the Head

There are both superficial and deep muscles of the head. A number of superficial muscles are primarily derived from portions of the platysma and are involved in producing actions identified as those of facial expression, e.g., eye, ear, nose and lip movements and are not included in this discussion. The following jaw muscles are derivatives of simple jaw adductors seen in primitive vertebrates.

## Masseter m.

The heavy muscle projecting prominently beneath and posterior to the eye and making up the cheek region in the cat is the masseter [Figure 2–21]. Although this muscle's construction consists of three separate layers of fibers whose directions are distinct, we will not attempt to dissect them.

**Origin:** From the zygomatic arch

**Insertion:** Masseteric fossa and adjacent portions of the mandible

**Action:** Elevation of mandible

## Temporalis m.

This a massive muscle occupying the temporal fossa of the skull [Figure 2–22].

**Origin:** Most fibers originate from the temporal bone and a few from the zygomatic arch

**Insertion:** Coronoid process of the mandible

**Action:** Elevates mandible

## Pterygoideus externus m.

This muscle of mastication is located ventral to the temporalis.

**Origin:** From the external pterygoid fossa that extends from the sphenopalatine foramen of the palatine to the foramen rotundum of the basisphenoid

**Insertion:** Ventral border of the medial aspect of the mandible

**Action:** Elevates the mandible

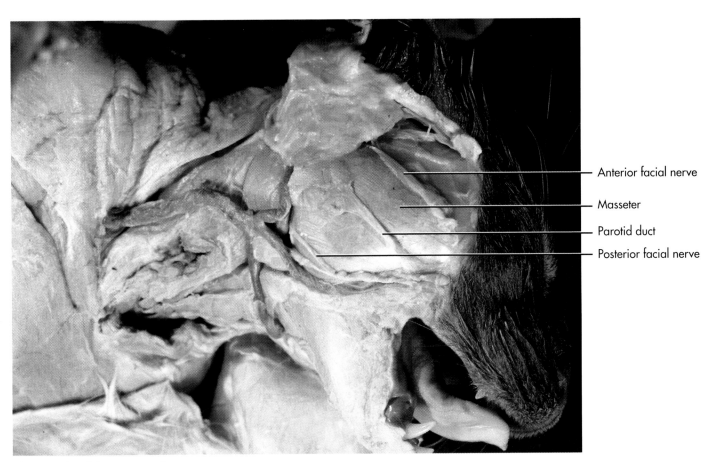

Anterior facial nerve

Masseter

Parotid duct

Posterior facial nerve

*Figure 2–21*    Jaw muscle I.

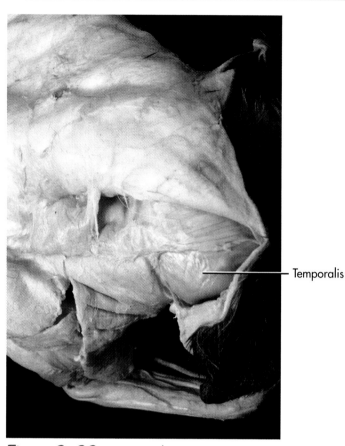

Figure 2-22 — Temporalis

**Figure 2-22** Jaw muscle II.

## Pterygoideus internus m.

A second muscle of mastication is located posterior to the previous muscle.

Origin: From the internal pterygoid fossa lying along the lateral surface of the pterygoid process and hamulus of the basisphenoid

Insertion: Angular process of the mandible and pterygoideus externus

Action: Synergistic with pterygoideus externus in elevating the mandible

## Shoulder Muscles

### Supraspinatus m.

This thick muscle lies in the supraspinous fossa of the scapula [Figure 2-19].

Origin: From the entire surface of the supraspinous fossa

Insertion: Greater tuberosity of the humerus

Action: Protracts the humerus

## Infraspinatus m.

This thick, but somewhat smaller muscle fills the infraspinous fossa [Figure 2-19].

Origin: From the surface of the infraspinous fossa

Insertion: Lateral surface of the greater tuberosity of the humerus

Action: Rotates the humerus laterally

## Teres major m.

This is a thick triangular muscle occupying the axillary border of the scapula [Figure 2-19]. Carefully separate the teres major from the infraspinatus.

Origin: Dorsal third of the axillary border

Insertion: Common tendon with the latissimus dorsi onto the medial surface of the shaft of the proximal end of the humerus

Action: Flexes and rotates the humerus medially

## Levator scapulae ventralis m.

This is a band-like muscle whose cranial end emerges from beneath the clavotrapezius and a part of which can be seen lying between the clavotrapezius and acromiotrapezius muscles [Figure 2-13 and Figure 2-14]. This muscle is not present in humans.

Origin: By two heads from the ventral surface of the transverse process of the atlas and from the basioccipital near the tympanic bulla

Insertion: The two heads unite forming a flat band that inserts onto the ventral border of the metacromion of the scapula and into the infraspinous fossa

Action: Pulls scapula craniad

## Acromiodeltoid m.

This flat muscle is positioned ventral to the levator scapulae ventralis and caudal to the clavobrachialis [Figure 2-13 and Figure 2-14].

Origin: Acromion of the scapula

Insertion: Surface of the spinodeltoid muscle

Action: Flexes the humerus and rotates it laterally

## Spinodeltoid m.

This muscle lies ventral to the acromiotrapezius and levator scapulae ventralis and caudal to the acromio-deltoid [Figure 2–13 and Figure 2–14]. The human deltoid is equivalent to the clavobrachialis (clavodel-toid), acromiodeltoid and spinodeltoid muscles of the cat.

**Origin:** Spine of the scapula

**Insertion:** Deltoid ridge of the humerus

**Action:** Synergistic action with the acromiodeltoid in flexing the humerus and rotating it outward

## Teres minor m.

This is a small, somewhat triangular muscle located between the infraspinatus and long head of the triceps brachii and beneath the spinodeltoid [Figure 2–23].

**Origin:** Axillary border of the scapula near the glenoid fossa

**Insertion:** Greater tuberosity of the humerus

**Action:** Synergistic action with the infraspinatus in rotating the humerus laterally

## Subscapularis m.

This large, medial, triangular muscle is located in the subscapular fossa [Figure 2–20a and Figure 2–20c].

**Origin:** Almost the entire subscapular fossa

**Insertion:** Dorsal border of lesser tuberosity of the humerus

**Action:** Adducts the humerus

# Muscles of the Upper Arm or Brachium

## Coracobrachialis m.

A very short band-like muscle that lies on the medial aspect of the shoulder joint in close proximity to the insertion of the subscapularis and the origin of the biceps brachii [Figure 2–20a and Figure 2–20c].

**Origin:** Coracoid process of the scapula

**Insertion:** Proximal end of humerus

**Action:** Adducts the humerus

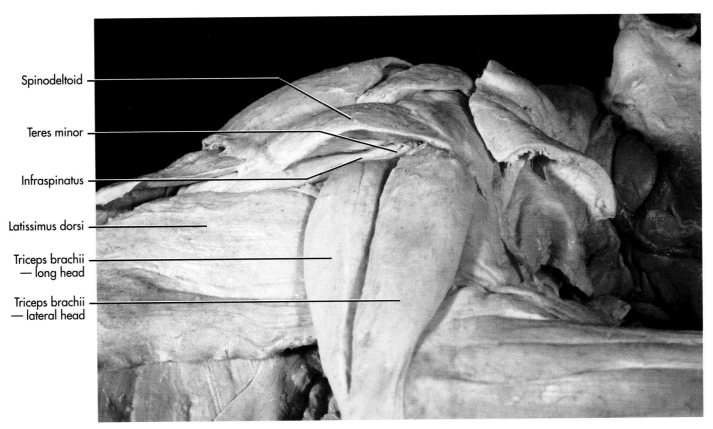

Spinodeltoid

Teres minor

Infraspinatus

Latissimus dorsi

Triceps brachii
— long head

Triceps brachii
— lateral head

**Figure 2–23**    Teres minor.

## Epitrochlearis m.

This delicate, flat muscle appears on the medial surface of the brachium and partially overlies the triceps brachii [Figure 2–20a and Figure 2–27a]. The muscle has no homolog in man.

**Origin:** From the lateral border of latissimus dorsi

**Insertion:** By a thin aponeurosis and continuous with the antebrachial fascia onto the olecranon process of the ulna

**Action:** Acts synergistically with the triceps brachii in extending the antebrachium

## Biceps brachii m.

This is a thick muscle lying on the cranial surface of the humerus [Figure 2–20a and Figure 2–20c]. In the human, this muscle has two heads, a long and a short head, while in the cat only the homolog of the long head occurs.

**Origin:** By a tendon above the glenoid fossa of the scapula

**Insertion:** By a tendon on the radial tuberosity

**Action:** Flexes the forearm synergistically with the brachialis, tends to supinate the manus and stabilizes the shoulder joint

## Triceps brachii m.

A very large, lateral muscle consisting of three heads that originate from separate sites, but with a common insertion [Figure 2–24].

**Origin:** (1) Lateral head — deltoid ridge of proximal end of humerus

        (2) Long head — Near glenoid fossa of axillary border of scapula

        (3) Medial head — consists of three parts all of which originate from the humerus

**Insertion:** By a common strong tendon onto the surface of the olecranon process of the ulna

**Action:** Extends the forearm

## Anconeus m.

A small triangular muscle that covers the lateral surface of the elbow [Figure 2–25].

**Origin:** Dorsal surface of the lateral epicondyle

**Insertion:** Lateral surface of the ulna

**Action:** Acts synergistically with the triceps brachii in extending the forearm

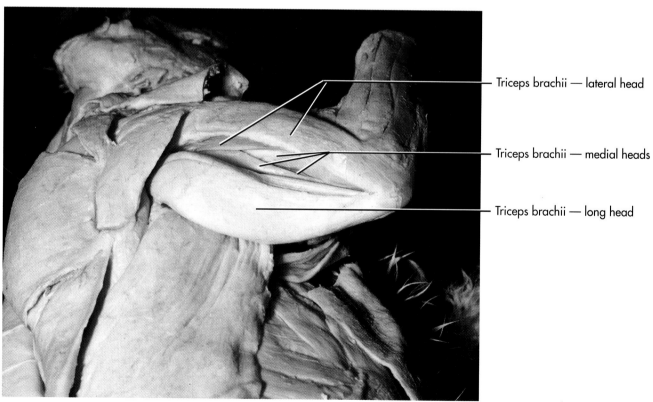

Triceps brachii — lateral head

Triceps brachii — medial heads

Triceps brachii — long head

**Figure 2–24** Triceps brachii.

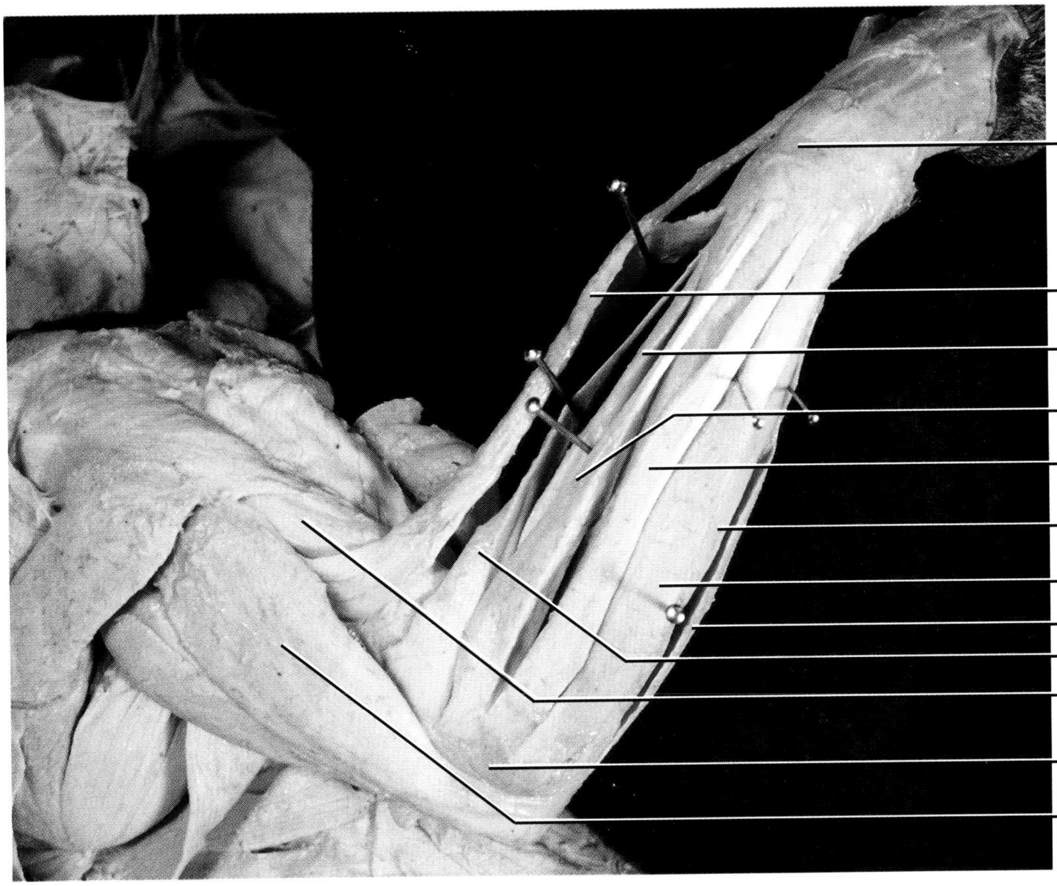
Extensor retinaculum
Brachioradialis
Extensor carpi radialis brevis
Extensor digitorum communis
Extensor digitorum lateralis
Flexor digitorum profundus — ulnar head
Extensor carpi ulnaris
Flexor carpi ulnaris — ulnar head
Extensor carpi radialis longus
Brachialis
Anconeus
Triceps brachii — lateral head

**Figure 2–25** Superficial forearm extensors.

### Brachialis m.

A lateral muscle that is located along the cranial surface of the humerus and lies partially obscured by the lateral head of the triceps brachii [Figure 2–25].

**Origin:** Lateral surface of the shaft of the humerus

**Insertion:** Lateral surface of ulna near semilunar notch

**Action:** Flexes the forearm or antebrachium and is synergistic with the biceps brachii.

## Muscles of the Forearm or Antebrachium

Notice that the antebrachium is covered with a two-layered connective tissue called the **antebrachial fascia.** The outer layer is loose and is a continuation of the subcutaneous fascia. The inner layer is in close contact with the underlying muscles and extends between the dorsal or extensor muscles and adheres very closely to their tendons. This sheet is continuous on the ventral or flexor surface and is closely attached to the pronator teres and radius. In the carpal area the fascia thickens to form a dorsal transverse ligament, the **extensor retinaculum** [Figure 2–25] and a ventral transverse ligament, the **flexor retinaculum** [Figure 2–27c] to hold the tendons of these muscles in place. It further continues dorsally as the fascia of the manus, while ventrally on the palmar surface it unites with the pad and is continuous with the tendon sheaths of the flexors.

At the level of the first phalanx, narrow, tough **annular ligaments** that surround the tendons of the flexor muscles are found in these sheets. During the dissection of the forearm muscles it is *imperative* to trace tendons of each of the muscles to their endpoint. Carefully remove the antebrachial fascia, being especially cautious in the region of the tendons, retinacula and the brachioradialis muscle. This is an area in which one can be destructively creative. Take great care in separating the muscles while maintaining their integrity. In other words, do not split muscles. The brachioradialis, the extensor carpi radialis longus, the extensor carpi radialis brevis and flexor digitorum profundus (ulnar head) muscles can be observed and identified in dorsal and ventral views of the antebrachium. You must be able to recognize them in both views.

## Brachioradialis m.

This narrow, bandlike muscle extends along the radial border of the antebrachium in company with blood vessels and a nerve [Figure 2–25].

**Origin:** Mid-shaft of the humerus

**Insertion:** Styloid process of the radius

**Action:** Supinates the manus

## Extensor carpi radialis longus m.

This is a slender muscle whose main mass lies on the radial side of the antebrachium, deep to the brachioradialis [Figure 2–25].

**Origin:** Lateral supracondyloid ridge of the humerus

**Insertion:** Thin tendon at the base of the second metacarpal

**Action:** Extends the manus

## Extensor carpi radialis brevis m.

This slender, somewhat shorter muscle, lies just medial to the extensor carpi radialis longus and must be carefully separated from it [Figure 2–25].

**Origin:** Lateral supracondyloid ridge of the humerus below the origin of the extensor carpi radialis longus

**Insertion:** Tendon at the base of the third metacarpal

**Action:** Extends the manus

## Extensor digitorum communis m.

A long slender dorsal muscle that partially overlies the extensor carpi longus and brevis [Figure 2–25]. The human muscle is called simply, extensor digitorum.

**Origin:** Lateral supracondyloid ridge of humerus below the origin of the extensor carpi radialis brevis

**Insertion:** Tendon divides into four slips that insert on the dorsal surface along the medial aspect of the three phalanges of the second, third, fourth and fifth digits

**Action:** Extension of second, third, fourth and fifth digits

## Extensor digitorum lateralis m.

A long slender dorsal muscle that lies lateral to the extensor digitorum communis [Figure 2–25]. Humans lack this muscle, but possess an extensor digiti minimi that inserts on the fifth digit only and extends the little finger.

**Origin:** Lateral supracondyloid ridge of humerus below the origin of the extensor digitorum communis

**Insertion:** Division of the tendon similar to that of the extensor digitorum communis, but may subdivide into three or four parts that insert along the dorsolateral surface of the phalanges of digits three, four, and five or two, three, four, and five, respectively

**Action:** Extends the digits with the extensor digitorum communis, synergistically

## Extensor carpi ulnaris m.

This long, slender muscle lies along the ulnar side of the antebrachium and is the last of the superficial extensors [Figure 2–25].

**Origin:** Lateral epicondyle of the humerus below the origin of the extensor carpi lateralis and ulna above the semilunar notch

**Insertion:** Base of the fifth metacarpal

**Action:** Extension of carpals of the ulnar side

## Supinator m.

This flat muscle surrounds the proximal end of the radius and lies under the extensor digitorum communis and lateralis [Figure 2–26].

**Origin:** From stabilizing elbow ligaments and the lateral epicondyle of the humerus

**Insertion:** Fibers pass obliquely to insert on the proximal third of the radius

**Action:** Supinates the forearm synergistically with the brachioradialis

## Abductor pollicis longus m.

A flat muscle whose oblique fibers occur between the radius and ulna, is located distal to the supinator [Figure 2–26].

**Origin:** Ventrolateral surface of the ulnar shaft and the dorsal surface of the radius

**Insertion:** On the radial side of the first metacarpal

**Action:** Extends and abducts the pollex (thumb, digit I). In the human, similar abduction and extension of the thumb involves the abductor pollicis longus and the extensor pollicis brevis, absent in the cat

## Extensor indicis m.

This very slender muscle lies deep to the extensor carpi ulnaris. It may consist of a single muscle or two separate muscles with a common origin [Figure 2–26].

**Origin:** Lateral surface of the ulna

**Insertion:** At the base of the radius; if the muscle is single with a single tendon, it inserts on the second phalanx of the second digit; if the muscle is single with a divided tendon, both may insert on the second phalanx of the second digit or one may insert on the second digit and one on the pollex (digit I); if there are two muscles, an extensor digiti I, inserts by means of a tendon on the pollex and an extensor digiti II inserts on digit II

**Action:** Extends the first and second digits; in man, extensor digiti I and extensor digiti II are represented by the extensor pollicis longus and the extensor indicis proprius, respectively

## Flexor carpi ulnaris m.

A muscle having a humeral and ulnar head that lies along the ulnar side of the ventral aspect of the lower forearm [Figure 2–27a and Figure 2–27b].

**Origin:** Humerus near the medial epicondyle (humeral head), lateral surface of the olecranan of the ulna (ulnar head)

**Insertion:** Pisiform bone of the carpals

**Action:** Wrist flexor

## Flexor digitorum superficialis m.

This is a muscle that occurs in two parts, superficial and deep, that inserts on the digits [Figure 2–27a and Figure 2–27b]. The superficial head is the widest of the flat, bandlike muscles of the ventral surface of the

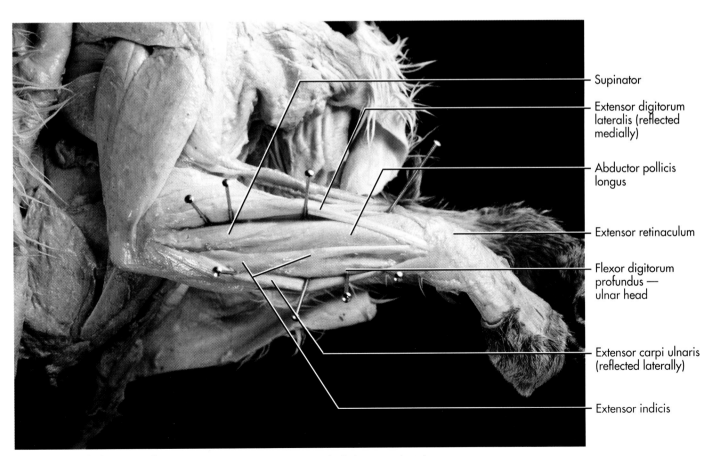

*Figure 2–26*   Deep forearm extensors, supinator, and abductor policis longus.

lower forearm. The deep head lies on the surface of the tendon of the flexor digitorum profundus. A palmaris longus m. is present in the human, but not in cats. Some authors, however, describe the superficial portion of flexor digitorum superficialis as the palmaris longus.

**Origin:** Superficial head — medial epicondyle of the humerus; Deep head — tendon of two humeral heads of the flexor digitorum profundus

**Insertion:** The tendons of the two heads pass under the flexor retinaculum and split to insert on either side of the middle phalanx of digits 2–5

**Action:** Flexes the digits

## Flexor carpi radialis m.

A thin muscle that extends from the humerus to the manus [Figure 2–27a].

**Origin:** Medial epicondyle of the humerus

**Insertion:** Bases of the second and third metacarpals

**Action:** Flexes the wrist

## Pronator teres m.

This ventral muscle is oriented obliquely over the upper surface of the forearm [Figure 2–27a and Figure 2–27b]. In the human there are two heads, a humeral head and an ulnar head.

**Origin:** Medial epicondyle of the humerus

**Insertion:** Middle of the medial border of the radius

**Action:** Pronation of the manus by rotating the radius

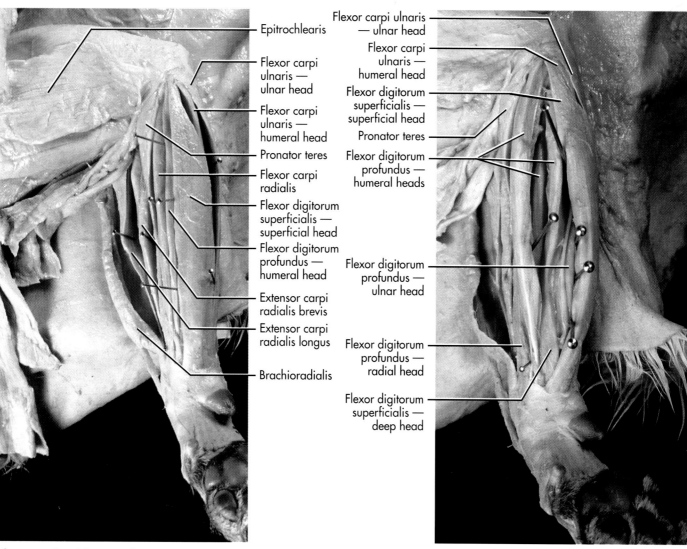

**A**　Superficial forearm flexors

**B**　Deep forearm flexors

***Figure 2-27***　Medial forearm muscles.

## *Flexor digitorum profundus m.*

This is a deep five-headed muscle whose tendons are united at the wrist [Figure 2–27b and Figure 2–27c].

**Origin:** Most of the radial border of the ulna (ulnar head), middle third of the radius, interosseous ligament between the radius and ulna and nearby shaft of the ulna (radial head), medial epicondyle of the humerus (three humeral heads)

**Insertion:** Five tendons join at the wrist to form a strong, wide, white, glistening band that subdivides into five tendons to insert on the bases of the distal phalanx of digits 1–5

**Action:** Flexes all digits

## *Pronator quadratus m.*

A deep muscle whose fibers extend obliquely between the distal ends of the ulna and the radius. To find this muscle, separate the tendon and radial head of the flexor digitorum profundus and the tendon of flexor carpi radialis. Look for a flat, bluish purple muscle covered by shiny fascia. Carefully slit the fascia to reveal the oblique fibers of this muscle [Figure 2–27c].

**Origin:** Distal part of the ventral border of ulna

**Insertion:** Distal surface of the ventral border of the radius

**Action:** Rotates the radius and is synergistic with the pronator teres

## Muscles of the Manus ━━━

### Lumbricales m.

These are small intrinsic muscles of the manus.

**Origin:** By slips from the common tendon of flexor digitorum profundus

**Insertion:** Base of the first phalanx of digits 2–5

**Action:** Bends digits radially

A number of additional small intrinsic muscles associated with the metacarpals and digits will not be treated here. You might wish to examine them independently.

## Muscles of the Thigh ━━━

### *Sartorius m.*

This is a muscle that appears as a narrow thick band laterally. This is deceiving, however, because it continues as a thin band extending almost halfway across the medial surface of the cranial aspect of the thigh [Figure 2–28, Figure 2–29, and Figure 2–30]. Use caution in dissecting this muscle since it often has fat and extensive connective tissue associated with it.

**Origin:** Crest and ventral border of the ilium

**Insertion:** Patella, tibia, and fascia of the knee

**Action:** Adducts and rotates the femur, extends the shank

**★★Sew and cut this muscle.**

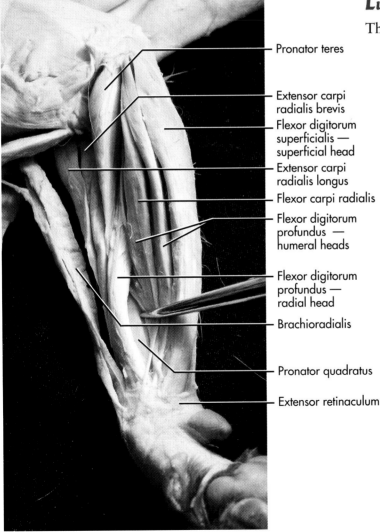

Pronator teres

Extensor carpi radialis brevis

Flexor digitorum superficialis — superficial head

Extensor carpi radialis longus

Flexor carpi radialis

Flexor digitorum profundus — humeral heads

Flexor digitorum profundus — radial head

Brachioradialis

Pronator quadratus

Extensor retinaculum

***C*** Pronator quadratus

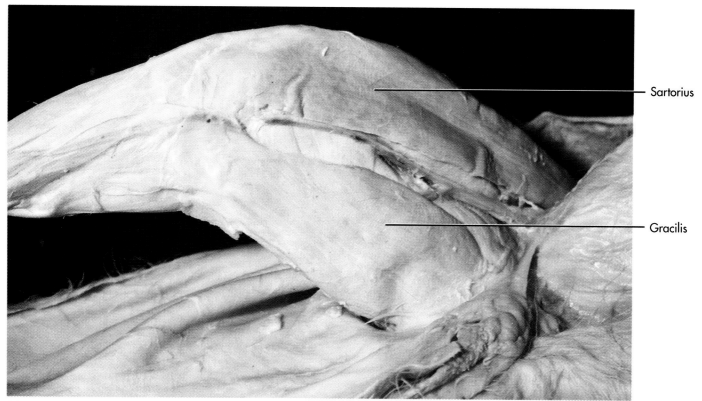

**Figure 2-28**   Medial thigh muscles.

Sartorius

Gracilis

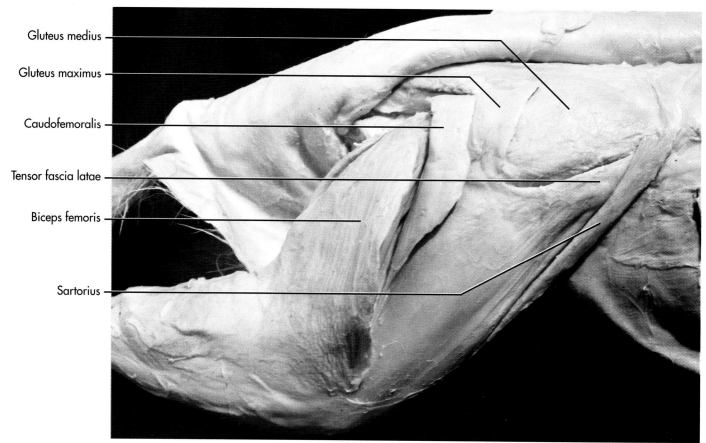

Gluteus medius

Gluteus maximus

Caudofemoralis

Tensor fascia latae

Biceps femoris

Sartorius

**Figure 2-29**   Lateral thigh muscles.

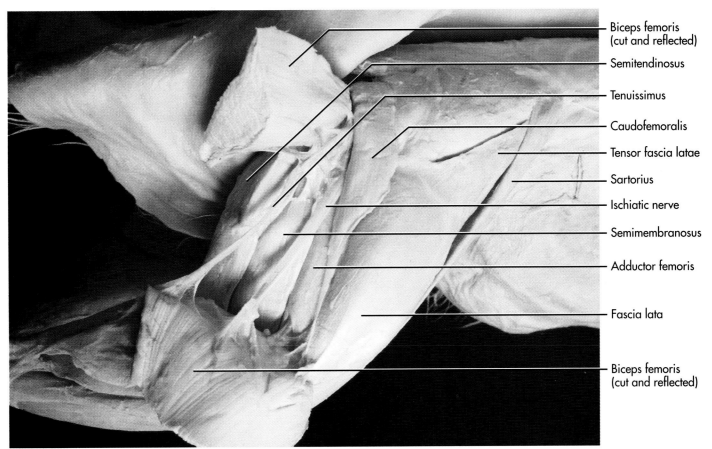

Biceps femoris (cut and reflected)
Semitendinosus
Tenuissimus
Caudofemoralis
Tensor fascia latae
Sartorius
Ischiatic nerve
Semimembranosus
Adductor femoris
Fascia lata
Biceps femoris (cut and reflected)

**Figure 2-30**  Lateral thigh muscles: biceps femoris cut to expose underlying muscles.

### Gracilis m.

This is another thin muscle that occupies the caudal half of the medial surface of the thigh [Figure 2–28]. Since the insertion is an aponeurosis, you may tend to be overzealous in cleaning the surface of this muscle and destroy it.

**Origin:** Symphysis of the ischium and pubis

**Insertion:** A thin aponeurosis on the medial surface of the tibia and continuous with the fascia of the shank

**Action:** Adducts and retracts the leg

**★★Sew and cut this muscle.**

### Biceps femoris m.

This large, thick muscle covers almost three-fourths of the lateral surface of the thigh [Figure 2–29 and Figure 2–30]. Like the gracilis, care must be exercised when dissecting near the insertion. This muscle will

only be cut and not sewn. There are three major concerns when bisecting the biceps: (1) the very delicate tendon of the caudofemoralis is closely applied to the undersurface of the cranial aspect of the biceps, (2) the tenuissimus lies just beneath the caudal edge of the biceps, and (3) the sciatic nerve is positioned under and approximately in the middle of the biceps. Avoid cutting any of these. This is another muscle that was first described in the human where it originates as two heads (bi-ceps), one from the ischial tuberosity and the second from the femur, while in other mammals, e.g., the cat, it possesses a single head.

**Origin:** Ischial tuberosity

**Insertion:** Proximal one-third of the tibia and lateral patella

**Action:** Abducts thigh and flexes the shank

**★★This muscle will only be cut. Be extremely careful to avoid severing the underlying tenuissimus, sciatic nerve, and tendon of the caudofemoralis.**

## Tenuissimus m.

This is an extremely slender muscle that is strongly adherent to the biceps femoris [Figure 2–30]. This muscle is absent in humans.

**Origin:** Transverse process of second caudal vertebra

**Insertion:** In common with the biceps femoris

**Action:** Synergistically assists the biceps femoris in abducting the thigh and flexing the shank

## Caudofemoralis m.

Just cranial to the biceps femoris, with its major mass lying beneath that muscle, is the caudofemoralis [Figure 2–29 and Figure 2–30]. Again, care must be exercised when dissecting this muscle since it is often associated with fat and connective tissue and is inserted by way of a very thin, narrow tendon that adheres closely to the medial surface of the biceps femoris. The caudofemoralis is missing in humans.

**Origin:** Transverse processes of second and third caudal vertebrae

**Insertion:** Thin tendon along the lateral border of the patella

**Action:** Abducts the thigh and extends the shank

The semitendinosus, the semimembranosus, and the adductor femoris muscles can be observed and identified in both lateral and medial views of the thigh. You will be expected to identify them in both views.

## Semitendinosus m.

This is a long muscle that forms the caudal border of the thigh [Figure 2–30 and Figure 2–31].

**Origin:** Ischial tuberosity

**Insertion:** Medial surface of the tibia

**Action:** Flexes the shank

## Semimembranosus m.

A thick muscle, cranial to the semitendinosus and lying on the medial aspect of the thigh, is the semimembranosus [Figure 2–30 and Figure 2–31].

**Origin:** Ischial tuberosity and ramus of the ischium

**Insertion:** Medial epicondyle of the femur and adjacent medial surface of the tibia

**Action:** Extends the thigh

## Adductor femoris m.

This broad muscle lies cranial to and partially covered by the semimembranosus [Figure 2–30 and Figure 2–31].

**Origin:** Ramus of pubis and ischium

**Insertion:** Shaft of femur

**Action:** Adducts thigh

## Adductor longus m.

Cranial to the adductor femoris is the thin adductor longus that appears as a triangle that is just caudal to the femoral vessels and saphenous nerve, all of which lie in the iliopectineal fossa [Figure 2–31].

**Origin:** Craniomedial border of the pubis

**Insertion:** Middle portion of the linea aspera of the femur

**Action:** Adducts thigh

## Pectineus m.

This small triangular muscle lies just beneath the femoral vessels and saphenous nerve [Figure 2–31]. Often, fat may obscure the pectineus and will have to be carefully removed.

**Origin:** Cranial border of pubis

**Insertion:** Proximal shaft of the femur

**Action:** Adducts the thigh

## Iliopsoas Complex

This complex consists of a thick muscle mass that is almost entirely obscured by the abdominal musculature and includes the iliacus and psoas major. To observe, make a two inch lateral incision through the abdominal musculature.

## Iliacus m.

The most lateral and slightly dorsal portion of the complex is the iliacus [Figure 2–31].

**Origin:** Ventral border of the ilium

**Insertion:** Lesser trochanter of the femur

**Action:** Flexes and rotates the thigh

## Psoas major m.

This is the largest portion and occurs in the middle of this complex [Figure 2–31].

**Origin:** Bodies of the last thoracic and all of the lumbar vertebrae

**Insertion:** Lesser trochanter of the femur

**Action:** Flexes and rotates the thigh

## Psoas minor m.

This is a very thin muscle occurring medial to the psoas major [Figure 2–31]. This muscle is missing in a high percentage of humans.

**Origin:** Bodies of the last thoracic and first few lumbar vertebrae

**Insertion:** Pubis, by a long, narrow, conspicuous glistening tendon

**Action:** Flexes vertebral column

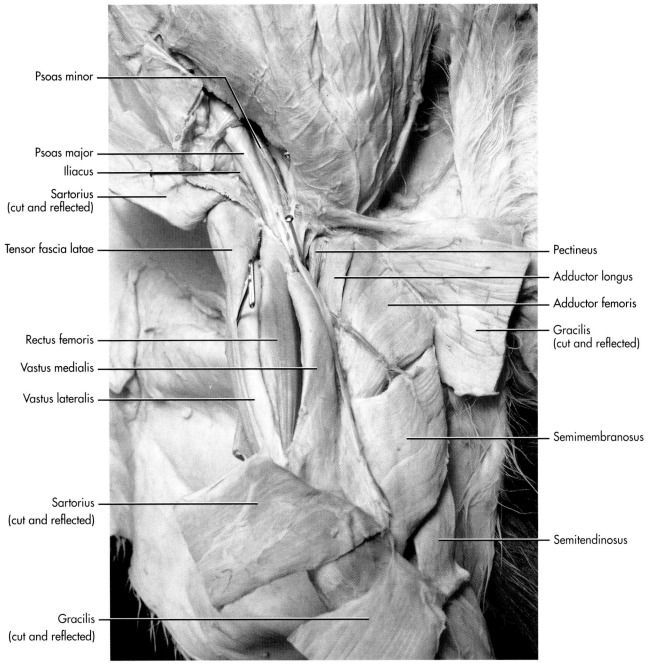

**Figure 2–31** Thigh muscles, muscles of the iliopsoas complex, psoas minor.

## Quadratus lumborum m.

This is a deep, flat muscle that lies ventral to the lumbar portion of the vertebral column. This muscle will be best observed during the dissection of the viscera.

**Origin:** From the last rib and last few thoracic and lumbar vertebrae

**Insertion:** On the transverse processes of the lumbar vertebrae and on part of the ilium

**Action:** Bends the vertebral column laterally

## Tensor fascia latae m.

This rather thick triangular muscle largely covers the cranial portion of the vastus lateralis and abuts the caudal border of the sartorius and the cranioventral border of the gluteus medius [Figure 2–29, Figure 2–30, and Figure 2–31]. Extreme care should be exercised in loosening the fascia lata from the caudal edge of the vastus lateralis. Do not shred or destroy the fascia lata.

**Origin:** Ventral border of the ilium, fascia of surrounding hip muscles

**Insertion:** Into the fascia lata. The fascia lata continues distally and covers part of the vastus lateralis and vastus medialis and then inserts on the surface of the patella

**Action:** Tightens the fascia lata and helps to extend the shank

## Quadriceps Complex

Four component muscles make up this complex that lies on the craniolateral and craniomedial aspects of the thigh and is the powerful extensor of the shank.

## Vastus medialis m.

This is the most medial of the four components [Figure 2–31 and Figure 2–32].

**Origin:** Shaft of the femur

**Insertion:** Crosses the patella and inserts by means of the patellar ligament on the tibial tuberosity

**Action:** Extends the shank

## Rectus femoris m.

This is a spindle shaped muscle that rests between the vastus medialis and the vastus lateralis and is distinguished by a shiny covering of fascia.[Figure 2–31 and Figure 2–32].

**Origin:** From the ilium near the acetabulum

**Insertion:** In common with the vastus medialis and lateralis

**Action:** Extends the shank

## Vastus lateralis m.

This is a large flat muscle that covers the cranial and lateral surface of the thigh [Figure 2–31 and Figure 2–32].

**Origin:** Shaft and greater trochanter of the femur

**Insertion:** In common with the vastus medialis and rectus femoris

**Action:** Extends the shank

## Vastus intermedius m.

This is the deepest of the quadriceps muscles and can be seen by carefully separating the rectus femoris and vastus lateralis [Figure 2–32].

**Origin:** Almost the entire shaft of the femur

**Insertion:** In common with the other three members of this complex

**Action:** Extends the shaft

# Muscles of the Shank ━━━━

Beware of the tough fascia surrounding the shank muscles. Carefully remove this tissue and while doing so, avoid the destruction of the tendons of insertion of the thigh muscles. The shank muscles are roughly divided into extensors and flexors. A distinct band of connective tissue, the extensor retinaculum, holds the cranial extensor muscle tendons in place [Figure 2–33].

## Tibialis cranialis m.

This large, flat, meaty muscle lies on the craniolateral aspect of the tibia [ Figure 2–33].

**Origin:** Proximal end of the tibia and fibula

**Insertion:** Along the medial surface of the first metatarsal after passing beneath the extensor retinaculum

**Action:** Flexes the pes

## Extensor digitorum longus m.

This large muscle lies beneath the tibialis cranialis and only a narrow strip is evident caudal to it on the lateral surface of the shank [Figure 2–33]. Carefully loosen this muscle from the tibialis cranialis.

**Origin:** Lateral epicondyle of the femur

**Insertion:** The tendon, after passing under the extensor retinaculum, is subdivided into four slips that insert on the dorsal surface of the second and third phalanges of digits 2–5

**Action:** Extends the digits

## Extensor hallucis longus m.

This is a muscle lying deep to the tibialis cranialis and the extensor digitorum longus.

**Origin:** Anterior surface of the fibula

**Insertion:** Generally in common with the tendon of the tibialis cranialis on the first metatarsal

**Action:** Flexes the pes

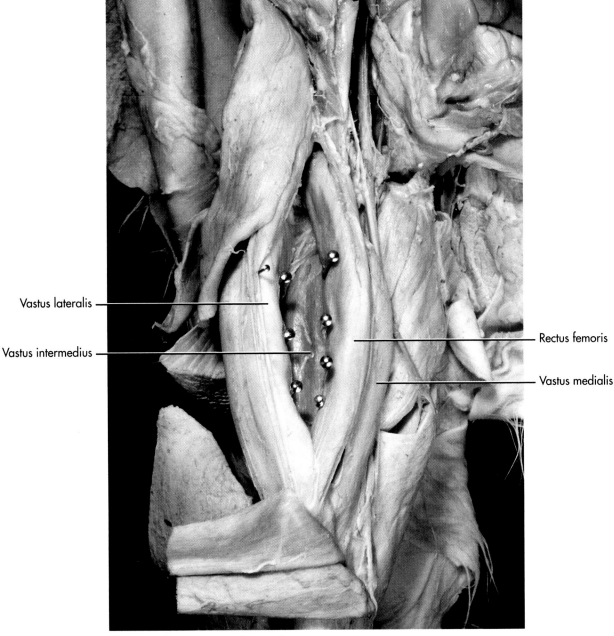

Vastus lateralis

Vastus intermedius

Rectus femoris

Vastus medialis

***Figure 2–32*** Quadriceps femoris complex.

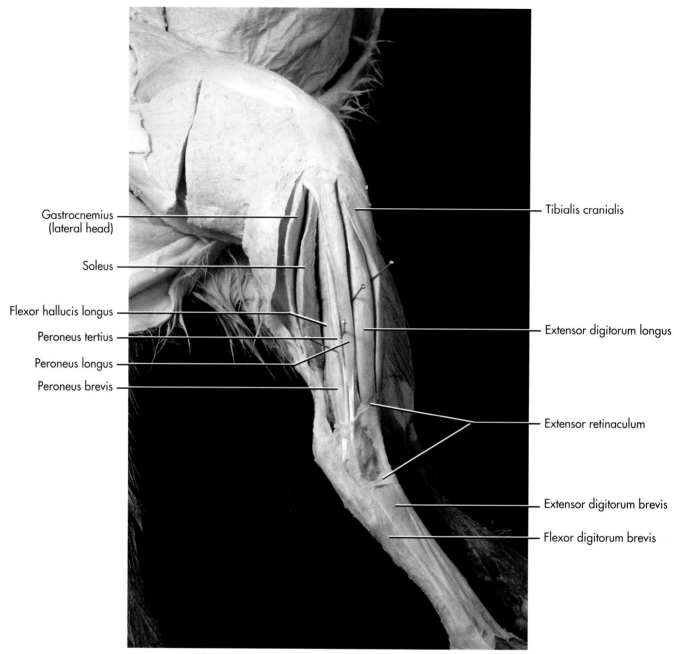

Gastrocnemius (lateral head)

Soleus

Flexor hallucis longus

Peroneus tertius

Peroneus longus

Peroneus brevis

Tibialis cranialis

Extensor digitorum longus

Extensor retinaculum

Extensor digitorum brevis

Flexor digitorum brevis

***Figure 2-33*** Lateral shank muscles.

## Peroneus longus m.

This is one of three peroneus muscles on the lateral surface of the shank. It is the most superficial of this group [Figure 2–33].

**Origin:** Head and lateral surface of the shaft of the fibula

**Insertion:** Proximal ends of all five metatarsals

**Action:** Flexes the pes

## Peroneus tertius m.

This is a slender muscle lying beneath the peroneus longus [Figure 2–33].

**Origin:** Lateral surface of the fibula

**Insertion:** Its tendon lies in the groove of the lateral malleolus and passes along the lateral margin of the foot and inserts on the first phalanx of the fifth digit.

**Action:** Flexes foot and abducts and extends fifth digit

## Peroneus brevis m.

The shortest of the three peroneus muscles, peroneus brevis, lies posterior to the other two [Figure 2–33].

Origin:    Distal half of the fibula

Insertion:    *Note that the tendon of peroneus brevis passes in common with the tendon of peroneus tertius within the groove of the lateral malleolus and finally inserts on the base of the fifth metatarsal on the lateral side

Action:    Extends the foot

## Popliteus m.

This is a triangular muscle that wraps obliquely around the posterior aspect of the knee from the femur to the tibia [Figure 2–34].

Origin:    Lateral epicondyle of the femur

Insertion:    Medial aspect of the proximal end of the tibia

Action:    Flexes and medially rotates the leg

## Flexor digitorum longus m.

This is a long slender muscle on the medial aspect of the shank just posterior to the tibia [Figure 2–34].

Origin:    Head of the fibula and shaft of the tibia

Insertion:    Forms a common broad tendon extending over the plantar surface of the foot, then dividing into four discrete tendons that insert on the base of the terminal phalanx of each toe

Action:    Flexes toes and pes

## Flexor hallucis longus m.

This somewhat larger muscle lies lateral to the flexor digitorum longus on the posterior aspect of the shank. [Figure 2–33 and Figure 2–34].

Origin:    From the shaft of the fibula and shaft of the tibia

Insertion:    In common with the flexor digitorum longus

Action:    Flexes toes and pes

## Tibialis caudalis m.

This is a flat, slender muscle that lies beneath the flexor digitorum longus and between the flexor digitorum longus and flexor hallucis longus [Figure 2–34]. Notice the prominent tendon of this muscle.

Origin:    From the head of the fibula, proximal end of the tibia and adjacent aponeurosis

Insertion:    By means of a long slender tendon onto the plantar surface of the navicular and medial cuneiform

Action:    Extensor of the pes

## Gastrocnemius m.

The gastrocnemius is the major contributor to most of the bulky posterior muscle mass of the lower leg known as the calf [Figure 2–33 and Figure 2–34]. It possesses two heads, a lateral and a medial head.

Origin:    The lateral head arises from the lateral border of the patella, the superficial fascia of the shank, the sesamoid bone located above the lateral epicondyle of the femur and an aponeurosis from the plantaris and adjacent tibia. The medial head originates from the sesamoid bone above the medial epicondyle of the femur and its distal adjacent shaft.

Insertion:    By means of a common powerful tendon, the Achilles tendon, formed by the individual tendons of the gastrocnemius, the soleus, and the plantaris muscles, that inserts on the proximal end of the calcaneus

Action:    Extends the pes

## Plantaris m.

The plantaris lies beneath the gastrocnemius and can be seen protruding between the proximal ends of the heads of this muscle [Figure 2–34]. Care must be exerted in dissecting this muscle away from the two heads of the gastrocnemius.

Origin:    From the sesamoid above the lateral epicondyle of the femur and the lateral border of the patella

Insertion:    Passes through the center of the Achilles tendon over the calcaneus and serves as the origin of the flexor digitorum brevis on the ventral aspect of the pes

Action:    Acts synergistically with the gastrocnemius and the soleus to extend the pes

## Soleus m.

This is a flat muscle located beneath the plantaris [Figure 2–33].

**Origin:** Proximal part of the fibula

**Insertion:** In common with the tendon of the gastrocnemius and contributes to the formation of the Achilles tendon

**Action:** Synergistic extension of the pes with the gastrocnemius and plantaris

## Triceps surae m.

The gastrocnemius and the soleus muscles have sometimes been considered a calf muscle with three heads.

## Muscles of the Pes

### Extensor digitorum brevis m.

This thin muscle covers the dorso-lateral surface of the tarsus and metatarsus [Figure 2–33 and Figure 2–34].

**Origin:** From the proximal ends of metatarsals 3–5

**Insertion:** By three tendons that split into a medial and lateral slip that both terminate on the dorsal and lateral surface of the first phalanx

**Action:** Extends the toes

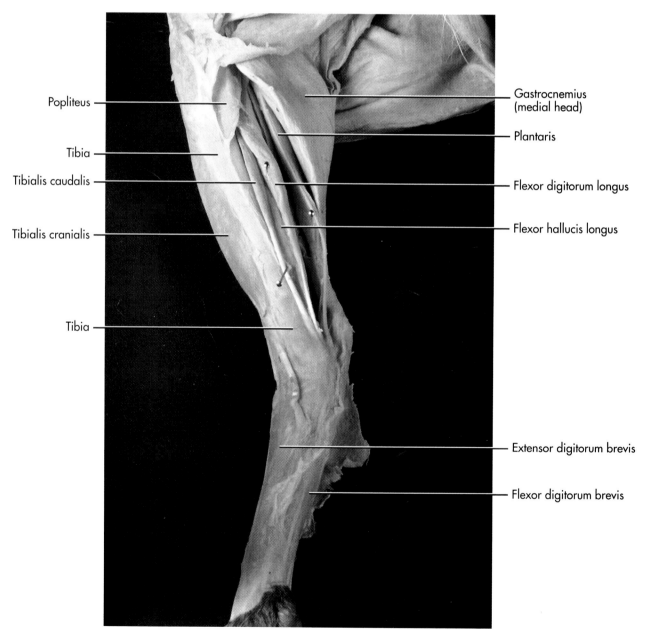

Popliteus

Tibia

Tibialis caudalis

Tibialis cranialis

Tibia

Gastrocnemius (medial head)

Plantaris

Flexor digitorum longus

Flexor hallucis longus

Extensor digitorum brevis

Flexor digitorum brevis

***Figure 2–34*** Medial shank muscles.

### Flexor digitorum brevis m.

This muscle lies on the plantar surface of the foot [Figure 2–33 and Figure 2–34].

**Origin:** An extension of the plantaris tendon

**Insertion:** By four tendons to the second phalanx of digits 2–5

**Action:** Flexes the toes

In addition, there are a number of small muscles associated with the tarsus, metatarsus and phalanges that will not be individually described. Various intricate movements are caused by them.

# Muscles of the Hip ━━━━

Carefully remove the tough fascia covering the hip region. Reidentify the tensor fascia latae, the caudofemoralis and the biceps femoris [Figure 2–29].

### Gluteus maximus m.

The gluteus maximus is a thin trapezoidal muscle lying just anterior to the caudofemoralis [Figure 2–29]. In humans, this muscle is massive and makes the major contribution to nice "buns."

**Origin:** From transverse processes of the last sacral and first caudal vertebrae, as well as adjacent fascia

**Insertion:** Onto the surface of the greater trochanter of the femur

**Action:** Abducts the thigh

**★★After this muscle has been identified and isolated, slide a probe under the muscle perpendicular to the fibers in the region of the belly and with a sharp scalpel cut along the top of the probe, using the probe as a hard surface to prevent cutting into important muscles beneath it. Do not sew this muscle.**

### Gluteus medius m.

This muscle, in the cat, is a very thick muscle sandwiched between the cranial tensor fascia latae and caudal gluteus maximus [Figure 2–29].

**Origin:** From the crest and lateral surface of the ilium, transverse processes of the last sacral and first caudal vertebrae and adjacent fascia

**Insertion:** Proximal end of the greater trochanter of the femur

**Action:** Abducts the thigh

**★★Extreme care must be exercised in dissecting this muscle from the important, underlying musculature with which you will be dealing, shortly.** After cutting and reflecting the gluteus maximus muscle, you should be able to identify the flattened posterior portion of the pyriformis extending from beneath the caudal edge of the gluteus medius muscle. Note the sciatic nerve passing obliquely under the pyriformis muscle. The cranial edge of the gluteus medius is very thick and must be loosened from the muscular part of tensor fascia latae. Lift the cranial edge of the gluteus medius and observe the shiny, spindle-shaped gluteus minimus muscle. Insert a probe beneath the caudal edge of the gluteus medius and perpendicular to the direction of the muscle fibers, continuing until it emerges beneath the cranial edge. Be careful that the probe remains dorsal to the pyriformis and gluteus minimus muscles. With a sharp scalpel, cut through the belly of the gluteus medius along the dorsal edge of the probe. **Do *not* sew this muscle.**

### Pyriformis m.

This fan-shaped muscle lies under both of the superficial gluteus muscles [Figure 2–35a and Figure 2–35b]. As mentioned earlier, notice that the sciatic nerve passes under this muscle.

**Origin:** From transverse processes of the last two sacral and first caudal vertebrae

**Insertion:** Proximal end of the greater trochanter of the femur

**Action:** Abducts the thigh

**★★Insert a probe perpendicular to the fibers of the pyriformis approximately 3/4 of the distance from the point of origin, beneath the caudal edge until it emerges cranially. Take care *not* to pick up the sciatic nerve with the muscle. With a sharp scalpel, cut through the pyriformis, following the top edge of the probe. Do *not* sew this muscle.**

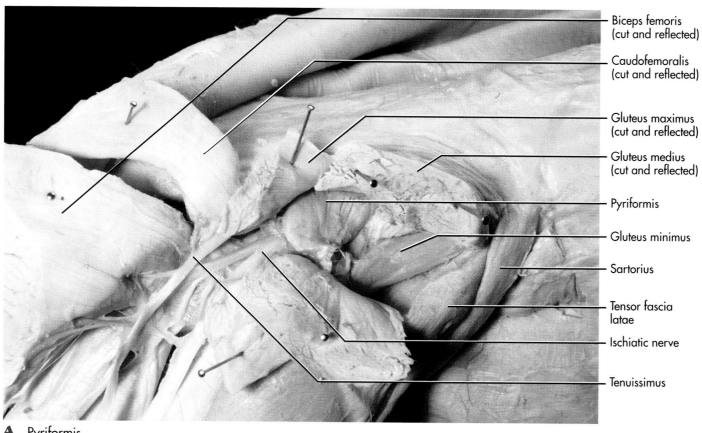

Biceps femoris
(cut and reflected)

Caudofemoralis
(cut and reflected)

Gluteus maximus
(cut and reflected)

Gluteus medius
(cut and reflected)

Pyriformis

Gluteus minimus

Sartorius

Tensor fascia
latae

Ischiatic nerve

Tenuissimus

**A** Pyriformis

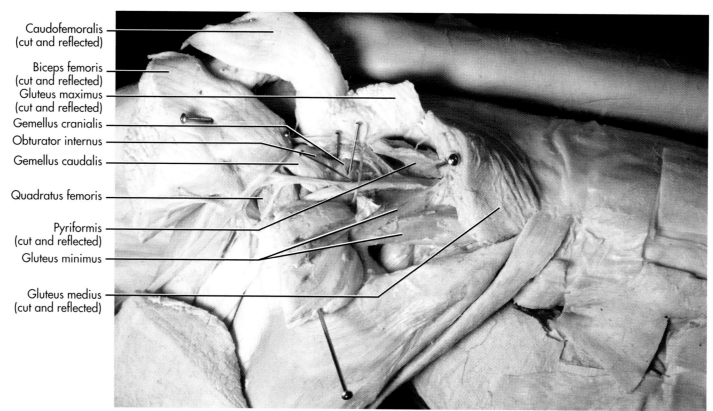

Caudofemoralis
(cut and reflected)

Biceps femoris
(cut and reflected)

Gluteus maximus
(cut and reflected)

Gemellus cranialis

Obturator internus

Gemellus caudalis

Quadratus femoris

Pyriformis
(cut and reflected)

Gluteus minimus

Gluteus medius
(cut and reflected)

**B** Deep hip muscles underlying pyriformis (note the pin in the middle of gemellus cranialis)

*Figure 2-35* Deep hip muscles.

## Gluteus minimus m.

This muscle consists of an anterior shiny, spindle-shaped portion and a flat, fan-shaped posterior portion [Figure 2–35a and Figure 35b].

**Origin:** From the lateral surface of the ilium

**Insertion:** Greater trochanter of the femur

**Action:** Abducts and rotates the thigh outward

## Articularis coxae m.

This is a small, flat muscle lying beneath gluteus minimus and between the heads of the vastus lateralis and rectus femoris [Figure 2–35c]. It does not exist in humans.

**Origin:** Ilium cranial to the acetabulum

**Insertion:** Dorsal surface at the proximal end of the femur

**Action:** Assists in flexion and rotation of the thigh

## Gemellus cranialis m.

This is a fan-shaped muscle lying below the pyriformis and closely abutting the caudal border of the gluteus minimus [Figure 2–35b].

**Origin:** From the dorsal edge of the ilium and ischium

**Insertion:** Area anterior to the apex of the greater trochanter of the femur

**Action:** Abducts and rotates the thigh

## Coccygeus m.

This is a deep hip muscle lying dorsal to gemellus cranialis and often mistaken as part of it.

**Origin:** In common with gemellus cranialis, the dorsal edge of the ilium and ischium

**Insertion:** Proximal caudal vertebrae

**Action:** Contributes to the pelvic wall and bends the tail laterally.

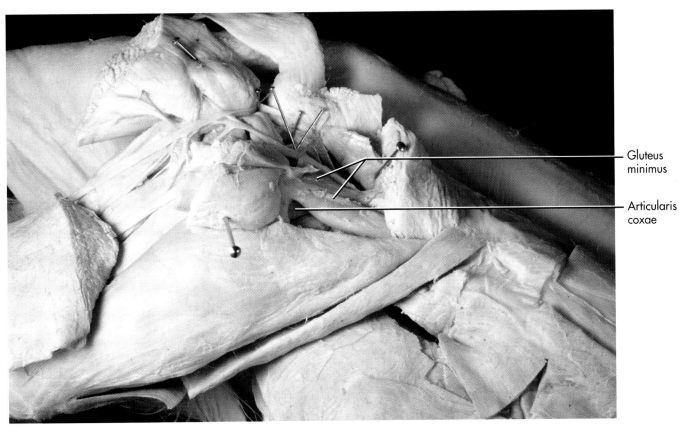

Gluteus minimus

Articularis coxae

**C** Articularis coxae

## Obturator internus m.

This muscle is located directly caudal to the gemellus cranialis [Figure 2–35b]. Although in lateral view, it appears as a small triangular muscle, its actual area is considerably more extensive.

**Origin:** Along the medial surface of the ramus of the ischium from the symphysis to the tuberosity

**Insertion:** The muscle passes laterally over the dorsal border of the ischium to insert into the trochanteric fossa of the femur

**Action:** Abducts the thigh

## Gemellus caudalis m.

This flat muscle lies caudal to and is overlapped by the obturator internus [Figure 2–35b].

**Origin:** From the dorsolateral surface of the ischium

**Insertion:** In common with the tendon of the obturator internus into the trochanteric fossa

**Action:** Abducts the thigh

## Quadratus femoris m.

The last of the visible deep hip muscles is short and thick and frequently appears brownish [Figure 2–35b].

**Origin:** Lateral surface of the ischial tuberosity

**Insertion:** Along the ventral borders of the greater and lesser trochanters

**Action:** Retraction of the thigh

## Obturator externus m.

Even though one might expect this muscle to be easily visible from the external surface, it actually is deeply buried beneath some of the hip muscles already studied. To observe this muscle, carefully separate the gemellus caudalis and quadratus femoris muscles.

**Origin:** From the lateral surface of the pubis and ischium near the border of the obturator foramen

**Insertion:** Into the trochanteric fossa of the femur

**Action:** Rotates and retracts the thigh

# Tail Muscles

A number of intrinsic muscles perform the typical tail movements of a feline, e.g., straight carriage, lateral bending and the nervous twitching and lashing motions prior to pouncing upon some unsuspecting object. Several of these are continuations of the lumbar muscles discussed previously, e.g., the extensor caudae medialis, a continuation of the multifidus spinae, raises the tail.

# Body Cavities and Mesenteries

**3**

## Opening the Cat

Exposure of the body cavities is not difficult if one looks before one leaps! Place the cat ventral side up on the tray. Palpate the sternum to locate the xiphoid process and remember that the sternum in the cat is elongate so do not panic if it appears that you are too far posterior. Also, note that the xiphoid process is cartilaginous and will feel softer than the sternum. A good muscle dissection should have left you with the xiphihumeralis muscle in the chest area. The xiphoid process occurs approximately 1/4 to 1/2 inch cranial to the posterior edge of this muscle. During the following procedure, refer to Figure 3–1.

All of the following instructions apply to the skinned side of the cat. Make a one inch horizontal incision through all muscle layers and connective tissue about 1/4 inch posterior to the tip of the xiphoid process with your scalpel (Incision 1). Take care to only cut through the muscles and not damage underlying organs. Insert your finger into the incision to determine whether you have penetrated the body cavity and to locate the diaphragm. There is a high probability that you have made your incision just posterior to the diphragm. The diaphragm is a muscular partition separating the thoracic and abdominal cavities that feels similar to a taut balloon.

With scissors, extend the incision laterally on both sides toward the back of the cat along the curved contour of the diaphragm about 3–4 inches on each side (Incision 2). With a scalpel, very carefully loosen the diaphragm from the body wall allowing it to come to rest on the liver. From the original horizontal incision, make a caudally directed longitudinal incision one-half inch to one side of the midline. While you are making this incision pull the abdominal wall up and watch for a

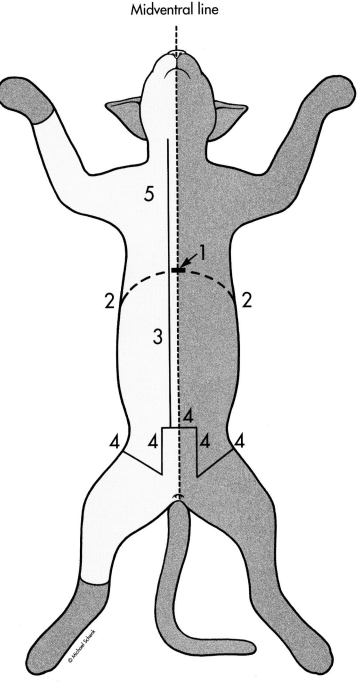

**Figure 3–1** Incisions to expose internal organ systems.

midventral mesentery attaching the urinary bladder to the wall (Incision 3). When within about 1/2 inch of this mesentery, *stop*. Laterally, cut about one inch to either side of the midline and then continue these cuts to the caudal end of the abdominal cavity to form a small door-like structure (Incision 4). If your specimen is a male, be careful not to destroy the spermatic cord, the inguinal canal or vas deferens. The cord can be recognized because it contains not only the vas deferens but also injected blood vessels lying on the medial aspect of the leg and passing over the brim of the pelvis continuing through the inguinal canal and through the abdominal muscles. Extend the incisions laterally from the caudal cuts (above), again avoiding the inguinal canal and spermatic cords.

To expose the organs of the thoracic cavity, with scissors cut from the xiphoid process cranially (toward the head). Your incision should be 1/2 inch from the midventral line of the skinned side of the specimen (Incision 5). As you approach the neck region you will be cutting through muscles in which major blood vessels and nerves occur (arteries — red, veins — blue,

nerves — white). To avoid destroying these structures, we recommend that you cut through one muscle at a time. Firmly grasp the thoracic wall of the skinned side and reflect back until you hear a cracking sound. Gently lift the opposite side with the intact skin and observe the mesentery adhering to the midventral body wall. Carefully, with your scalpel release the mesentery from the body wall allowing it to fall on the surface of the underlying organs. Just lateral to the attachment of this mesentery, on either side, observe an artery and vein adhering to the inner surface of the ventral thoracic wall. Again, with your scalpel, release these vessels from this surface. If necessary, remove some of the muscle. Now, with both hands grasp the rib cage on the unskinned side and quickly reflect back the thoracic wall until you hear a cracking sound.

Until you have read the next sections, **do not** remove or disturb any tissues that might appear fatty or membranous, particularly, the greater omentum [Figure 3–2]. To preserve these delicate membranes, it is highly recommended that the mesenteries be studied before consideration of the viscera.

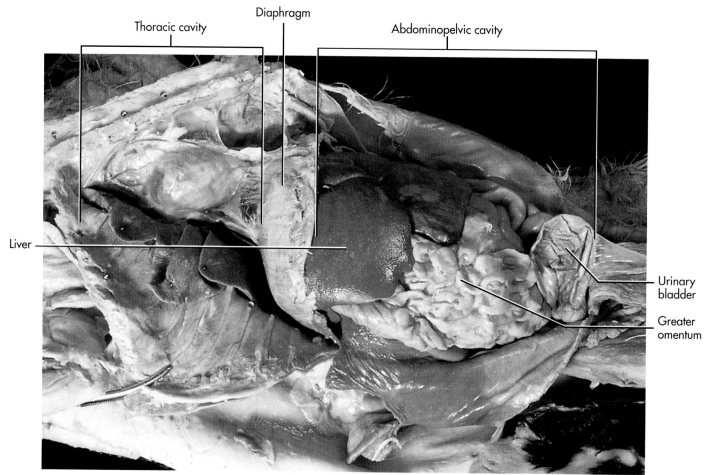

***Figure 3–2***   Incisions to expose internal organ systems.

# Body Cavities or Coelomic Cavities

Among both invertebrates and vertebrates we see bodies that have evolved with body cavities lined with mesenteries allowing ogans that are suspended within them to move independently of the general body surface. In general, this has allowed animals to develop a number of important characteristics and to become larger and more mobile.

Vertebrate body cavities are typically lined with a shiny membrane called a serosa. The serosa lining the body wall is known as the **parietal** layer and the outer covering reflected over the surface of most organs suspended in these cavities is a continuation of this membrane called the **visceral** serosa. In reality, what we refer to as a cavity in the living animal is a potential space containing a small amount of lubricating fluid, allowing free sliding movement of the organs. Mesenteries are membranes suspending organs within the cavities and extending between the parietal and visceral layers.

In mammals, including the cat or human, the **coelomic cavity** is divided into a **thoracic** and **abdominopelvic** (peritoneal) cavity by the unique muscular diaphragm [Figure 3–3]. The thoracic cavity is further subdivided into a more or less central **pericardial** cavity surrounding the heart and paired lateral

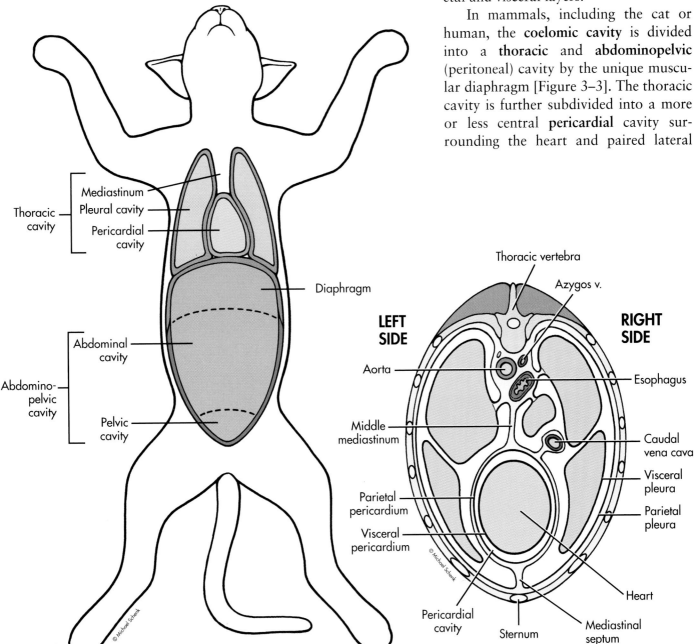

**Figure 3-3** Body cavities.

pleural cavities containing the lungs. Between the two **pleural** cavities is a potential space, the **mediastinum**, in which is located the heart and its cavity, the esophagus, the trachea, major blood vessels, nerves, and some endocrine organs all of which are held in place by loose connective tissue.

The abdominopelvic cavity is arbitrarily divided by an imaginary line drawn from the ilial crest to the pubic rim, defining an abdominal space and a pelvic space. In the abdominal cavity are suspended primarily digestive organs while in the pelvic cavity are urinogenital organs and the distal organs of the digestive tract [Figure 3–3].

## Mesenteries of the Thoracic Cavities

The pleural cavities are delimited by the **parietal pleura** as a glistening membrane that continues as the reflected **visceral pleura,** the outer covering of the lungs. The joined left and right medial parietal pleurae form the **mediastinal septum.** It is located both ventral and dorsal to the pericardium and continues anterior to the heart and adheres to the organs residing in the mediastinum. Take note that the ventral portion of the mediastinal septum is that membrane that you loosened from the mid-ventral thoracic body wall when

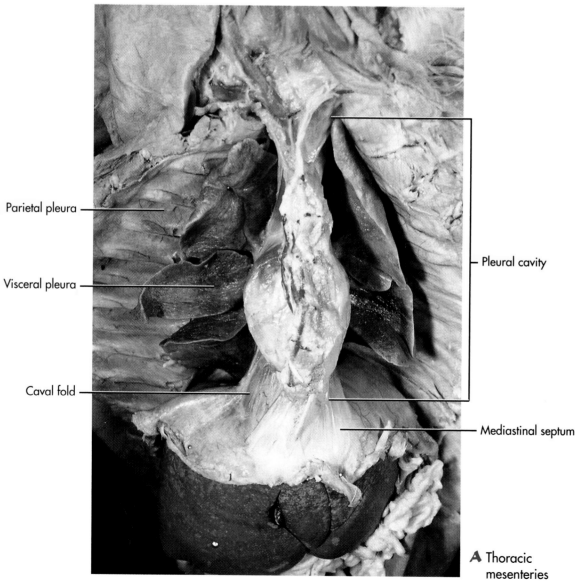

Parietal pleura

Visceral pleura

Caval fold

Pleural cavity

Mediastinal septum

**A** Thoracic mesenteries

*Figure 3–4* Thoracic mesenteries and pericardia.

Pulmonary ligament

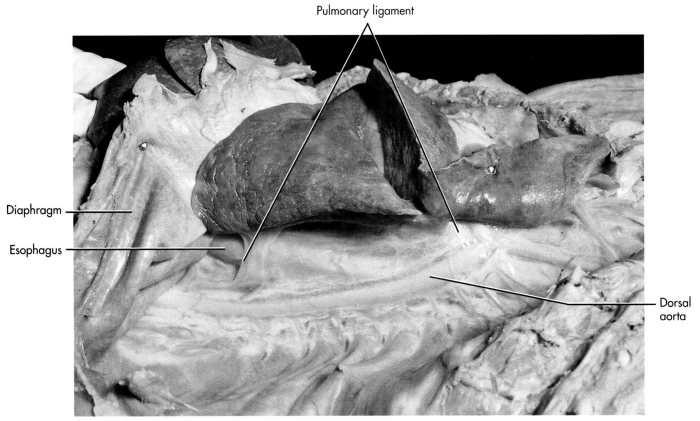

Diaphragm

Esophagus

Dorsal aorta

**B**   Thoracic mesenteries

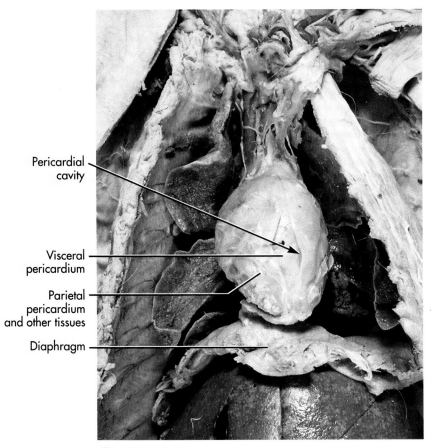

Pericardial cavity

Visceral pericardium

Parietal pericardium and other tissues

Diaphragm

**C**   Pericardia

you "opened the cat." The right postero-ventral portion of the mediastinal septum forms a pocket, the **caval fold**, into which projects the small accessory lobe of the right lung. Notice that a large blue blood vessel, the posterior vena cava, adheres to the medial portion of this mesentery. With your fingers, very carefully pull one of the lungs laterally and observe the stretched mesentery, the **pulmonary ligament** [Figures 3–4a and Figure 3–4b].

The serosal membranes associated with the heart are similar in their relationships to those of the pleural membranes and their association to the lungs. With a pair of scissors make a slit in the ventral portion of the pericardial sac to appreciate the **pericardial cavity**. The **parietal pericardium** defines the potential space called the pericardial cavity and then reflects over the surface of the heart as the **visceral pericardium** [Figure 3–4c]. In contrast to the pleura, the parietal pericardium is intimately associated externally with other tissues forming the pericardial sac.

# Mesenteries of the Abdominopelvic Cavity

Carefully separate the diaphragm from the liver and identify the whitish area, the **central tendon of the diaphragm,** where the muscles of the diaphragm converge. This is also the site of contact between the liver and the diaphragm. Three ligaments can be identified between the diaphragm and the liver. The most prominent of these is the **falciform ligament** found between the left and right halves of the liver and extending to the ventral abdominal wall. The thickened free margin of this membrane is the **round ligament,** a remnant of a fetal blood vessel. The continuation of the falciform ligament on either side of the central tendon of the diaphragm is the **coronary ligament** [Figure 3–5].

The very conspicuous and fragile **greater omentum** must be handled with caution [Figure 3–6]. It lies over most of the visceral organs, holding them in place, and is liberally laced with fat, since it is the site of fat storage. Quite often, the greater omentum is tucked among the coils of the small intestine and may even be attached by strands of serosa to the dorsal parietal peritoneum. Carefully loosen the omentum with your fingers from the intestinal loops, clipping, if necessary, the strands anchoring it dorsally.

The greater omentum is a double layered, apron-like mesentery extending from the greater curvature of the stomach and attaching to the dorsal wall of the peritoneal cavity. The **ventral layer** of this two-layered mesentery, attached to the greater curvature of the stomach and extending to the pelvic region, turns back on itself toward the stomach as the **dorsal layer** [Figure 3–7]. It then passes dorsal to the stomach, incorporating the tail of the pancreas and ultimately attaches to the dorsal peritoneal wall. That portion of the ventral layer of the greater omentum, extending from the stomach to the spleen is called the **gastrosplenic ligament** [Figure 3–6].

The potential space between the dorsal and ventral layers is the **omental bursa.** To demonstrate this cavity, carefully separate the two layers and with your scissors cut along the bottom of the apron. Slowly pull the two layers apart and observe the "sac-like cavity." The opening of this sac, the **epiploic foramen,** opens dorsally into the peritoneal cavity, thereby establishing continuity between the omental bursa and the peritoneal cavity. As you are holding the two layers

**Figure 3–5**   Ligaments associated with the liver and diaphragm.

Round ligament

Falciform ligament

Coronary ligament

Central tendon of the diaphragm

Diaphragm

Liver

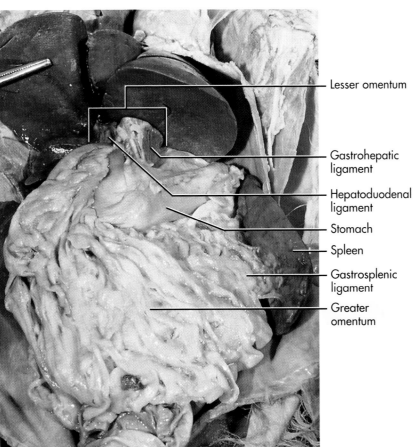

Lesser omentum

Gastrohepatic
ligament

Hepatoduodenal
ligament

Stomach

Spleen

Gastrosplenic
ligament

Greater
omentum

**Figure 3-6**   Greater and lesser omentum.

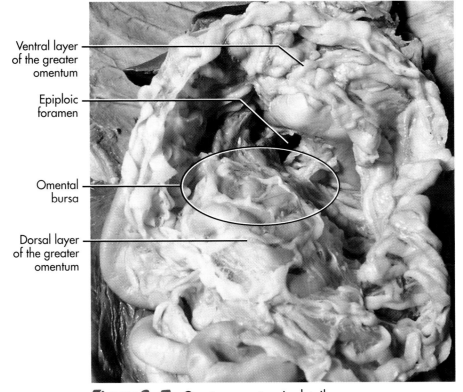

Ventral layer
of the greater
omentum

Epiploic
foramen

Omental
bursa

Dorsal layer
of the greater
omentum

**Figure 3-7**   Greater omentum in detail.

of the omentum, have your partner shine a pen light between the layers, while peering craniad to observe this opening [Figure 3–7]. The foramen opens dorsally and just to the right of the lesser omentum, discussed below.

A much less extensive mesentery extending from the liver to the lesser curvature of the stomach and the duodenum is the **lesser omentum**. That portion of this mesentery between the liver and the stomach is known as the **gastrohepatic ligament** and the continuation of this mesentery between the liver and the duodenum is the **hepatoduodenal ligament** [Figure 3–6]. Part of the caudate lobe of the liver projects ventrally into this mesentery. Blood vessels, "bile ducts," nerves and lymphatic vessels pass on the right through the free surface of this mesentery.

A short, somewhat inconspicuous mesentery, the **hepatorenal ligament**, stretches from the caudate lobe of the liver to the parietal peritoneum covering the right kidney [Figure 3–8]. Do not destroy this ligament, since there is no corresponding ligament on the left side.

Also on the right side is an oftentimes more conspicuous and fragile, trianglar mesentery, the **duodenocolic fold**, extending from the duodenum to the mesocolon [Figure 3–9]. On the left side of the peritoneal cavity and extending from the dorsal layer of the greater omentum to the opposite side of the mesocolon is another triangular **gastrocolic ligament** [Figure 3–9].

From the dorsal body wall, the large intestine (colon) is suspended by a part of the dorsal mesentery, the **mesocolon** [Figure 3–9 ]. To appreciate its extent, gently pull the colon ventrally. At the same time, observe that the duodenocolic fold and gastrocolic ligament merge with the mesocolon at opposing acute angles.

Gently lift the coils of the small intestine and observe the extensive mesentery suspending and supporting this organ. Notice the wealth of blood vessels coursing through this

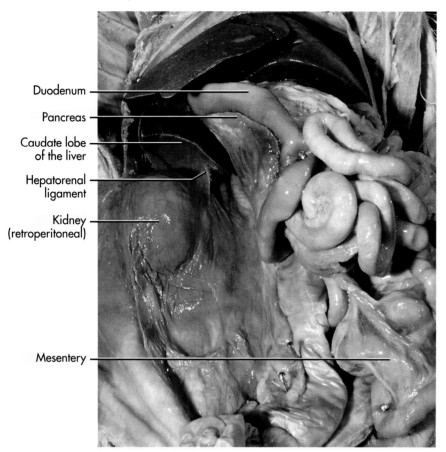

Duodenum

Pancreas

Caudate lobe
of the liver

Hepatorenal
ligament

Kidney
(retroperitoneal)

Mesentery

**Figure 3-8** Hepatorenal ligament.

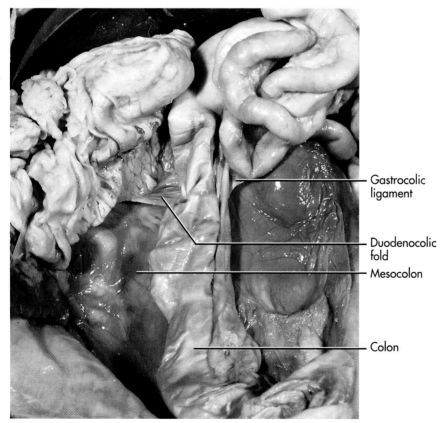

Gastrocolic
ligament

Duodenocolic
fold

Mesocolon

Colon

**Figure 3-9** Mesenteries of the abdominopelvic cavity I.

mesentery. That portion of this mesentery that supports the duodenum and the head of the pancreas is called the **mesoduodenum**, while the remainder that supports the jejunum and ileum is the **mesentery** proper [Figure 3–10].

Three prominent mesenteries anchor the urinary bladder in the abdominopelvic cavity. The **median vesical ligament** extends from the ventral surface of the urinary bladder to the ventral body wall. Both sides of the urinary bladder are anchored to the lateral body wall by the **lateral vesical ligaments**. Along the free edge of the lateral ligaments runs the **round ligament** that is the remnant of the fetal umbilical arteries that carried oxygen poor blood to the placenta [Figure 3–11]. There is a generous rounded pad of fat attached to each of the lateral vesical ligaments and may often mask them.

If your specimen is a female, an elongated **broad ligament** supports the internal reproductive structures. The most extensive part of the broad ligament is the **mesometrium** supporting the uterus. The portion of the broad ligament, much less extensive, and supporting the ovary is the **mesovarium** and the least extensive, supporting the uterine tubes (oviducts) is the **mesosalpinx**. The cranial end of the ovary is attached to the body wall by a thickened **suspensory ovarian ligament**. The caudal end of the ovary is held in place by a second thickened band called the **ovarian ligament**, extending between the ovary and the cranial end of the uterine horns. Almost perpendicular and lateral to the mesometrium is the **round ligament** [Figure 3–12]. It is the female counterpart of the gubernaculum in the male, that will be discussed in the reproductive system.

If your specimen is a male, mesenteries associated with the reproductive system are largely outside the main body cavities and will be discussed with the reproductive system.

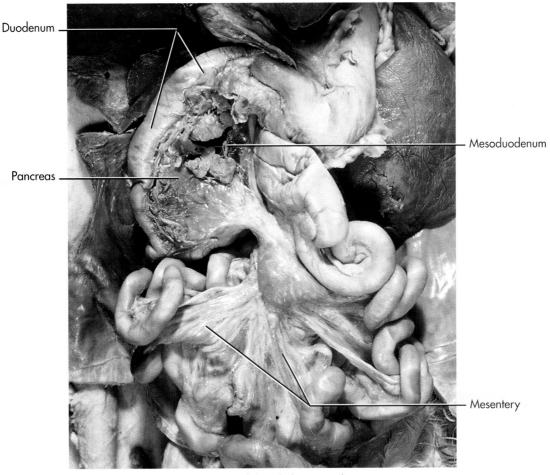

**Figure 3-10**   Mesenteries of the abdominopelvic cavity II.

Duodenum

Pancreas

Mesoduodenum

Mesentery

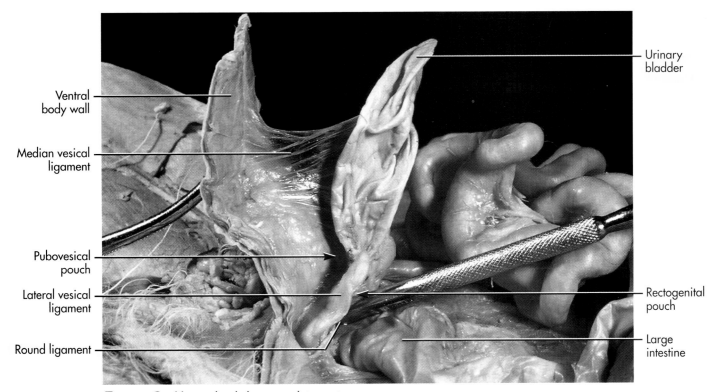

**Figure 3-11**   Male abdominopelvic region.

Ventral body wall

Median vesical ligament

Pubovesical pouch

Lateral vesical ligament

Round ligament

Urinary bladder

Rectogenital pouch

Large intestine

Ovarian ligament

Ovary

Suspensory ovarian ligament

Broad ligament
- Mesosalpinx
- Mesovarium
- Mesometrium

Uterine horn

Round ligament

**Figure 3-12** Mesenteries of the female reproductive system.

Extensions of the abdominopelvic cavity into the pelvic region occur in both sexes. In the male, that part of the cavity that extends between the large intestine and the urinary bladder is the **rectogenital pouch** and the cavity that extends between the urinary bladder and the ventral body wall is the **pubovesical pouch** [Figure 3–11].

In contrast, in females, since the uterus passes between the large intestine and the urinary bladder, there are three spaces versus the two in males. The **rectogenital pouch** occurs between the large intestine and the uterus, the **vesicouterine pouch** lies between the uterus and the urinary bladder and the **pubovesical pouch** is in the same position as in the male, between the urinary bladder and the ventral body wall [Figure 3–13].

Mesenteries and cavities in humans are very similar. A very obvious outward sign of one of the functions of the greater omentum (fat accumulation) in humans is known as a "beer belly."

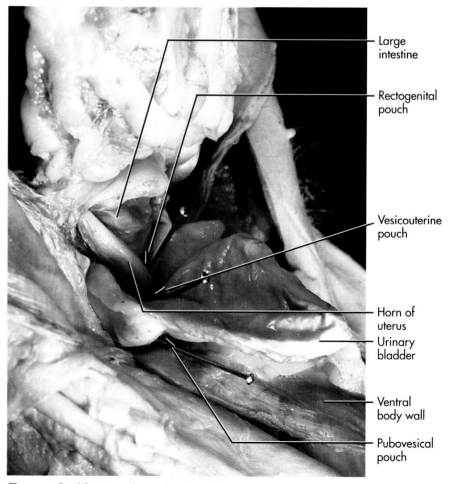

Large intestine

Rectogenital pouch

Vesicouterine pouch

Horn of uterus

Urinary bladder

Ventral body wall

Pubovesical pouch

**Figure 3-13** Female abdominopelvic region.

# Digestive System 4

The typical digestive system of a vertebrate such as the cat, consists of a tube with two openings, an anterior mouth and a posterior anus. This tube has become differentiated into a number of specialized areas that we recognize as the organs of the alimentary canal. The entire alimentary canal is lined by a mucous membrane often exhibiting specialization in various organs. Although the obvious function of a mucous membrane is secretion of mucus, other functions include enzyme secretion, HCl secretion, hormone secretion, etc. Embryological derivatives of the tube, e.g., the liver and pancreas, are physically integrated into the system, usually by means of ducts.

There are other organs whose functions are critical to the proper function of the rest of the digestive system. The teeth that figure so prominently in the skull of the skeletal system, the salivary glands that are modified mucous glands, and the tongue all contribute to the proper function of the digestive system.

The main function of the digestive system is to mechanically and chemically process food into absorbable molecules so that an animal can survive and prosper nutritionally in order to carry out its life processes. Teeth obviously are involved in capturing and holding food and reducing it to chunks that are mixed with salivary secretions containing digestive enzymes and mucus that make it possible for the food to slide down the digestive tract without damaging the lining. The tongue moves the food from the oral cavity into the pharynx and initiates the swallowing reflex. By muscular activity the food is propelled through the regions of the alimentary canal, the pharynx, the esophagus, the stomach, and the small and large intestine. Into the small intestine the secretions of the accessory organs, the liver and pancreas, are added to the secretions of the digestive tract proper. As the food passes through the alimentary canal it is reduced to a form easily absorbed and made available to all parts of the body. The undigested end product of these processes is fecal material eliminated through the anus.

## Salivary Glands and Ducts

In order to examine the salivary glands, carefully remove surface connective tissue along the lateral aspect of the head and neck and the surface of the masseter muscle, being especially cautious not to destroy blood vessels, nerves, and nervelike structures that may be salivary ducts. The parotid gland and its duct are particularly vulnerable to damage while attempting to clean the area below the ear and over the masseter muscle.

The salivary glands are paired and located along the lateral surface of the head beneath connective tissue and skin [Figure 4–1]. The largest of these paired glands, located ventral to the ear is the **parotid**. It is a large, diffuse, lobulated structure that is intimately associated with overlying connective tissue and can be easily misidentified and removed while trying to expose the gland. The parotid duct emerges from approximately the midpoint of the anterior surface of the gland, crosses the masseter muscle, and enters the vestibule (space between the teeth and the inside of the lip) of the oral cavity where it opens opposite the third upper premolar tooth. Two similar appearing bands, one above the parotid duct (the **anterior branch of the facial nerve**), and one below the parotid duct (the **posterior branch of the facial nerve**), serve as reference points in identification of the duct [Figure 4–1].

The **mandibular** gland also referred to as the submaxillary, is located just ventral to the parotid and posterior to the angular process of the mandible. It, too, is lobular, but the lobes are less diffuse giving the impression that this gland is smoother and more well

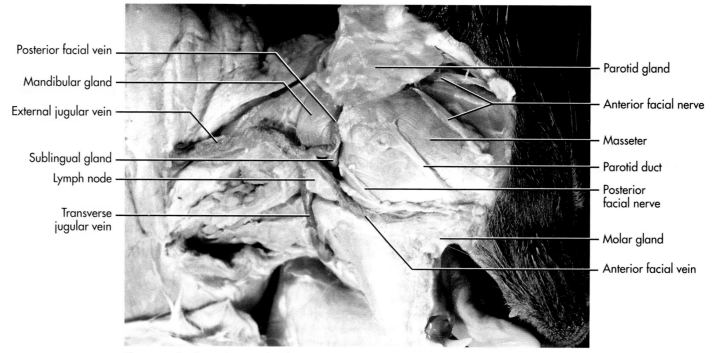

Posterior facial vein

Mandibular gland

External jugular vein

Sublingual gland

Lymph node

Transverse jugular vein

Parotid gland

Anterior facial nerve

Masseter

Parotid duct

Posterior facial nerve

Molar gland

Anterior facial vein

**Figure 4-1**  Salivary glands.

defined. Each duct can be identified emerging from beneath the anterior edge of the gland and continuing laterally and beneath the digastric and under the mylohyoid muscles, entering the floor of the oral cavity and opening at the base of a small papilla just anterior to the lingual frenulum [Figure 4–2]. In the vicinity of this gland are generally one or two lymph nodes that can be easily mistaken for the mandibular. These may vary in size and when large may be particularly confusing.

The **sublingual** gland is the smallest of the three. It is conical and certainly the smoothest of the three, and often adheres to the anterior surface of the mandibular gland. This gland wraps around the proximal end of the mandibular duct. The sublingual duct is inconspicuous and runs parallel to the mandibular duct and also opens in the floor of the oral cavity in the vicinity of the mandibular duct [Figure 4–1].

In the cat, two other glands, a molar and a zygomatic, are considered to be part of the salivary system. The **molar** gland occurs at the angle of the jaw and is located immediately beneath the skin and embedded in the surrounding connective tissue. It

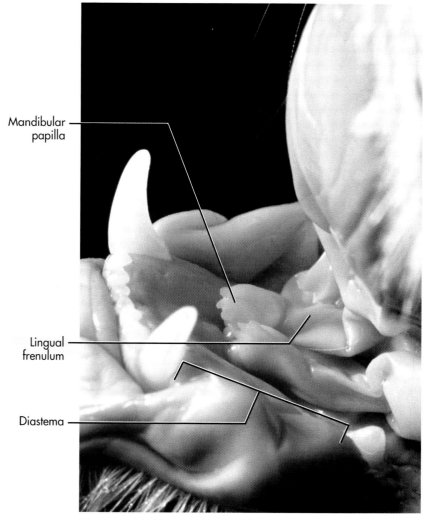

Mandibular papilla

Lingual frenulum

Diastema

**Figure 4-2**  Mandibular gland papillae.

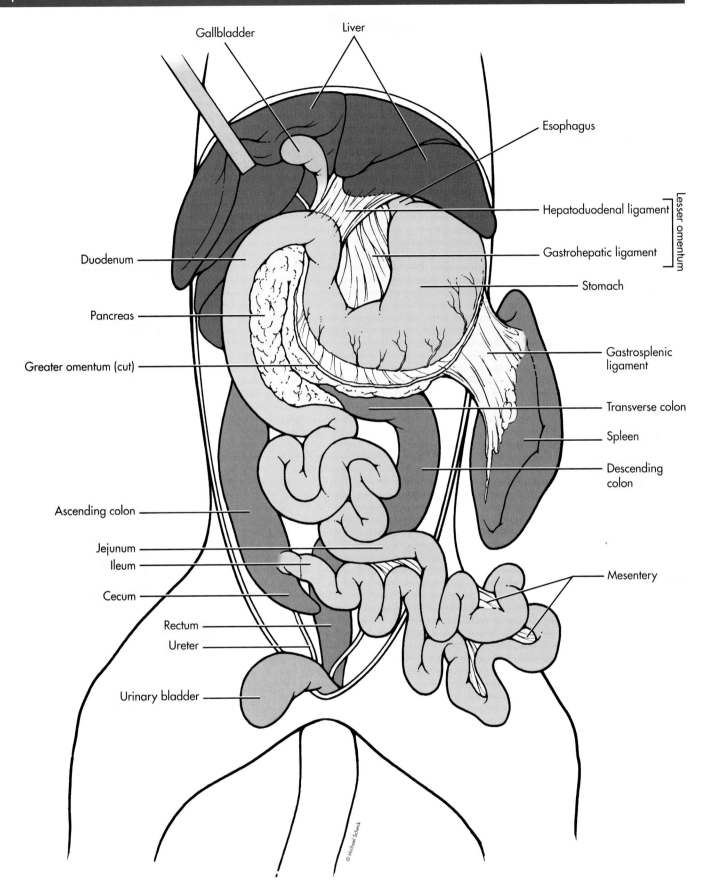

**Figure 4-3** Lower digestive system schematic.

has a brownish-gray, granular appearance, and may vary in prominence. Several inconspicuous, small ducts open on the inner surface of the cheek [Figure 4–1]. The **zygomatic** or infraorbital gland lies in the floor of the orbit of the eye. It opens by means of a small duct into the posterolateral portion of the roof of the mouth. This gland is difficult to find without removing an eye and we do not recommend that it be done.

In humans, the salivary glands are the parotid, the submandibular (mandibular in the cat), and sublingual. The position of the parotid is similar to that of the cat and its duct (Stensen's) opens in the vestibule opposite the second maxillary molar. The submandibular gland is located medial to the mandible beneath the mucous membrane of the oral cavity and its duct (Wharton's) opens in about the same position as in the cat. The sublingual gland lies anterior to the submandibular along the base of the tongue. Its ducts (Rivinus) open into the floor of the oral cavity along the base of the tongue and directly above the gland. In contrast to the cat, humans do not have molar or zygomatic glands.

## Alimentary Canal ━━━━━━━

In order to facilitate observation of the anatomy of the oral cavity, the pharynx and the larynx, we will describe two methods of exposing these areas. One of them results in a specimen where the oral cavity, pharynx, and larynx are presented as dorsal and ventral halves while the other is a bisected left and right half. Each possesses its own advantages. The first that we describe is performed with an electrical craniotomy saw and may best be done as a class demonstration. To prepare the cat for this operation, make an incision with a scalpel through the skin from the nose to the back of the neck. Peel the skin back from the incision about 2–2½ inches [Figure 4–4]. The next steps are probably best performed by the instructor and a laboratory assistant. While the assistant holds the head steady on the dissecting tray, generally locking the thumbs around the ears, and holding either side of the head tightly, the instructor uses the craniotomy saw to bisect the entire head, including the mandible. **Both the person doing the**

**cutting and the holding assistant must keep their eyes on the saw at all times! Be sure to wear safety glasses.** This is really not as dangerous as it might sound but both individuals should be cautious. The completed bisection may require some minor cutting of the tongue and the laryngeal area with a scalpel. This technique permits viewing of various head organs, e.g., the brain, pituitary gland, nasal conchae, sinuses as well as the relationship of such cavities as the oral and pharyngeal and other difficult to demonstrate organs and openings like the palatine tonsils and the opening of the auditory tube into the nasopharynx [Figure 4–5].

The second dissection is more difficult to perform and should be completed after the salivary glands, ducts, and facial nerves associated with the masseter muscles have been identified. With a sharp scalpel cut through the masseter muscle to the ramus of the jaw on either side, avoiding the parotid duct and posterior facial nerve, if at all possible. Use a pair of bone shears to cut through the ramus of the jaw. An audible crunch will be heard and, when completed, should result in your being able to depress the lower jaw. It will be necessary to cut through the juncture of the palatoglossal arches and soft palate to gain full access to the pharyngeal area [Figure 4–6]. This dissection has the advantage of allowing observation of the entire hard and soft palates, the tongue, lingual and labial frenula, opening of the nasopalatine duct, etc. It further avoids some damage to the circulatory and nervous systems that may result from the bisection.

***Figure 4–4*** Head prepared for dissection.

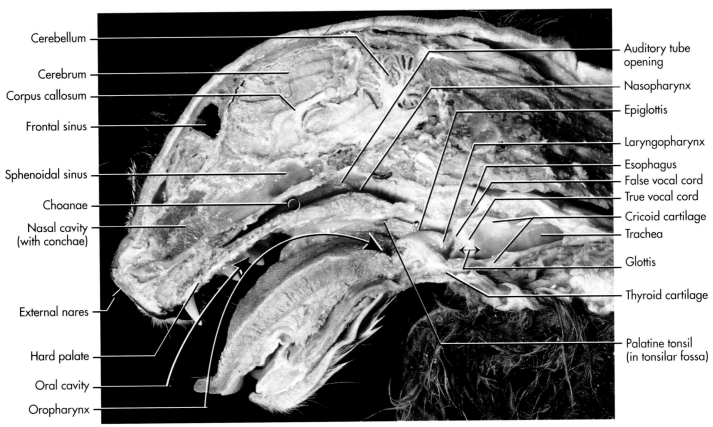

Cerebellum
Cerebrum
Corpus callosum
Frontal sinus
Sphenoidal sinus
Choanae
Nasal cavity (with conchae)
External nares
Hard palate
Oral cavity
Oropharynx

Auditory tube opening
Nasopharynx
Epiglottis
Laryngopharynx
Esophagus
False vocal cord
True vocal cord
Cricoid cartilage
Trachea
Glottis
Thyroid cartilage
Palatine tonsil (in tonsilar fossa)

**Figure 4-5**   Bisected head.

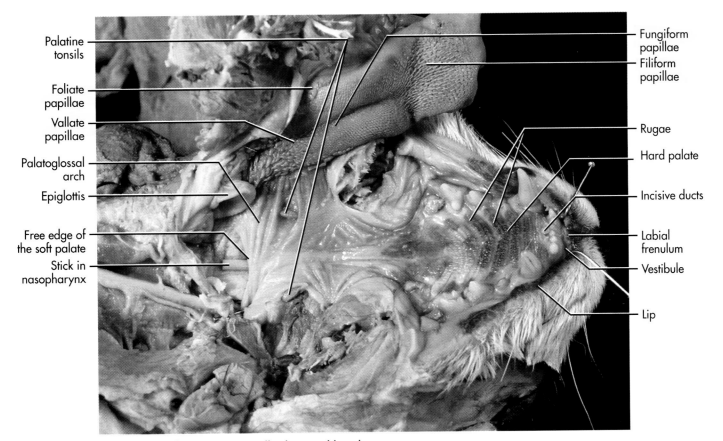

Palatine tonsils
Foliate papillae
Vallate papillae
Palatoglossal arch
Epiglottis
Free edge of the soft palate
Stick in nasopharynx

Fungiform papillae
Filiform papillae
Rugae
Hard palate
Incisive ducts
Labial frenulum
Vestibule
Lip

**Figure 4-6**   Dorso-ventrally dissected head.

## Mouth or Oral Cavity

The mouth or oral cavity is defined externally by the lips along its border. The **lips** are a pair of folds whose inner surface is covered by a mucous membrane and whose outer surface is hairy. The space between the lips and the teeth is called the **vestibule**. In the vestibule, the **labial frenulum**, a fold of tissue, connects the upper and lower lips at the midline to their respective gumlines [Figure 4–6].

The **oral cavity** proper is the area of the mouth extending from the lingual side of the teeth to the entrance of the oropharynx [Figure 4–5]. The dental formula of mammals often indicates specializations for dietary habits. In the cat, this formula is:

$$\frac{3\,\text{incisors:}\,1\,\text{canine:}\,3\,\text{premolars:}\,1\,\text{molar}}{3\,\text{incisors:}\,1\,\text{canine:}\,2\,\text{premolars:}\,1\,\text{molar}}$$

The numbers in the numerator of the formula represent the teeth rooted in half of the maxilla and the numbers in the denominator of the formula represent the teeth rooted in one half of the mandible. To determine the total number of teeth, multiply the teeth in each half jaw by two for a total of 30. Note that the teeth of the cat are highly adapted for a carnivorous diet. Recall that the small, wedge-shaped incisors are adapted for nipping, the elongated conical canines for stabbing and holding prey and the blade-like molariform teeth for cutting and shearing.

The respective dental formula for humans is:

$$\frac{2\!:\!1\!:\!2\!:\!3}{2\!:\!1\!:\!2\!:\!3}$$

Note that the human canines are shorter and blunter and the molariform teeth are flattened and adapted for grinding since humans are described as omnivores, meaning that a combination of plant and animal food is consumed.

The space between the lower canine and premolars in the cat is called a **diastema** [Figure 4–2]. Humans do not possess a diastema.

### Tongue

The **tongue** is a very mobile, muscular organ that plays an important versatile role in the life of the cat. It is used as an organ of food manipulation, swallowing, drinking, and grooming. The **lingual frenulum** anchors the tongue in the anterior floor of the oral cavity and is one of the most obvious structures there. The frenulum becomes obvious when the tongue is lifted [Figure 4–7a].

On the surface of the tongue are four types of projections known as **papillae** [Figure 4–7b]. The most numerous are the **filiform**, which in cats are located on most of the surface of the tongue. Anteriorly, they appear spiky and are used in grooming or as rasping devices to remove tissue from bones. Posteriorly, they

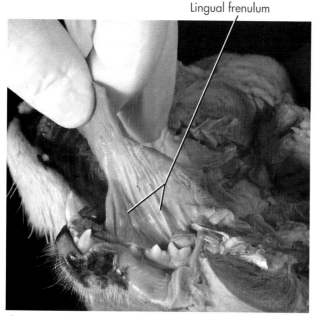

**A** Lingual frenulum

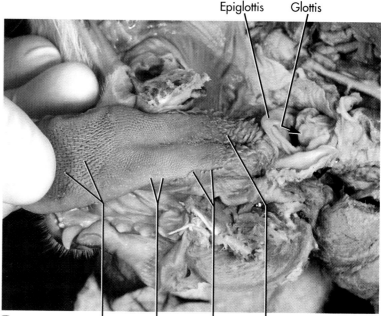

**B** Papillae

*Figure 4–7* Tongue.

are less pointed. **Fungiform** papillae are mushroom shaped, less numerous and scattered among the filiform papillae. **Vallate** papillae are larger, round papillae isolated by shallow grooves and arranged in a V configuration near the root of the tongue. The apex of the V is oriented toward the pharynx. Frequently, these papillae are difficult to distinguish. The **foliate** papillae are leaf-shaped and are located on the posterolateral aspect of the tongue. Taste buds, microscopic structures important in detecting chemicals identifiable in tasting food, are located in fungifom, vallate, and foliate papillae.

The human tongue is very similar to the cat. Filiform papillae are less acute, vallate are more numerous, and foliate papillae are missing. Fungiform and vallate papillae house the tastebuds.

## Palate

The roof of the oral cavity is formed anteriorly by the **hard palate** and posteriorly by the **soft palate**. The hard palate consists of a bony shelf constructed of the palatine processes of both the premaxilla and maxilla and the palatines. The hard palate is covered by tissue formed into a series of folds known as **rugae**. The soft palate consists of connective tissue and muscle and extends from the caudal end of the hard palate to its free edge. At the anterior end of the hard palate and directly posterior to the incisors are a pair of ducts, the **incisive ducts**, whose openings are distinguished by a small nipplelike structure [Figure 4–6]. These ducts lead to vomeronasal organs whose function amplifies olfaction in mammals who are good smellers. The human palate is similar to the cat with the exception of incisive ducts and reduced rugae. In humans, the absence of the incisive ducts is probably correlated with the reduced sense of smell.

## Pharynx

The pharynx, a space shared by the digestive and respiratory systems, extends from the oral cavity to the larynx. It is arbitrarily subdivided into three regions, the **nasopharynx**, the **oropharynx**, and the **laryngopharynx** [Figure 4–5]. The dorsal nasopharynx extends from the internal nares (choanae) to the free edge of the soft palate. Through this passage movement of air for respiration and olfaction occurs. Make a small slit in the soft palate and insert a probe into the nasopharynx or observe this space in a bisected specimen. In the lateral walls of this portion of the pharynx are the paired **auditory tube openings**, better seen in the bisected specimen [Figure 4–5]. These tubes connect the air filled middle ear cavity with the nasopharynx and are important in equalization of air pressure.

The oropharynx is the space bounded laterally by the **palatoglossal arches** and extends from approximately the base of the tongue to the free edge of the soft palate [Figure 4–5 and 4–6]. The **fauces**, the space between the arches marks the transition between the oral cavity and pharynx. Air, food, and liquids pass through the oropharynx on their way to the trachea and the esophagus, respectively. Two small lymphoid masses, the **palatine tonsils**, lying in shallow depressions, the **tonsilar fossae**, are located in the laterodorsal walls of the oropharynx [Figure 4–5 and Figure 4–6].

The laryngopharynx is that part of the pharynx continuing from the tip of the epiglottis to the glottis, an opening into the larynx [Figure 4–5].

## Esophagus

Movement of food and liquids from the pharynx into the esophagus involves a process called swallowing. During this activity, the larynx is elevated and pulled up against the epiglottis, covering the glottis or opening into the respiratory tract, thereby preventing the food or liquids from entering it and facilitating passage of these materials into the esophagus.

The **esophagus** is a collapsible muscular tube, capable of being greatly expanded, that passes through the mediastinum dorsal to the trachea. Characteristic wavelike muscular movements (peristalsis) in the walls of the esophagus propel the foodstuff through this tube to the stomach. In mammals, the thoracic and abdominopelvic cavities are separated by a muscular partition known as the diaphragm that plays an essential role in breathing and through which the esophagus passes. At its distal end, the esophagus terminates in a ring of smooth muscle, the **cardiac sphincter**, permitting movement of material from the esophagus into the stomach and functioning primarily in preventing reflux of the bolus (food mixed with saliva and oral enzymes) back into the esophagus [Figure 4–8].

## Stomach

This expanded part of the alimentary tract serves as a temporary storage area for food and liquids. Modified

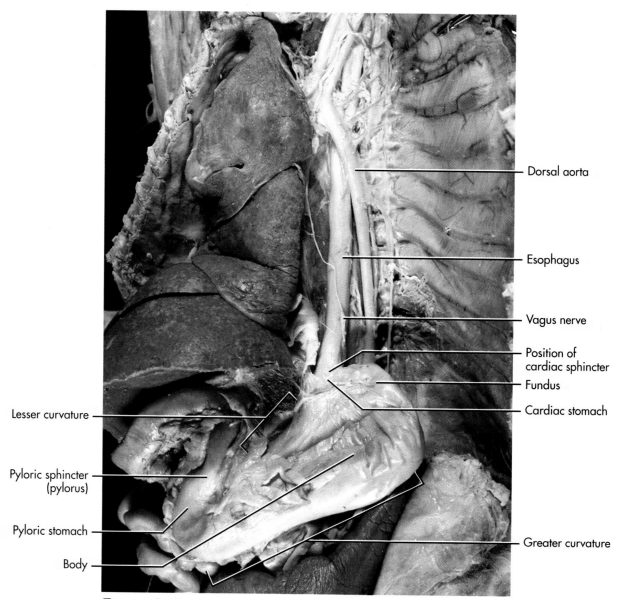

Lesser curvature

Pyloric sphincter (pylorus)

Pyloric stomach

Body

Dorsal aorta

Esophagus

Vagus nerve

Position of cardiac sphincter

Fundus

Cardiac stomach

Greater curvature

**Figure 4–8**   Esophagus and stomach.

cells lining this organ secrete hydrochloric acid to facilitate the action of a proteolytic enzyme also secreted in the stomach. In the stomach the bolus is further processed through segmenting and peristaltic movements that eventually advance the mass toward the intestine.

The stomach is a J-shaped organ lying mainly on the left side of the body. The covex left margin is known as the **greater curvature** and the concave right margin is known as the **lesser curvature**. Remember that the lesser omentum occurs between the liver and the lesser curvature of the stomach and the proximal end of the duodenum as the gastrohepatic and hepatoduodenal ligaments, respectively. From the greater curvature hangs the greater omentum. On the left side, the triangular gastrocolic ligament extends from the greater omentum to the mesocolon. That portion of the stomach below the cardiac sphincter is the **cardiac** end and the narrow portion connected to the intestine is the **pyloric** region. A muscular valve, the **pyloric sphincter** (pylorus), located at the distal end of the pyloric region regulates the movement of the stomach contents into the intestine. The large inflated portion between these two ends consists of the upper **fundus** and lower **body** [Figure 4–8].

Carefully make an incision along the greater curvature from the fundus to the pyloric area of the stomach making sure to avoid the greater omentum. If the stomach is full, carefully remove some of the material to observe the **gastric rugae** or folds in this organ that allow it to expand perceptively when food is eaten.

## Small Intestine

From the stomach the contents of the alimentary canal move into the small intestine. In this region of the alimentary canal, most of the major chemical digestion of carbohydrates, proteins, and fats takes place. Some of the digestive enzymes are a structural part of the cells of the luminal epithelium of the small intestine while other essential enzymes and digestion facilitators are released from the pancreas and biliary system (liver and gall bladder) through ducts into the small intestine. This region is also another area where segmentation and peristalsis mix and move the contents along the alimentary tract. This is the major absorption site of nutrients and water in the digestive tract.

The lengthy small intestine actually occupies a minimal abdominal volume since it is greatly coiled. The small intestine is regionally subdivided into three areas, the **duodenum**, the **jejunum**, and the **ileum** [Figure 4–9]. Mesenteries play an important role in maintaining the position of the small intestine. The mesoduodenum supports the duodenum and head of the pancreas while the mesentery proper supports the jejunum and ileum. Observe the obvious lymph nodes associated with the mesentery proper. The triangular duodenocolic fold, on the right side of the body, anchors the duodenum to the mesocolon.

The very short proximal part of the small intestine about 12 to 18 cm (5–7 in) in length in an adult cat, known as the duodenum, extends from the pylorus to the position of the duodenocolic fold. The distal-most portion of the small intestine is the ileum and the middle portion is the jejunum.

At the junction of the ileum and the large intestine, on the righthand side of the body, is a doughnut-shaped muscular **ileocecal valve**, which, like the pylorus regulates the movement of the contents of the small intestine into the large intestine as well as prevents the reflux of contents into the small intestine [Figure 4–10].

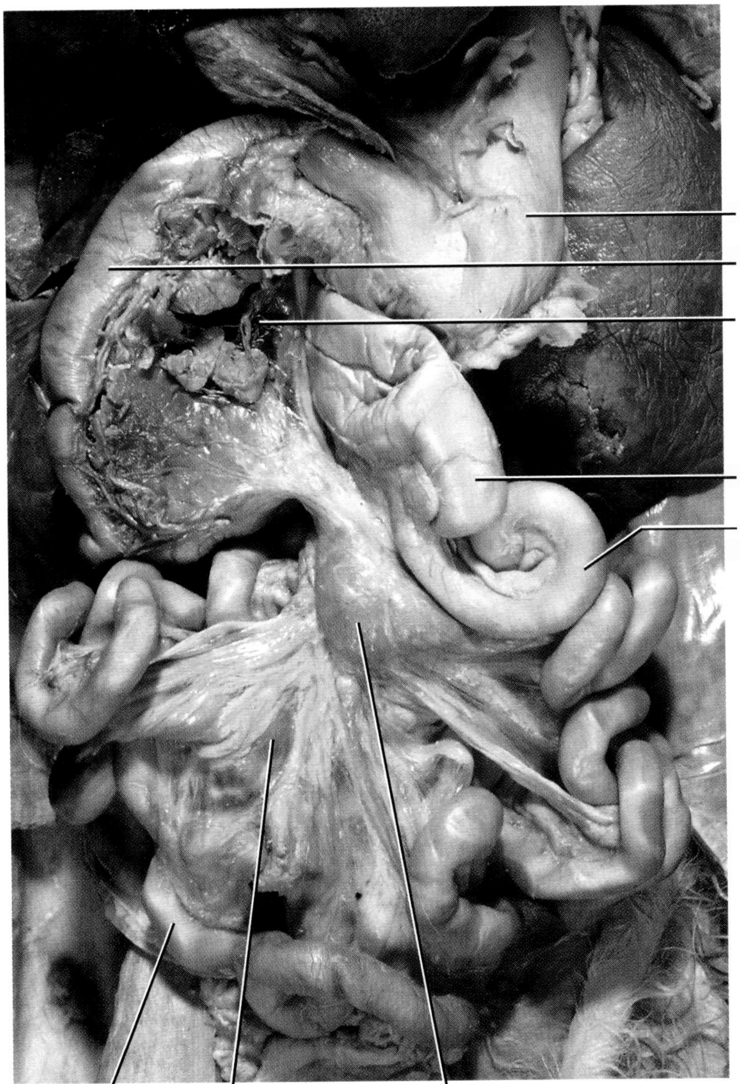

Stomach

Duodenum

Mesoduodenum

Cecum

Ileum

Jejunum　　Mesentery　　Mesenteric lymph node

**Figure 4–9** Regions of the small intestine.

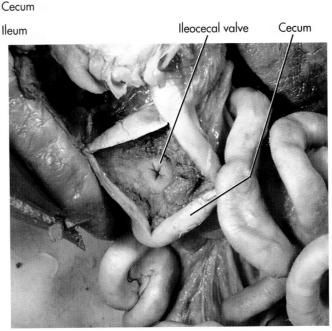

Ileocecal valve　　Cecum

**Figure 4–10** Ileocecal valve.

Carefully make a small incision with a sharp scalpel in the wall of the ileum at the site of the ileocecal valve and observe its shape. You may have to clear any contents in this area to observe this valve.

## Large Intestine

Further absorption of water occurs in this region along with fermentation, rotting of undigested material, and vitamin synthesis by resident colonies of bacteria. The vitamins are absorbed across the mucosa of the large intestine. The end result is the production of gases and semisolid feces that are eliminated from the body through the anus.

Anatomically, the proximal part of the large intestine is a blind diverticulum, the **cecum**. In humans, an elongate, fingerlike tube, the appendix, extends from the cecum. Cats do not possess an appendix.

From the cecum, the colon continues cranially on the right side of the body as the **ascending colon**, makes a left hand turn, crosses the abdominal cavity to the left side as the **transverse colon** where it curves caudally and continues as the **descending colon** terminating as the **rectum** [Figure 4–11]. The mesocolon suspends the large intestine from the parietal peritoneum of the dorsal wall. With the exception of the sigmoid colon in the human, this portion of the digestive tract is similar to that of the cat. The anus is the caudal opening of the digestive tract and is surrounded by sphincter muscles. A pair of scent glands, the **anal glands**, open into the rectum near the **anus** [Figure 4–11]. Secretions are important in territorial

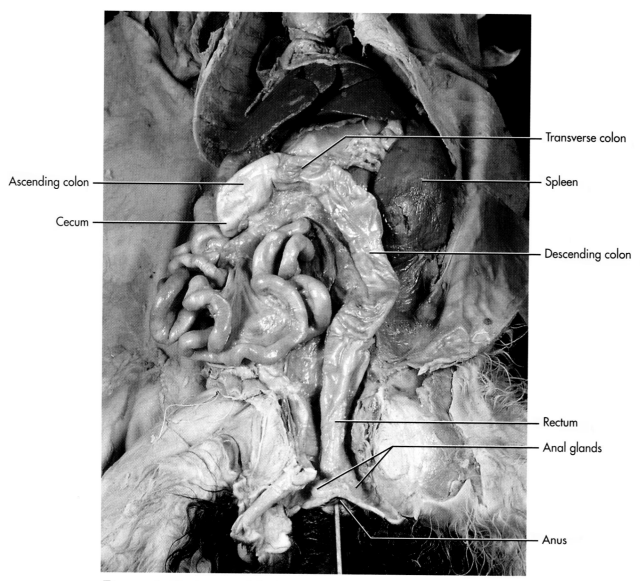

**Figure 4–11**  Regions of the large intestine.

marking and sexual attraction. Unfortunately, humans have no scent glands, but their alimentary canal is similar to the cat.

## Accessory Digestive Organs ▬

### Liver

The largest internal organ in most mammals is the dome-shaped liver that rests directly below the diaphragm. Among its many functions are chemical syntheses, detoxification, storage of metabolic products, bile production, etc. Actually, if you cannot pinpoint an organ where a particular function occurs, a good guess is the liver.

In the cat, the prominent, reddish-brown liver is divided into six lobes. A deep cleft from which the falciform ligament extends from the liver to the ventral body wall, separates the left and right halves. Identify **a left medial** and a left **lateral lobe.** Adjacent and to the right of the falciform ligament is the small **quadrate lobe,** which is partially united with the **right medial lobe.** The gall bladder is located in a semicircular depression, the cystic fossa, between the quadrate and right medial lobes. Just posterior to the right medial lobe is the **right lateral lobe.** The **caudate lobe,** just posterior to the right lateral lobe and sometimes

appearing like a subdivision of that lobe, extends into the lesser omentum [Figure 4–12]. Observe the hepatorenal ligament extending between the caudate lobe and the right kidney.

The point at which the liver and the diaphragm actually contact one another is the site of the **central tendon of the diaphragm** [Figure 4–13]. Note that the falciform ligament continues as the coronary ligament to each side of the central tendon of the diaphragm. Also find the round ligament on the free surface of the falciform ligament. It represents the remnant of the umbilical vein of the cat during its fetal life when this vessel was essential in returning oxygenated blood from the placenta. The lesser omentum connects the liver to the lesser curvature of the stomach and to the duodenum.

An important digestive function of the liver involves secretion of a solution containing bile salts that are important in emulsifying fats, reducing the size of the fat globule, and increasing the surface area of the fat so that enzymatic digestion is facilitated. Additionally, bile is involved during fat absorption. Bile is secreted by liver cells and stored in the "bag" called the **gall bladder.** A number of ducts are associated with the liver and gall bladder. Many small hepatic ducts converge to form two or more quite prominent

Gall bladder (in cystic fossa)

Right medial lobe

Right lateral lobe

Quadrate lobe

Left medial lobe

Left lateral lobe

Caudate lobe

**Figure 4–12** Lobes of the liver.

**hepatic ducts** leading from the left lobes and right lateral lobe of the liver that join the **cystic duct**, draining the gall bladder, forming the **common bile duct** [Figure 4–14a and Figure 4–14b]. The common bile duct that extends parallel with the hepatic portal vein (appearing as a robust yellow vessel in triply injected cats) and the relatively small hepatic artery (appearing as a red vessel) empties into the duodenum. All of these structures, with the exception of the hepatic ducts, accompanied by nerves and lymphatic vessels, form a tough tendinous right lateral border of the hepatoduodenal ligament of the lesser omentum.

To observe the duct system, carefully isolate with forceps, the common bile duct (a tannish or greenish, flat structure) within the border of the hepatoduodenal ligament beginning at its distal end where it joins the main pancreatic duct opening into the duodenum marked by a small pimplelike bump known as the **hepatopancreatic ampulla** (ampulla of Vater) [Figure 4–14a and Figure 4–14b]. The common bile duct is fragile and can easily be torn. From the ampulla it extends toward the liver where it is joined by the hepatic ducts from various lobes of the liver as well as the often greenish cystic duct leading from the gall bladder.

You may have noticed that the gall bladder and surrounding liver tissue may be stained an olive green, the typical color of bile. Exposure of the hepatic ducts that have a tendency to shred and tear requires careful removal of hepatic tissue using forceps in a picking motion. The cystic duct is perhaps the easiest to find since it extends from the posterior end of the gall bladder. It is through this system of ducts that the bile is released under the influence of digestive tract hormones and fatty foodstuff in the chyme (intestinal contents).

In the human, there are only four lobes of the liver — the right and left separated by the falciform ligament, and a caudate and quadrate. The ductwork and functions are very similar.

## Pancreas

This organ is actually one that is comprised of tissues derived from two different embryonic sources. Therefore, it should not be too surprising for you to learn that parts of it function as an endocrine gland producing essential hormones that control various metabolic activities throughout the body and the other portion

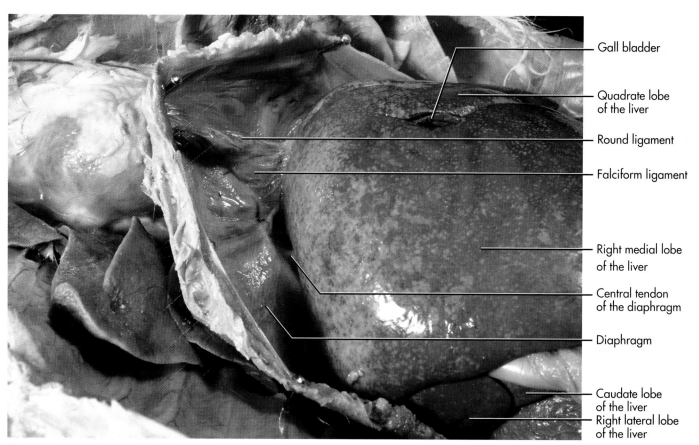

Gall bladder

Quadrate lobe of the liver

Round ligament

Falciform ligament

Right medial lobe of the liver

Central tendon of the diaphragm

Diaphragm

Caudate lobe of the liver

Right lateral lobe of the liver

*Figure 4–13*   Relationship of the liver and diaphragm.

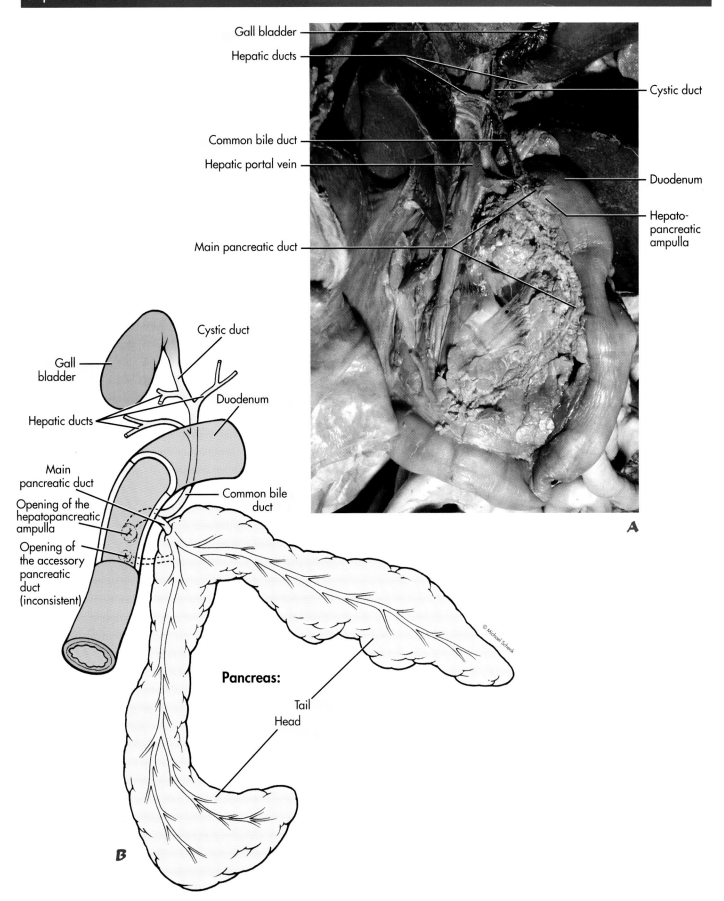

**Figure 4-14** Ducts of the pancreas and bilary system.

produces essential digestive enzymes and a buffering solution of sodium bicarbonate, a cat's own antacid supply, actually only affecting the acidity of the small intestine rather than providing gastric relief.

The appearance of this organ is lobulated and glandular. It is the tannish, elongated organ whose **head** (**duodenal portion**) lies within the mesoduodenum and whose **tail** (**gastrosplenic portion**) lies within the dorsal part of the greater omentum near the greater curvature of the stomach [Figure 4–15]. Each part is drained by a duct, but the **main pancreatic duct** is associated with the duodenal part and it is this duct that joins the common bile duct in the **hepatopancreatic ampulla** on the duodenum [Figure 4–14a and Figure 4–14b]. An accessory duct often drains the gastrosplenic portion independently.

To observe the main duct, carefully and gently pick away pancreatic tissue along the duodenal border of the duodenal portion of the pancreas, starting from the ampulla and working toward the head end, taking

special care to preserve all red-injected and yellow-injected blood vessels in the process. This duct is whitish with smaller branches feeding into it and is especially delicate. The accessory duct, leading from the gastrosplenic portion, quite often, is not as robust as the main duct and opens a short distance below the ampulla. This duct is often difficult to locate and may be absent in some cats. The pancreas and ducts in the human are very similar.

### Spleen

The **spleen** is a large lymphoid organ often discussed with the digestive system because it occurs in the peritoneal cavity, along with the viscera. This large, tonguelike organ lies on the left side of the body and is anchored in the ventral layer of the greater omentum, the gastrosplenic ligament [Figure 4–11]. In humans the spleen is soft and fist-sized.

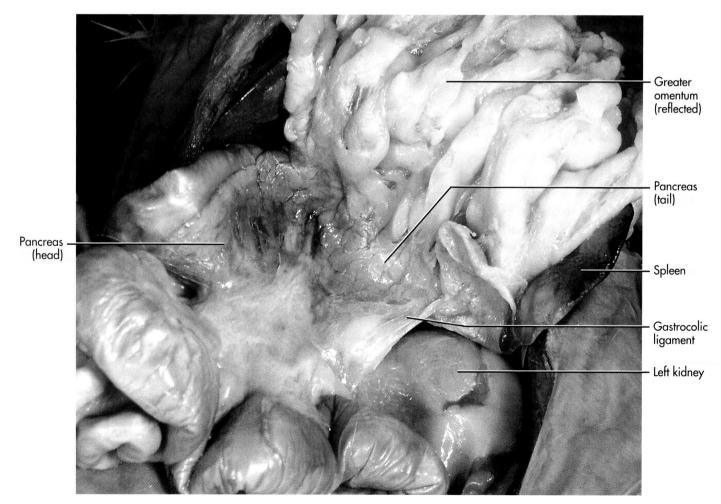

Pancreas (head)

Greater omentum (reflected)

Pancreas (tail)

Spleen

Gastrocolic ligament

Left kidney

*Figure 4–15*   Pancreas.

# Respiratory System

Gas exchange of oxygen and carbon dioxide is a life sustaining function of the respiratory system. Among most adult tetrapod vertebrates, cats and humans included, the organs facilitating this exchange are the lungs. They are located internally and generally found within the thoracic cavity of the body. The process of gas exchange, diffusion, occurs across the moist lungs into capillaries. The spongy lungs are made up of great numbers of gas-filled small spheres or alveoli where this diffusion takes place. The vast number of alveoli makes it possible to maximize the surface area in a reasonably sized organ such as the lung.

A system of tubes, the trachea, various bronchi and bronchioles conveys the oxygen-rich air from the atmosphere to the lungs and the oxygen-poor air back to the atmosphere [Figure 5–1]. The diameter of these tubes decreases while the number increases as they extend from the nasal cavity to the alveoli. The overall effect is to increase the respiratory surface area dramatically.

Among some reptiles and all mammals the palate described in the digestive system separates the oral and the nasal cavities. In the digestive system of mammals, the palate serves as the roof of the oral cavity and as the floor of the nasal cavity of the respiratory system. This "shelf" allows a mammal to chew and hold food items in the mouth and breathe at the same time. It also allows mammals to smell (taste) food for this reason.

Because some organs are common to the digestive and respiratory systems, we suggest that the digestive system be dissected first.

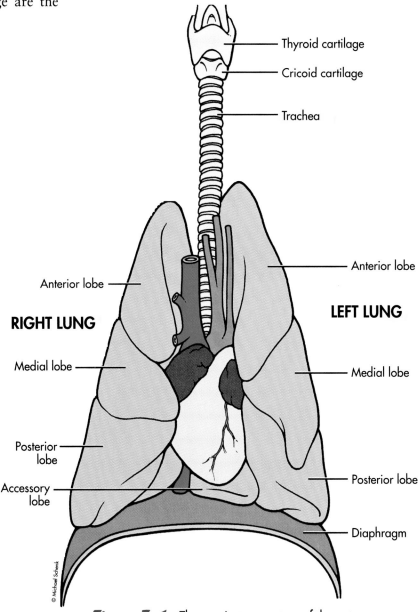

**Figure 5–1**  The respiratory system of the cat.

## Openings and Spaces

The pathway by which air moves from the atmosphere to the alveoli begins through the **nostrils** or **external nares** and into the **nasal cavities**. In these cavities the air is warmed, moistened, filtered, and smelled. From the cavities it passes through the **internal nares**, or **choanae**, and into the **nasopharynx**, one part of a more extensive region called simply the pharynx, a space shared with the digestive system. The nasopharynx extends from the internal nares to the free edge of the soft palate. The air then moves into the **laryngopharynx**, extending from the hyoid to the esophagus and larynx. From this space, the air moves into the larynx (see Figure 4–5).

## Larynx, Trachea, and Bronchi

Before the **larynx** is dissected, locate the paired thyroid glands situated on either side of the trachea, just posterior to the larynx [Figure 5–2]. In particular, be aware of the isthmus, a narrow band of tissue that extends at various angles between the two lobes.

This important structure is cartilaginous and consists of several single and paired elements. One of the single elements is the **epiglottic cartilage** that strengthens the **epiglottis**. The function of the epiglottis is to prevent the contents of the oral cavity from entering the trachea during swallowing. As the material is swallowed, the larynx is pulled anteriorly by muscles, causing the epiglottis to block off the **glottis**, a slit between the vocal cords. Air passes into the larynx through this slit. To view the epiglottis in a bisected specimen, see Figure 4–5. With a specimen dissected into a dorsal and ventral half, pull the tongue forward while peering into the pharyngeal region and observe the epiglottis.

A second, very large single cartilage noticeable ventrally is the

**thyroid cartilage** [Figure 5–2 and Figure 4–5]. Observe that this cartilage is continuous dorsally. To see this structure better, you should remove the musculature obscuring it. In humans, this cartilage is commonly called the Adam's apple and exhibits a distinct sexual dimorphism, i.e., in males it is much more prominent.

Posterior to the thyroid is the ring-shaped **cricoid cartilage** [Figure 5–2 and Figure 4–5]. The dorsal wall of the larynx consists primarily of the broad part of this cartilage. You may also want to clear musculature from this cartilage.

Small, paired cartilages, the **arytenoid** cartilages [Figure 5–2], sit on the dorsal rim of the cricoid cartilage and abut the dorsal projections of the thyroid

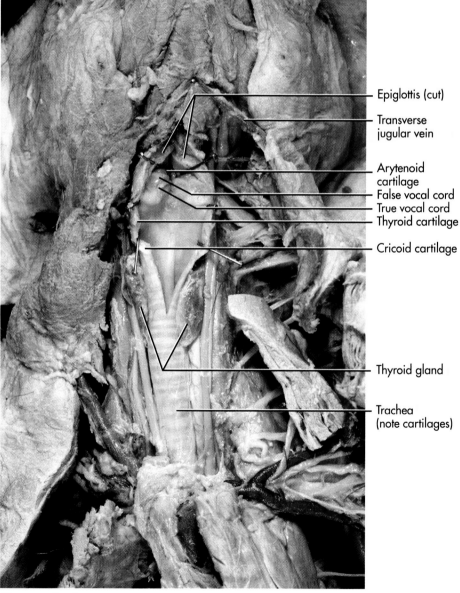

Epiglottis (cut)

Transverse jugular vein

Arytenoid cartilage
False vocal cord
True vocal cord
Thyroid cartilage

Cricoid cartilage

Thyroid gland

Trachea (note cartilages)

**Figure 5–2**  Larynx, trachea, and thyroid glands.

cartilage. Some other, inconspicuous cartilages are part of the larynx, but are difficult to see. In humans, these cartilages, the cuneiform and the corniculate, are more easily identified, in addition to the cartilages described in the cat.

With a sharp scalpel, make an incision in the mid-ventral wall of the larynx, perhaps extending it into the trachea posteriorly. With scissors, continue the cut anteriorly, cutting the epiglottis. These directions apply only to dorsoventral head dissection. Carefully reflect the walls of the larynx. Observe two pairs of tissue folds at the cranial end of the larynx. The anterior folds, the **false vocal cords**, often appearing tannish, extend from the arytenoid cartilages to the epiglottis. The posterior folds, the **true vocal cords**, appearing as whitish bands, extend from the arytenoid cartilages to the thyroid cartilage [Figure 5-2 and Figure 4-5]. Vocalization in cats is the result of air movement across the true vocal cords, while purring seems to related to the vibration of the vocal cords during air movement through the glottis. In humans, the false vocal cords are not involved in sound production.

The **trachea** extends posteriorly from the larynx to the root of the lungs [Figure 5-2 and Figure 4-5]. This large diameter respiratory tube is the main passageway for air from the larynx to the lungs. Observe the C-shaped cartilages that reinforce the wall of the trachea, with the dorsal open space of the "C" reinforced with muscle. This anatomical configuration allows compression during the act of swallowing but prevents collapse during respiration. The lobulated, glandular tissue, the thymus, lying along the ventral aspect of the trachea and heart should be conserved. This important endocrine gland varies in size with the age of the animal, also true in human beings.

Division of this tube within the tissue of the lungs occurs with a resulting interconnected network of air conducting tubes often referred to as a bronchial or respiratory tree. The first division of the trachea forms the **primary bronchi**. These are subdivided sequentially into **secondary** and **tertiary bronchi** [Figure 5-3]. Further branching results in bronchioles and alveolar ducts which terminate in alveoli, illustrating the decreasing diameter but increasing surface area mentioned in the introduction. The supporting cartilage of

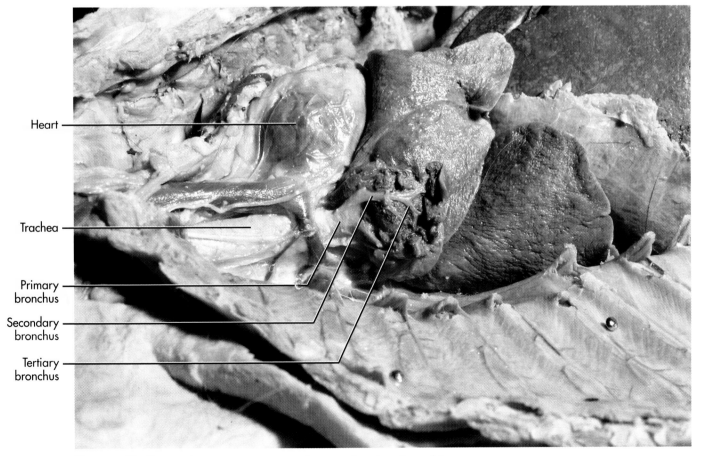

*Figure 5-3* Trachea: primary, secondary, and tertiary bronchi.

these tubes decreases proportionately to the increased surface area and elasticity of the tree.

To observe the primary bronchi, reflect the lungs medially and carefully pick away lung tissue at the level of the root of the lungs. Be careful to avoid the pulmonary vessels in this area that enter and leave the lung at the hilus. The bronchi appear as whitish, shiny tubes containing cartilage. Since the rest of the tree is enclosed within the lungs, we do not recommend further dissection. Your instructor may wish to provide a demonstration dissection.

## Lungs

The organs known as lungs are spongy, primarily due to the terminal structures of the respiratory tree called alveoli. Air moves through the tubular network into the alveoli, small, thin terminal air sacs, where gas exchange occurs. The left lung is subdivided into three lobes, the **anterior, medial,** and **posterior.** The right lung is also similarly divided with the exception of the posterior that is further subdivided forming an **accessory lobe.** Remember that this lobe of the lung projects into a mesentery pocket called the caval fold, while its left hand mesentery is the mediastinal septum [Figure 5–4]. In addition, remember that the lungs are suspended within the pleural spaces by the pulmonary ligaments [Figure 3–4b]. In human beings, a similar pattern of organ construction occurs with the exception of the number of lobes of the lungs. In humans, the left lung is subdivided into two lobes while the right has three.

## Diaphragm

The often mentioned muscular partition between the thoracic and abdominopelvic cavities is the **diaphragm** [Figure 5–4]. Mammals are the only vertebrates in which is found a complete muscular separation of these two cavities. Through this partition passes the esophagus, the posterior vena cava, and the aorta.

This organ is an essential component involved in the process of respiration. When this dome-shaped muscular partition contracts, moves posteriorly and flattens, the volume of the pleural cavities increases, with a concommitant decrease of pressure, and air moves into the respiratory tract. In contrast, when the diaphragm relaxes and returns to its domed position, the volume of the pleural cavities decreases and the pressure increases with the result that air moves into the atmosphere, again according to the laws of gas physics.

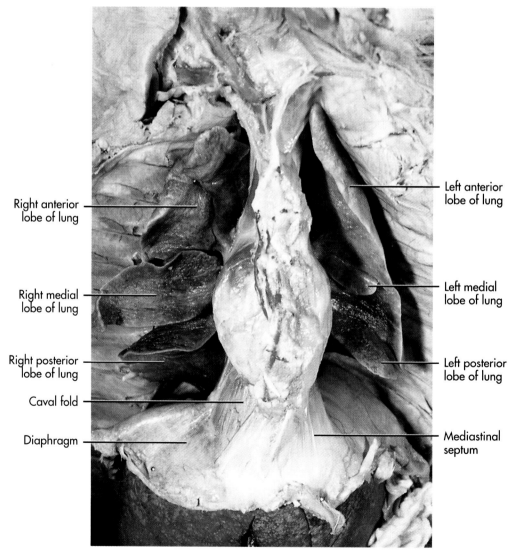

*Figure 5–4*   Lobes of the lungs.

# Urogenital System 6

As the name of this system suggests, it is a combination of two different systems. In mammals, as in many other vertebrates, the excretory and reproductive systems are closely interrelated, not only anatomically, but also embryologically. In particular, most of the terminal ductwork in males is common to both systems. Development of the reproductive systems in both sexes begins with an indifferent stage. Genetically, the sex is determined, but in the early stages of development there are no morphological differences in the gonads and external genitalia. Under the influence of testosterone, normal development of the reproductive system of male mammals progresses, whereas female reproductive structures develop in the absence of testosterone.

In spite of the interrelationships of the excretory and reproductive systems, the functions are worlds apart. In both sexes, the excretory system functions in maintaining the homeostatic balance of fluids, electrolytes, glucose, hormones, proteins, metabolic waste products, and other chemical substances. This balance is mediated through filtration, reabsorption, secretion, and elimination of excess chemicals above normal blood threshold levels. The structure and function of the excretory system in the two sexes is virtually identical from the kidneys to the urethra. In males, the pre-prostatic urethra is purely urinary while the rest of this tube functions as a part of both the excretory and reproductive systems. In females the entire urethra is urinary.

The functions of the testes and the accessory glands of the male reproductive system include sex hormone and semen production (sperm and associated glandular fluids). Hormones are important to maintain "maleness" and continued stimulation of semen production. While urine passes from the urinary bladder to the outside by way of the entire length of the urethra, semen, on the other hand, travels only along

that part of the urethra distal to the prostate gland to the outside. Deposition of the seminal fluid into the female reproductive tract is one of the functions of the penis.

The functions of the ovaries are production of sex hormones and oocytes and secretions by accessory glands in the female reproductive system. The system of "tubes" in the female reproductive apparatus is adapted for the receipt of semen from the male during intercourse, movement of the sperm to effect fertilization, and subsequent possible implantation and continued nourishment and maintenance of the developing embryo in the uterus.

## Excretory System

### Kidney

The kidney is the fundamental organ of this system. The primary functional units of this organ are the nephrons. The nephron consists of a cup-like Bowman's capsule with an elongate tubule extending from it. A specialized arterial capillary, the glomerulus, is intimately associated with the capsule. Also associated with the tubules of the nephron are other capillaries, numerous blood vessels, and nerves. The volume of blood that courses through the kidneys of mammals is impressive, e.g., in humans, the total blood volume of about 5 liters filters through the glomerulus approximately every 40 minutes. The end product of the filtration, reabsorption and secretion of the nephron is urine. In humans, in spite of the large volume of filtrate, 180 liters, resulting during a 24 hour period, only about 1 liter of urine is eliminated.

The kidneys are paired, retroperitoneal ("behind" the parietal peritoneum), organs that are surrounded by fat deposits in the dorsal portion of the lumbar region. Notice that the position of the right **kidney** is slightly more posterior than the left due to the posterior extension of the caudate lobe of the liver on the right side. Take note of the hepatorenal ligament extending between the caudate lobe and the right kidney. It has no counterpart on the left side, therefore be careful to conserve this membranous structure [Figure 3–5 and Figure 6–1].

In order to observe the gross internal anatomy of the kidney, make a slit through the parietal peritoneum on the *left* side. Carefully separate the *left* kidney from the surrounding fat, taking care to expose it sufficiently to allow you to make a mid-frontal cut through the kidney. In life the kidney resembles a large kidney bean in color and in shape. The medial indentation is the **hilus** [Figure 6–1]. Through this

region passes the expanded proximal end of the ureter, the renal pelvis, renal arteries and veins, and nerves. Notice the tough, whitish, fibrous connective tissue encapsulating the kidney, the **renal capsule**. To better view this capsule, carefully peel it back, without removing it [Figure 6–2]. The outer narrow band of lighter tissue in the section is the granular **cortex**. The central darker region is the striated **medulla**. The glomerulus and portions of the nephron tubule are found in the cortex while other tubular regions of the nephron as well as collecting ducts are found in the medulla. The medulla of the kidney in the cat consists of a single pyramid with its base abutting the cortex and its vertex opening as the **papilla** into the **renal pelvis**, the expanded proximal end of the ureter. The

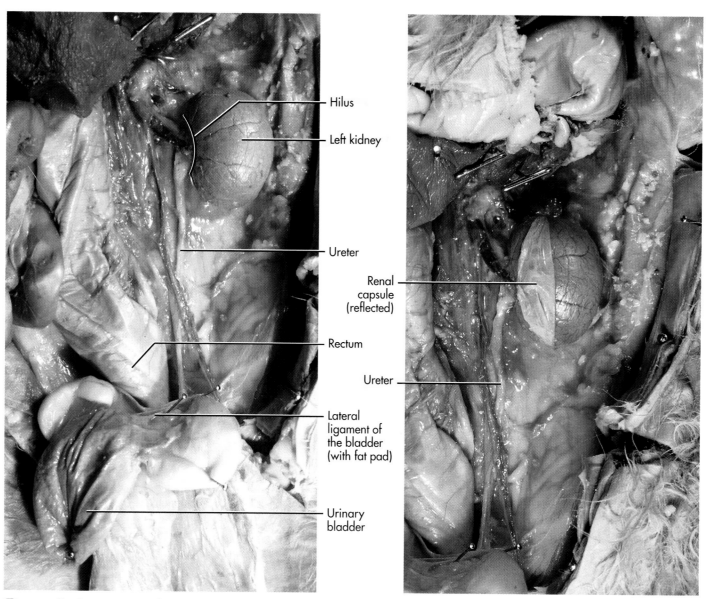

Hilus

Left kidney

Ureter

Renal capsule (reflected)

Rectum

Ureter

Lateral ligament of the bladder (with fat pad)

Urinary bladder

*Figure 6–1* Overview of excretory system.            *Figure 6–2* Renal capsule.

renal pelvis is located within the **renal sinus**, the space surrounding the renal pelvis [Figure 6–3]. Fat and blood vessels may be seen in the renal sinus. The structure of the human kidney is quite similar. The major difference is that the human kidney is multi-pyramidal with each of the pyramids terminating in a renal papilla that projects into areas known as calyces. The calyces, in turn, open into the renal pelvis.

## *Ureters, Urinary Bladder, and Urethra*

Ureters are tubes with muscular walls leading from the kidney to the urinary bladder. The **ureter** begins as the renal pelvis located within the sinus of the kidney, courses posteriorly in a retroperitoneal position, and passes through the lateral ligament of the urinary bladder to enter the urinary bladder [Figure 6–1]. The ureteral openings along with the urethral opening delineate a triangular area in the base of the bladder.

Carefully pick away the connective tissue and fat covering the *left* ureter exposing it from the hilus to the urinary bladder. Do not destroy the entire left lateral ligament of the bladder. In males, the vas deferens coils around the ureter at the base of the urinary bladder. *Do not* damage the vas deferens [Figure 6–4].

The saclike organ, the **urinary bladder**, is a reservoir for urine. When it is empty or in the relaxed state, it will appear small and have a muscular tone. As urine enters via the ureteral openings, the bladder expands to accommodate the incoming fluid. It may become greatly extended with urine and appears more saclike. The walls of the bladder consist of several layers — mucosal, submucosal, muscularis, and serosal. When the bladder is relaxed, its inner walls are folded into rugae. When filled, the rugae disappear because of stretching caused by accumulating urine. The free domed end of the urinary bladder is the **vertex** while the attached caudal end is the **fundus** [Figure 6–4].

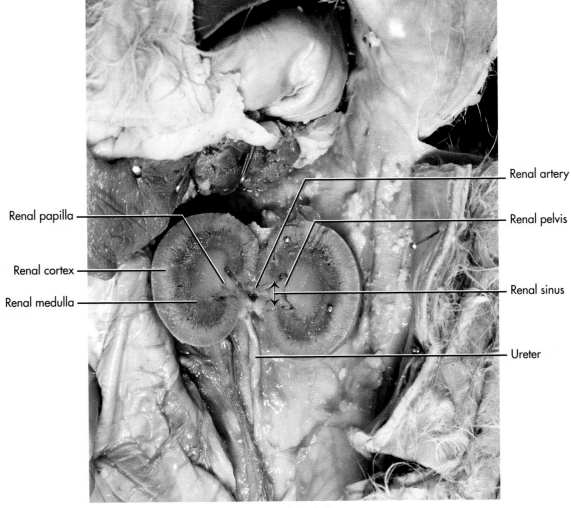

*Figure 6–3*   Internal anatomy of the kidney.

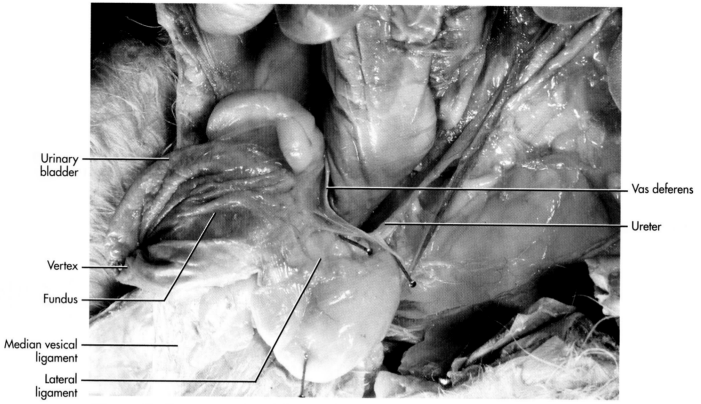

Urinary bladder

Vas deferens

Ureter

Vertex

Fundus

Median vesical ligament

Lateral ligament

**Figure 6–4**  Ureter and vas deferens in the male.

Remember that the bladder is held in position ventrally by the median ligament and on each side by the lateral ligaments, containing pads of fat.

Urine leaves the urinary bladder by way of the tubular **urethra** [Figure 6–7 and Figure 6–15]. Like the rest of the urinary tract, the walls of this tube are similarly constructed. Since this tube lies primarily in the pelvic canal, it will be seen during the dissection of the reproductive system.

In humans, the urinary system, with the exception of the aforementioned kidney differences, is very similar.

## Female Reproductive System —

The primary reproductive organs are the **ovaries**. Ovaries are small, oval organs, suspended from the dorsal body wall anteriorly by the **suspensory ovarian ligament** and posteriorly by the **ovarian ligament** connecting it to the cranial end of the uterine horns. Remember that the ovaries are further supported by a portion of the broad ligament, the **mesovarium** [Figure 6–5, Figure 6–6a and Figure 6–6b].

In reality, the ovaries are not physically connected to the tubes associated with the female reproductive system. Therefore, when the oocytes rupture through the serosa of the ovary they are swept into the **oviducts** or **uterine tubes**. In mammals, fertilization occurs in the upper third of the oviducts. The small, coiled oviducts lie lateral to the ovary and are suspended by another portion of the broad ligament, the **mesosalpinx**. The expanded proximal end of the oviduct, the **infundibulum**, is hoodlike and wraps around the ovary laterally and opens medially by way of the **ostium tubae**. Along its edges are small, finger-like projections, the **fimbriae**, whose movements are responsible for the sweeping of the oocyte into the tube. To observe these structures, carefully reflect the ovary and uterine tubes laterally [Figure 6–6a and Figure 6–6b]. To appreciate the ostium, carefully separate the edges of the infundibulum and insert a probe between them.

The uterine tubes merge into the larger diameter **horns of the uterus** (uterine horns). The two uterine horns fuse to form the **body** of the uterus and give the impression of a Y-shaped organ [Figure 6–5 and Figure 6–6a]. Successful fertilization results in implantation of early embryos in the uterine horns where development continues for nine to ten weeks, leading to birth of kittens, small versions of the adult. Recall

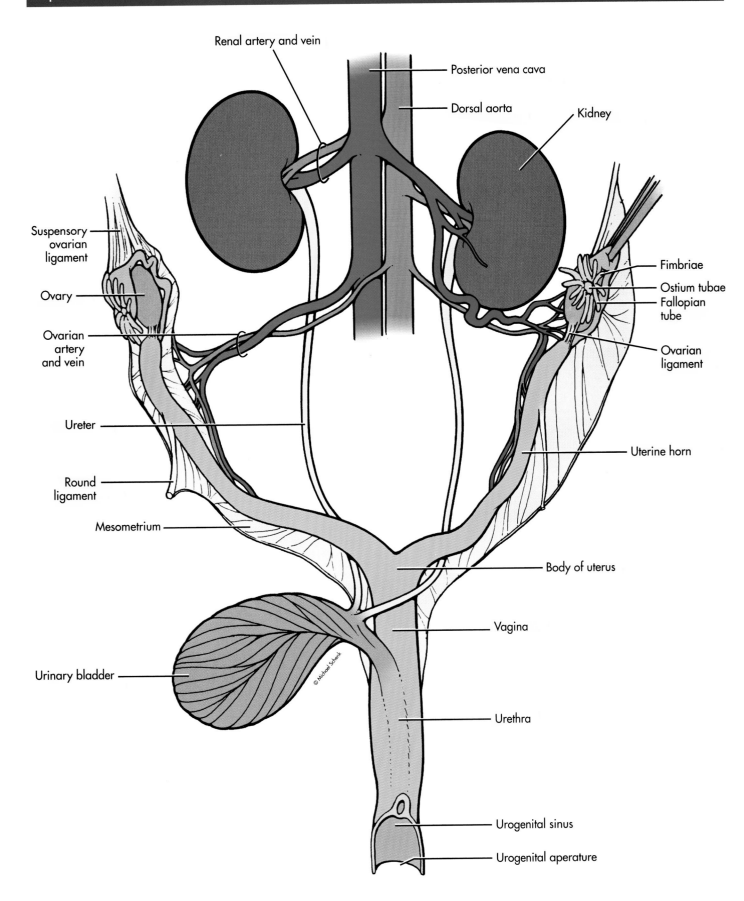

*Figure 6-5*　Female reproductive system.

**A**

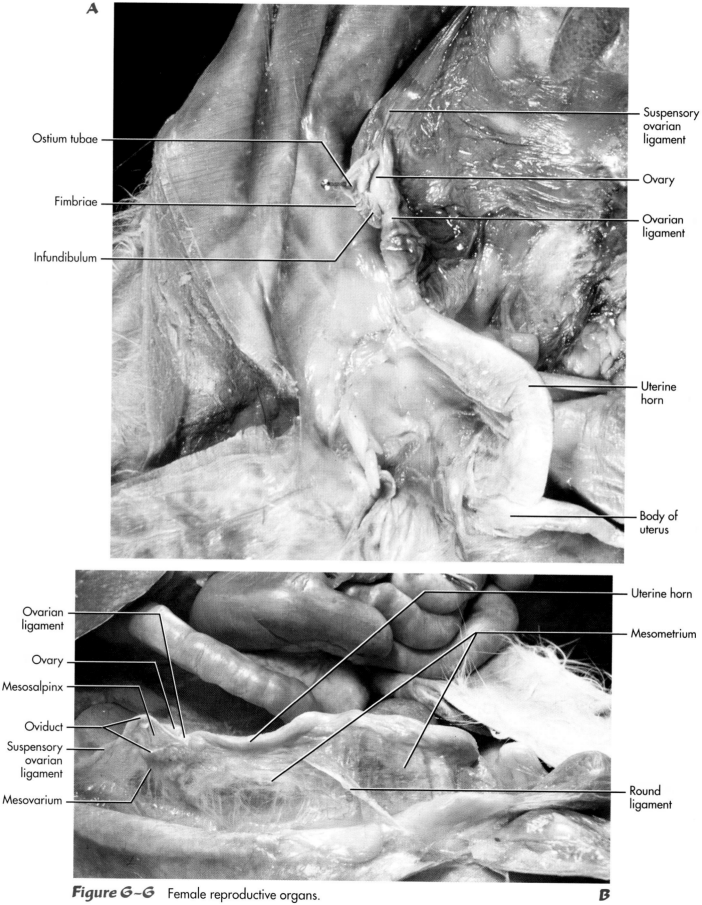

Ostium tubae

Fimbriae

Infundibulum

Suspensory ovarian ligament

Ovary

Ovarian ligament

Uterine horn

Body of uterus

Ovarian ligament

Ovary

Mesosalpinx

Oviduct

Suspensory ovarian ligament

Mesovarium

Uterine horn

Mesometrium

Round ligament

***Figure 6-6*** Female reproductive organs.

**B**

that the **mesometrium** of the **broad ligament** supports the horns of the uterus. Note the **round ligament** present in the mesometrium. It is homologous with the gubernaculum in the male.

To view the distal portion of the reproductive system, it is necessary to expose the pelvic cavity. While being cautious to avoid the median ligament of the bladder and blood vessels on the undersurface of the abdominal window, carefully make about a one-inch centrally located horizontal cut along the pelvic rim. Insert your index finger and palpate with your thumb externally to ascertain the position of the pubic symphysis that will feel like a shallow groove. This should correspond with the juncture of the medial muscles of the hindlegs that appears as a line overlying the symphysis. With a sharp scalpel make an incision through the leg muscle following the line formed by the muscle juncture. Often, the incision will follow the margin between the paired pubis and ischium closely and results in a clean separation of these bones. If that is not the case, with a pair of bone cutters, cut through the symphysis of the os coxae. Now, grasp the legs and break through the symphysis, exposing the organs of the pelvic cavity. Carefully clean the exposed area of fat and connective tissue, being especially careful not to remove associated blood vessels and nerves [Figure 6–7].

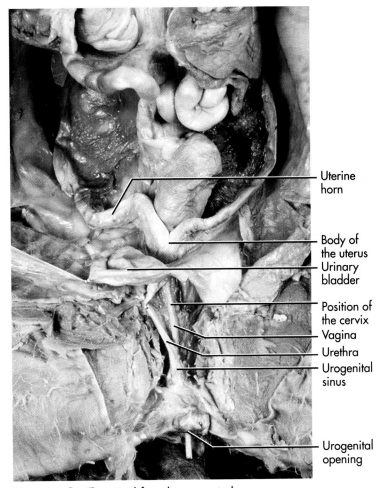

**Figure 6-7**   Distal female urogenital system.

Uterine horn
Body of the uterus
Urinary bladder
Position of the cervix
Vagina
Urethra
Urogenital sinus
Urogenital opening

To observe the anatomy of the distal portion of the urogenital system, with a pair of scissors beginning at the urogenital aperture, make a cut through the lateral wall of the canal. While making this short cut, continue until you observe the opening of the urethra and vagina into the urogenital sinus. Do not cut further [Figure 6–8].

The body of the uterus tapers distally to form the **cervix**, the neck-like region of the uterus, that protrudes into the vagina [Figure 6–7]. The cervix can be palpated externally as a sphincter-like region. The **vagina** extends from the cervix to the **urogenital sinus** where it opens as the **vaginal orifice** along with the **urethral orifice**, the opening of the

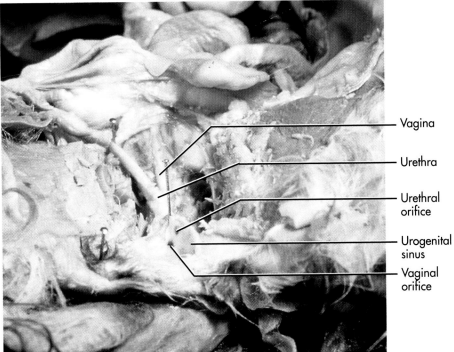

Vagina
Urethra
Urethral orifice
Urogenital sinus
Vaginal orifice

**Figure 6-8**   Female urogenital sinus with associated openings.

urethra, thus serving as a common canal for the genital and urinary systems. To observe these openings and other features of the urogenital system, reflect the cut ventral half of the canal. The urogenital sinus is quite long in the cat and opens to the outside through the **urogenital aperture**. In the cat, the **labia** are slight skin folds situated laterally around the urogenital aperture, that are not easily identifiable. Notice the small papillate **clitoris** resting in a shallow, midventral depression [Figure 6–8 and Figure 6–9]. This organ is partially homologous with the penis.

While describing the anatomy of the digestive system, the terminal portion of the rectum was not observable until the pelvic canal was exposed. Notice its position dorsal to the uterus as it continues to the outside through the anus. The **anal glands** are located on either side of the anus and open into the rectum. Cats use the secretions of these glands to mark their territories and also advertise their sex and sexual condition.

If a female cat is either pregnant, just given birth or suckling young, the paired mammary glands with their nipples extending along either side of the midventral line, will be very prominent [Figure 6–10 and Figure 6–11].

The anatomy of the human female is very similar with some minor differences. Among these are the absence of uterine horns, two pairs of labia, majora and minora, a more prominent clitoris,

and a cleftlike area between the labia minora, the vestibule of the vagina, where the urethra and the vagina open to the outside. Note that this condition is different from the female cat where there is a well defined urogenital sinus. Some further specialization of supporting ligaments is evident.

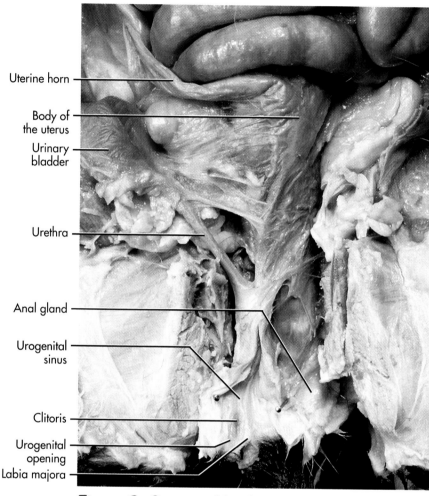

**Figure 6–9**  Terminal female urogenital system.

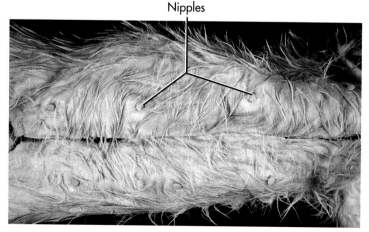

**Figure 6–10**  External features associated with mammary glands.

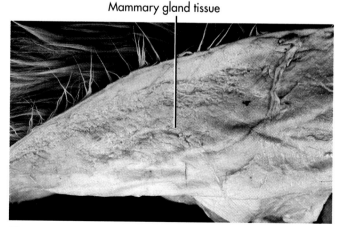

**Figure 6–11**  Internal mammary glands.

# Male Reproductive System ━━━

The primary reproductive organs in the male are the **testes**, egg shaped organs that are suspended externally within the **scrotum**, an obvious hairy sac protruding posteriorly just ventral to the anus. Take note also of the position of the sheath of the penis with its opening ventral to the scrotum. One of the major problems encountered with the male reproductive system is knowing where the spermatic cords leave the abdominal cavity through the abdominal wall and realizing that they lie in the fat of the inguinal (groin) area and can be cut or destroyed in the wink of an eye. This is the reason that you were warned to avoid removing fatty tissue in this region during the skinning and initial connective tissue cleaning process [Figure 6–12].

The dissection of the male reproductive system is somewhat more difficult and time consuming than the female. Begin by cautiously making a small cut (1/8 inch) through the skin of the posterior wall of scrotum. Carefully work the scissors under the skin and continue the incision to the anterior limit of the testis. Repeat the process on the other side. Now, carefully peel the scrotum laterally to expose the testis on both sides. Notice the abundant connective tissue, the **cremasteric fascia**, stretching between the inner wall of the scrotum and the white sac, the **cremasteric pouch**, surrounding the testis [Figure 6–13]. You will observe that the pouch abruptly narrows into a tubelike structure, the **spermatic cord**, at its anterior end. Within the spermatic cord lies the vas deferens, the spermatic artery and vein, lymphatic vessels, and nerves.

Leave one of the testes held in place by cremasteric fascia within the scrotum, but gently remove the other by loosening the cremasteric fascia. Do *not* cut the spermatic cord and detach the testis from the body of the cat; leave it attached. The organ you now observe is the testis enclosed within the cermasteric pouch. The pouch and its contents have the same relationship as any of the major ventral body cavities to the body proper, e.g., the abdominopelvic cavity. The tough, outer layer of the cremasteric pouch, the **tunica vaginalis communis**, is analogous to the body proper. Carefully nip through this outer covering and then continue the cut to expose the structures suspended within the sac. Notice the space between these enclosed structures and the sac. It is known as the **vaginal cavity** and is analogous to the potential space of the peritoneal cavity. The inner lining of the pouch is the **tunica vaginalis propria — parietal layer** and is

analogous to the parietal layer of the peritoneum. This layer comes together to form the mesentery-like **mesorchium** and then spreads over the surface of the structures, suspended within the vaginal cavity, as the **tunica vaginalis propria — visceral layer**, analogous to the visceral peritoneum of the abdominopelvic cavity [Figure 6–14]. The mesorchium can be demonstrated by gently grasping the structures of the spermatic cord and pulling them medially. Notice the thin, mesentery-like membrane anchoring these structures in place within the cord. The two layers of the tunica vaginalis propria can be seen as the inner shiny layer of the cremasteric pouch (parietal layer) and the outer shiny layer covering the testis (visceral layer).

A band of highly convoluted tubules, the **epididymis**, adheres to the dorsal portion of the testis. Observe the free anterior end, the **head**, the middle portion, the **body**, and the posterior **tail** of the epididymis. The **vas deferens** begins its journey as a somewhat convoluted tube from the tail of the epididymis and enters the spermatic cord, held in place by the mesorchium [Figure 6–15].

The descent of the testes in most male mammals has a very interesting developmental history. The testes begin their life in the abdominal cavity, but attached to the inner portion of the scrotum by a long band of connective tissue called the **gubernaculum** that passes through the lower abdominal wall on its way to the scrotum. As the fetus matures, the gubernaculum contracts, pulling the testes into the scrotum. As the testes move into the scrotum they are accompanied in their journey by a small bit of the peritoneal cavity (vaginal cavity) along with the parietal and visceral layers. So, really, it is not surprising that the organs suspended within the vaginal cavity have very similar relationships to the space and membranes of the peritoneal cavity. To see the gubernaculum, while holding the testis, gently pull the cremmasteric pouch wall at the posterior end of the testis and observe the short, tough fibrous band holding the tail of the epididymis tightly against the inner wall of the pouch [Figure 6–15].

Now, very carefully separate the spermatic cord from surrounding tissues and trace it anteriorly to an opening piercing the abdominal wall, the **external inguinal ring**. The cord passes through a short **inguinal canal** and the vas deferens enters the abdominal cavity through the **internal inguinal ring**. Notice also that the spermatic artery and vein enter and exit the spermatic cord at this point. Follow the vas deferens as it

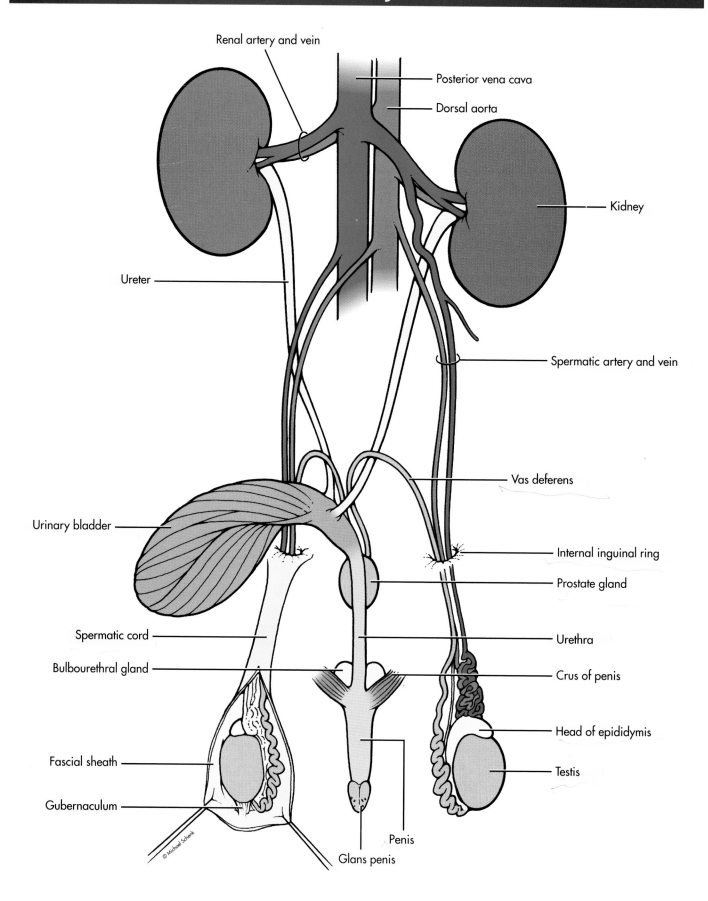

Renal artery and vein

Posterior vena cava

Dorsal aorta

Kidney

Ureter

Spermatic artery and vein

Vas deferens

Urinary bladder

Internal inguinal ring

Prostate gland

Spermatic cord

Urethra

Bulbourethral gland

Crus of penis

Head of epididymis

Fascial sheath

Testis

Gubernaculum

© Michael Schenk

Penis

Glans penis

*Figure 6-12* Male reproductive system.

courses dorsally around each of the ureters and urinary bladder [Figure 6–4 and Figure 6–15].

The next dissection should be completed preliminary to further work. Grasp the opening of the sheath of the **penis** with a pair of forceps and make a cut through the anterior wall of the sheath with scissors [Figure 6–15]. Continue the cut through the connective tissue along the shaft of the penis to expose it. Take care to avoid cutting into the penis itself.

To facilitate observation of the urethra, glands and other associated parts of the system, it is necessary to cut through the symphyses of the os coxae. As in the female, carefully make about a one inch cut through the abdominal wall along the rim of the pelvis, avoiding the median ligament of the bladder and blood vessels associated with the inner portion of the abdominal window cut when the cat was opened. Carefully palpate the slight depression between the pubes and with a sharp scalpel, cautiously make an incision, beginning with the depression and following the raphe between the gracilis muscles. Remember that the cut through the raphe will be quite deep. Now grasp the hindlegs and reflect them laterally to complete the separation of the two os coxae. It may be necessary to complete the separation by carefully

cutting through the ischiadic symphysis with the scalpel. At all times be careful not to cut into organs lying within the pelvic canal.

With some luck and good dissection you should be looking into the canal. Begin cleaning connective tissue from the tube leading from the urinary bladder, being careful to conserve associated blood vessels and nerves in the process. As you proceed distally an enlarged, whitish mass, the **prostate gland**, will be encountered. Dorsally, this is the point at which the vasa deferentia connect to the tube. That part of the tube extending from the urinary bladder to the prostate is the **urethra** and carries only urine. That part of the tube distal to the prostate is the **urogenital canal** that continues to the tip of the penis where it opens to the outside through the urogenital aperture. Both urine and semen are carried in the urogenital canal [Figure 6–15].

The distal portion of the urogenital canal is surrounded by a column of erectile tissue, the corpus spongiosum, that lies along the posterior surface of the penis when not erect. The distal portion of this erectile tissue caps the tip of the penis as the conical **glans penis**. The urogenital aperture opens at the tip of the glans. Notice the pocket of skin, the **prepuce**, that encloses the glans [Figure 6–14].

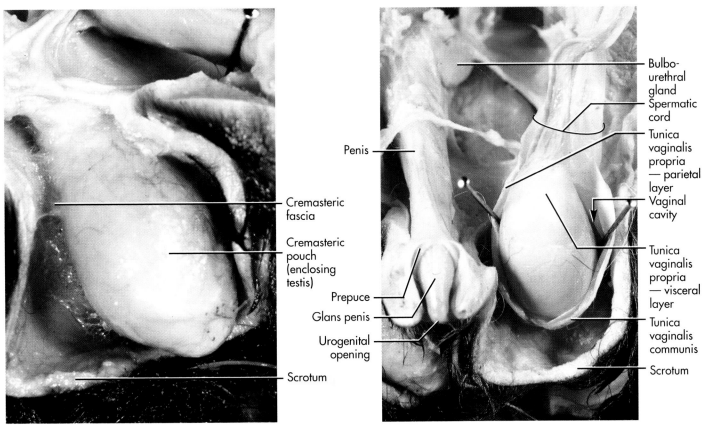

**Figure 6–13**   Testis in scrotum.

**Figure 6–14**   Testis with associated tunics.

A pair of erectile columns of tissue, the corpora cavernosa, lie along the anterior surface of the penis, when it is not erect. All three of these columns possess blood sinuses that bring about erection under the influence of sexual excitement. The proximal ends of the corpora cavernosa are attached to the ischia by bands of tough connective tissue called the **crura** of the penis (singular: crus). Each crus is covered ventrally by the ischiocavernosus muscle. Dorsal to each of the crura is a **bulbourethral gland** (Cowper's gland) that secretes lubricating fluid into the urogenital canal during sexual excitement [Figure 6–15].

As in the female, the male also possesses **anal glands** that are situated near the terminal end of the large intestine, near the anus [Figure 6–15]. These serve a similar function in males. Perhaps you have seen large cats, e.g., lions and tigers, in those wildlife documentaries on television as they back up to a bush or shrub and spray fluid on them. The fluid is forcefully ejected from their anal glands. Unneutered male domestic cats do something similar on furniture and other objects in their home territories, by the way, leading to odoriferous surroundings.

The male reproductive system in human males is quite similar to the cat, again with some exceptions. The inguinal canal in the human is considerably longer than in the cat. Since the abdominal wall is thinner in this region, it may be the site of an abnormal condition known as an inguinal hernia. The distal ends of the vasa deferentia enlarge into ampullae where they are joined by the ducts of the seminal vesicles to form the ejaculatory ducts, that in turn connect to the urogenital canal. The seminal vesicles secrete part of the fluid volume of the semen. The penis in humans is not contained within a sheath but hangs freely, attached proximally to the pubic symphysis by way of the crura.

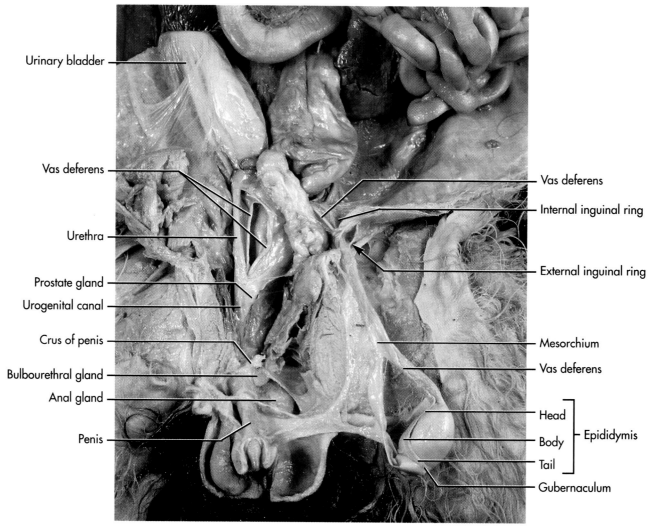

***Figure 6–15***   Male urogenital system.

# Endocrine System

Although the organs in this chapter are collectively known as a system, they are not physically connected in many cases. The functions of these organs, often known as glands, are exquisitely coordinated when they are operating normally. When they are not, often the result is a dysfunctional organism, cat or human. Secretions of these ductless glands, called hormones, act as regulatory chemicals, often interacting among themselves to control a complex series of cellular activities. The hormones are transported in the blood of the circulatory system to their target tissues where they are attracted to very specific receptor sites on the surface of these cells, mediating their characteristic activities.

In this chapter, individual endocrine glands will be identified with their position and function.

## Pituitary Gland or Hypophysis

This gland is connected to the ventral surface of the hypothalamus of the brain by a stalk (the infundibulum) and rests in the sella turcica of the sphenoid [Figure 7–1 and Figure 7–2]. It produces a myriad of hormones, many of which control secretions of other glands.

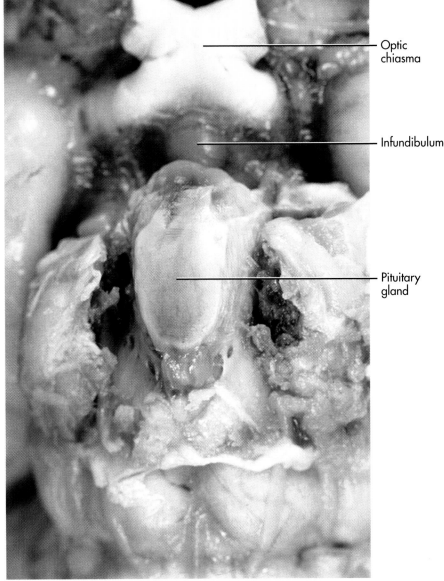

— Optic chiasma

— Infundibulum

— Pituitary gland

**Figure 7–1** Hypophysis.

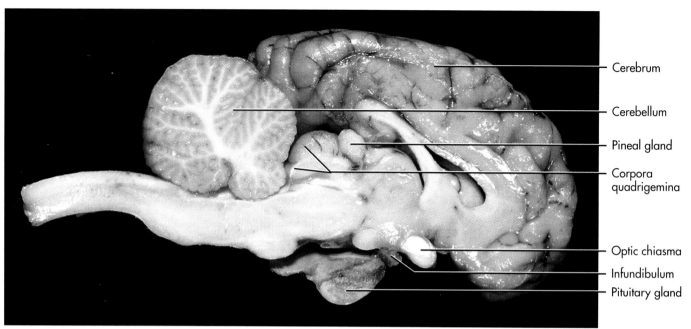

Cerebrum

Cerebellum

Pineal gland

Corpora quadrigemina

Optic chiasma

Infundibulum

Pituitary gland

**Figure 7–2**    Brain: sagittal section.

## Pineal Gland

The pineal gland projects from the dorsal surface of the brain [Figure 7–2 and Figure 7–3]. The hormone produced by this gland may play a role in the commencement of puberty.

Cerebral hemispheres

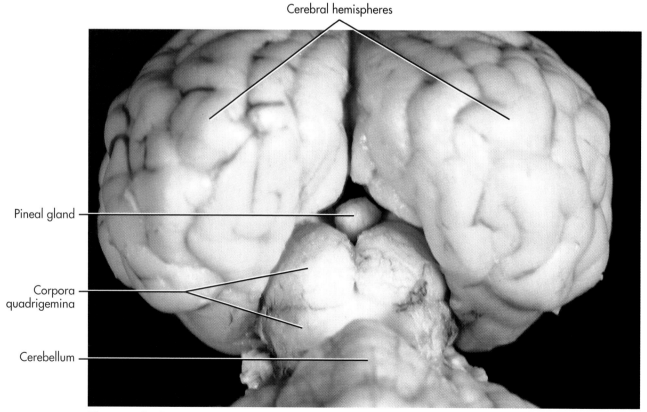

Pineal gland

Corpora quadrigemina

Cerebellum

**Figure 7–3**    Pineal gland.

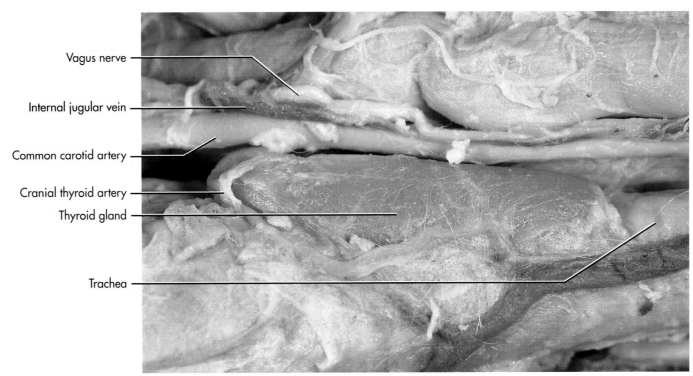

Vagus nerve
Internal jugular vein
Common carotid artery
Cranial thyroid artery
Thyroid gland
Trachea

**Figure 7-4**    Thyroid gland.

# Thyroid Gland

This endocrine gland is paired and lies on either side of the trachea just posterior to the larynx [Figure 7–4]. Commonly, the lobes of this gland are connected by a delicate, narrow band of tissue called the isthmus. Hormones produced by this endocrine tissue are involved in a wide range of metabolic activities, tissue maturation, sexual maturation, and other essential cellular activities such as energy utilization.

# Parathyroid Gland

These four very small glands are embedded in the dorsal surfaces of the thyroid glands but cannot be seen without visual aids. Their hormone secretion is critical to calcium balance.

# Thymus Gland

The thymus is a lobular gland that is very obvious in young mammals but may be difficult to find in older cats [Figure 7–5]. It lies on the ventral aspect of the trachea and may extend over the surface of the heart. During the juvenile period of mammalian life, the thymus functions as a source of specialized leukocytes that migrate to other tissues to participate in immune activities.

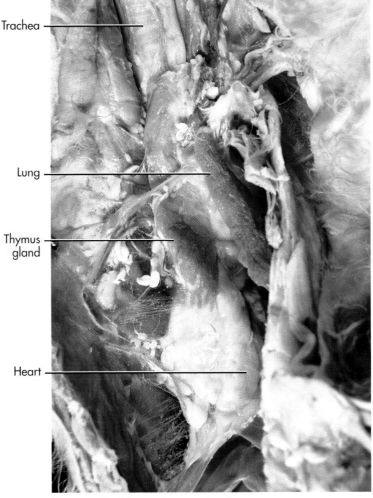

Trachea
Lung
Thymus gland
Heart

**Figure 7-5**    Thymus gland.

## Adrenal Glands

These small ovoid glands, in contrast to the human, do not cap the kidneys but are located a short distance anteriomedial to them [Figure 7–6]. This organ is constructed of two areas, the outer cortex and the inner medulla. The hormones secreted by the cortex regulate a number of metabolic activities while those of the medulla intensify and prolong the characteristic syndrome stimulated by the sympathetic portion of the autonomic nervous system.

Coeliac artery

Cranial
mesenteric artery

Dorsal aorta

Adrenolumbar vein

Adrenal gland

Renal vein

Kidney

**Figure 7–6**      Adrenal gland.

## Pancreas

The pancreas is a lobular gland located in the mesoduodenum and part of the gastrosplenic portion of the greater omentum [Figure 7–7]. This gland consists of two types of tissue, one that functions as endocrine tissue and the other that secretes chemicals involved in digestion. Hormones produced by the endocrine portion affect carbohydrate metabolism.

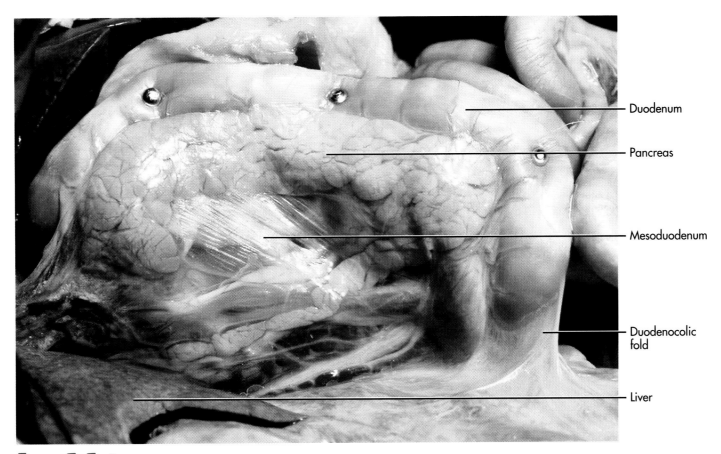

**Figure 7-7** Pancreas.

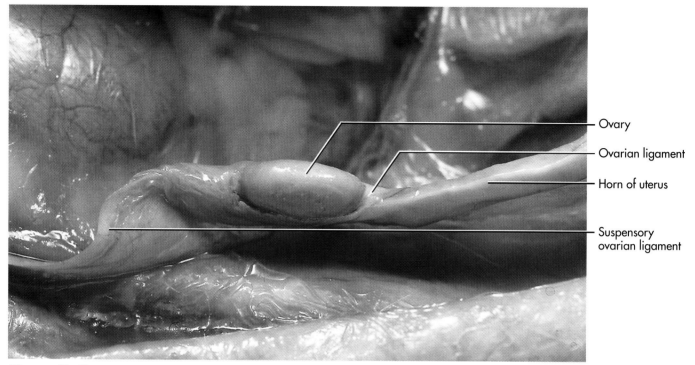

**Figure 7–8**    Ovary.

## Ovaries

These small, oval organs of the female reproductive system are located within the peritoneal cavity and suspended from the dorsal body wall [Figure 7–8]. The endocrine portion of the ovary produces female sex hormones that affect sexual and reproductive behavior.

## Testes

The testes, the male reproductive organs, located in the scrotum produce sex hormones affecting sexual and reproductive behavior [Figure 7–9].

## Other Endocrine Tissues

Tissues in the kidney and digestive organs produce hormones whose activities tend to be more localized and confined to the functions of the organs in which they are produced.

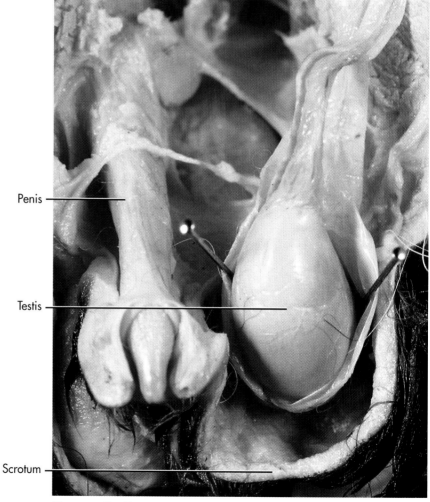

**Figure 7–9**    Testis.

# Circulatory System

The circulatory system consists of a network of continuous tubes connected to a muscular pump. This system, as its name implies, is responsible for the transportation, distribution, and circulation of various chemicals throughout the body. Examples of these activities include distribution of nutrients and transport of gases, hormones, and metabolites.

Although the circulatory system is continuous, it can be examined as individual components, (1) the heart, (2) the arteries, veins, arterioles, and venules that are generally connected by capillary beds, and (3) the blood. Components of the blood are the fluid plasma and circulating elements, erythrocytes, leukocytes, and platelets. These elements play an important role in gas transport, immune reactions, and blood clotting.

A major function of capillaries is the diffusion of water and any dissolved substances between the circulatory system and tissues in which they occur. Under normal physiological conditions, blood elements, and proteins occurring in the blood are too large to pass across the capillary wall. The overall result is that a small amount of fluid remains in the surrounding tissues. This fluid is returned to the circulatory system by way of lymphatic vessels that enter the systemic circulation in the neck and shoulder region.

Although mammalian hearts are all very similar in morphology, in the discussion that follows, the anatomy described is that of the sheep. Our recommendation is that the heart be cut with a sharp kitchen knife into dorsoventral halves preferably by your instructor.

## The Heart

### External Anatomy

The mammalian heart consists of two muscular pumps, the **right atrium** and **right ventricle**, that receive and pump oxygen-poor blood from the body to the lungs and the **left atrium** and **left ventricle** that

receive oxygen-rich blood from the lungs and pump it throughout the body [Figure 8–1 and Figure 8–2].

The heart is shaped somewhat like a blunt wedge, with its flattened **base** and more acute **apex** [Figure 8–1]. In the living mammal, including humans, the heart tilts to the left somewhat and projects into a membranous sac, the pericardium, in a potential space called the mediastinum. Therefore the left side of the heart lies against the diaphragm. The outer layer of the pericardium is fibrous and may be covered by the parietal pleura, as in the cat. Lining the potential space (pericardial) into which the heart projects is the serous membrane known as the parietal pericardium. The parietal pericardium reflects over the heart surface as the visceral pericardium.

The walls of the heart consist of three layers. The outer covering is a single layer of squamous epithelium that is really nothing more than the visceral layer of pericardium, also known as the epicardium or outermost layer of heart tissue. The muscular middle layer or myocardium makes up almost the entire tissue of the heart. The inner lining, continuous with the inner lining of circulatory vessels, also consists of a single layer of squamous epithelium known as the endothelium.

As you view the heart externally, perhaps your first impression is that the outer surface seems to be covered with an unusual amount of fat. At least among our students, that is often a common observation. Strange as it might seem, this is normal for the hearts of mammals.

The first determination that you should make is which side is dorsal and which is ventral. Remember that the heart as it rests in the normal living sheep's body has a dorsal and ventral aspect. In mammals, no matter how they walk, the **pulmonary trunk**, a major blood vessel that exits from the right ventricle, stretches from right to left across the ventral side of the heart [Figure 8–1]. Another vessel, the **aorta**, generally of greater diameter and slightly dorsal to the pulmonary trunk, also curves left. From the aorta branches the **brachiocephalic artery**. Carefully pick away fat between the pulmonary trunk and aorta until you discover a short ligamentous band connecting the two vessels. This represents the remnant of a fetal circulatory bypass, the **ligamentum arteriosum**, which allows most of the blood pumped into the pulmonary trunk during intrauterine life to be shunted into the systemic circulation and away from the nonfunctional lungs [Figure 8–1]. If you turn the heart over, you will probably notice that there are a greater number of vessels, the four **pulmonary veins** and the

**anterior** and **posterior vena cavas**, associated with the dorsal side [Figure 8–2]. In some specimens, the dorsal vessels are sometimes cut very close to the surface of the heart, leaving only openings or holes.

A shallow **atrioventricular groove** or **coronary sulcus**, marks the separation of the heart into the two anterior atria and the two posterior ventricles [Figure 8–2]. Encircling the heart in this groove is the main venous drainage of the heart, the **coronary sinus**. Venous blood returns to the heart from heart muscle through this channel. **Interventricular grooves** on the ventral and dorsal surfaces demarcate the division of the ventricle into right and left chambers [Figure 8–1 and Figure 8–2]. Major coronary blood vessels lie

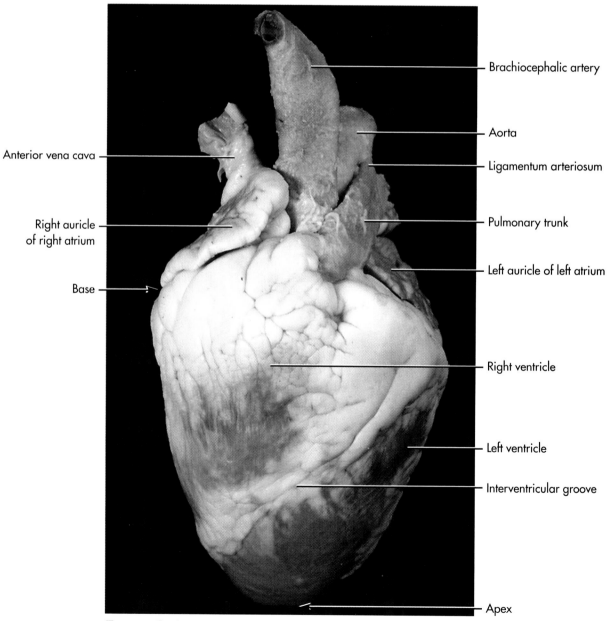

**Figure 8–1**   Heart: ventral view.

in these grooves, generally buried in a considerable amount of fat. Note that these grooves are oriented almost parallel to the left margin of the heart, giving the appearance that the left ventricle is larger. This is not an optical illusion, but due to the greater thickness of muscle in the left ventricle, evidently necessary to develop the pressures needed to pump oxygen rich blood throughout the systemic circulation. This disparity in ventricular thickness is very obvious upon examination of the cut surface of the muscular walls of both chambers. Also obvious, are two ear-like flaps, the **auricles**, attached to the atria [Figure 8–1 and Figure 8–2]. They increase the volume of each atrium somewhat.

## Internal Anatomy

In our treatment of the internal morphology we will describe the anatomy with respect to the incoming blood flow through the right pump, followed by the outgoing blood flow through the left pump. Be aware that both pumps function at the same time.

Blood enters the **right atrium** from the cranial region of the body by way of the **anterior vena cava** [Figure 8–3] and from the caudal region of the body via the **posterior vena cava** [Figure 8–3]. Locate the openings of these two major vessels in the inner wall of the right atrium. Notice that the atrial wall is thin compared to the ventricle. If there is a substantial section of these vessels remaining attached to your

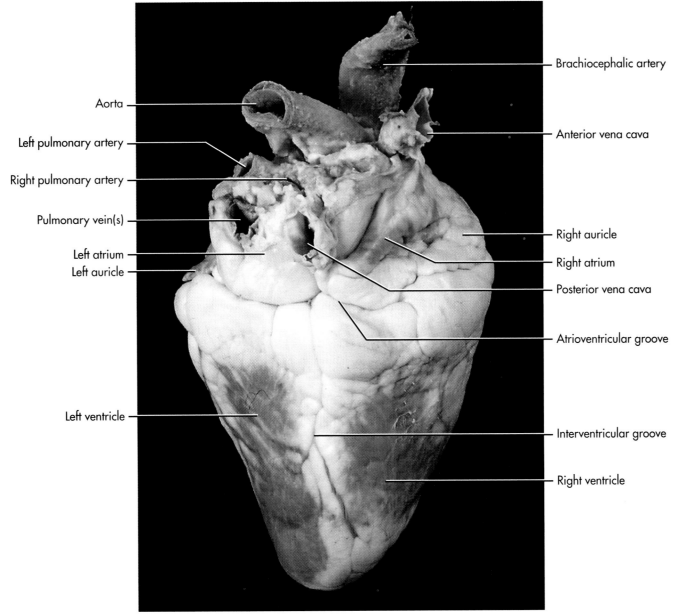

*Figure 8–2*  Heart: dorsal view.

specimen, notice that the posterior vena cava curves along the dorsal aspect of the lower left side of the heart, turning cranially to enter the right atrium. Additionally, locate the **opening of the coronary sinus** [Figure 8–3] situated caudal to the opening of the posterior vena cava. Venous blood from the heart, itself, drains into the right atrium through this opening. The inner wall of the auricle appears honeycombed because of the presence of muscular ridges, the **musculi pectinati** [Figure 8–4]. These muscular ridges also extend into the atrium. A depression, somewhat lighter in color than the surrounding tissue, sits just ventral to the entrance of the posterior vena cava in the **interatrial septum**. This area, the **fossa ovalis**, represents the position of an opening between the right and left atria that functions as a shunt during embryonic development [Figure 8–3].

Blood flows from the right atrium into the right ventricle through the **right atrioventricular valve** or **tricuspid valve**, taking its name from three flap-like structures or cusps — the **dorsal cusp** attached to the dorsal wall, the **lateral cusp** attached to the lateral wall, and the **medial cusp** attached to the medial wall [Figure 8–3 and Figure 8–4]. Attached to the apex of each cusp are cord-like structures, the **chordae tendineae**, extending to cone shaped **papillary muscles** in the wall of the right ventricle [Figure 8–3 and Figure 8–4]. Since the tricuspid valve is open, most of the ventricular filling is passive, but the final ventricular volume results from atrial contraction.

As the right atrium relaxes and the right ventricle contracts, high pressure in the ventricle has a tendency to cause backflow of blood into the atrium causing the valve to slam shut, but the contraction of the papillary muscles pulling on the chordae tendineae prevent the eversion of the cusps into the atrium. Notice that the inner walls of the ventricle are crisscrossed with muscular bands, the **trabeculae carneae**

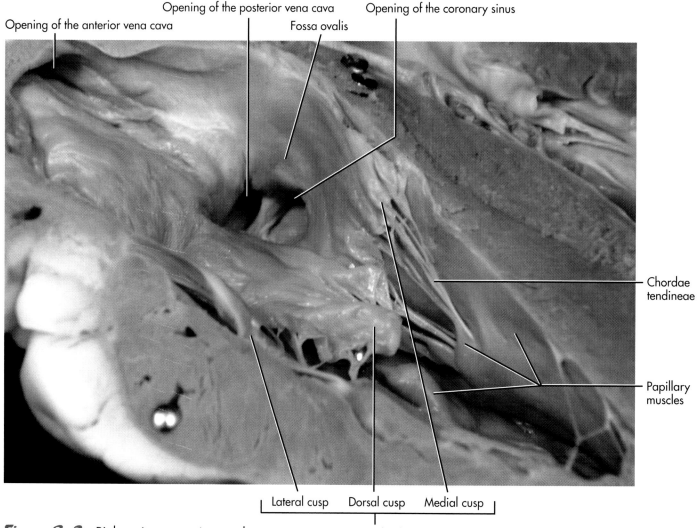

*Figure 8–3*   Right atrium: openings and anatomy.

[Figure 8–5]. A slender band of tissue, the **moderator band**, extends between the lateral and medial wall of the right ventricle [Figure 8–5].

Note that the **myocardium** of the right ventricle is thinner than that of the left ventricle, since pressures are lower in the right ventricle because blood pumped by the right side only travels to the lungs located close to the heart [Figure 8–6].

From the right ventricle, blood is pumped through the **pulmonary semilunar valve** into the pulmonary trunk. Three membranous pockets, each in the shape of a half moon, form this valve. The decrease in pressure in the ventricle as it relaxes, causes the blood, under high pressure in the pulmonary trunk, to backwash into the ventricle. This backwash is prevented by blood filling the pockets of the semilunar valve

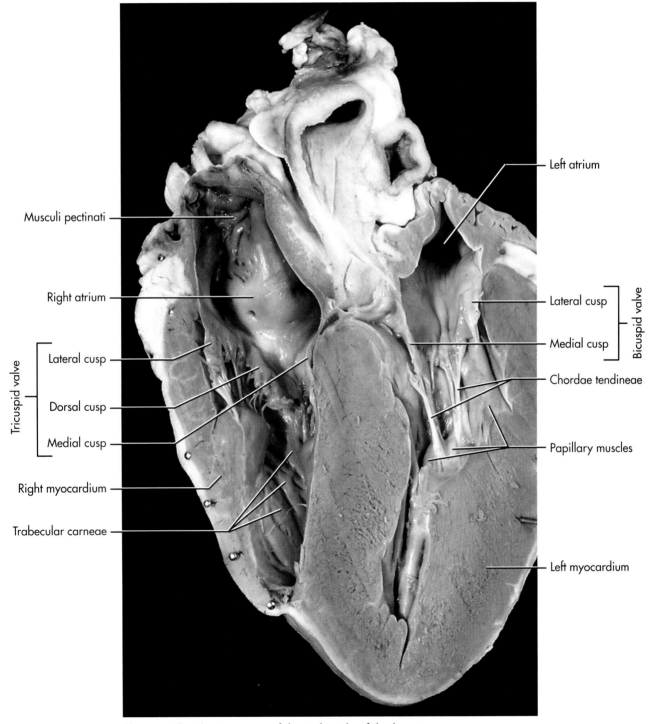

*Figure 8–4*   Anatomy of the right side of the heart.

which now slam shut. Blood is transported to the lungs where gas exchange occurs.

From the lungs, blood returns through the **pulmonary veins** to the left atrium. The two veins from each lung become confluent as they enter the atrium, sometimes giving the appearance of only two openings. Locate the openings of the pulmonary veins on the posterior aspect of the atrium [Figure 8–2]. Often, the pulmonary veins are removed close to the heart and appear only as holes in the left atrium.

The inner appearance of the left atrium is quite similar to the right atrium, with the exception that the musculi pectinati seem to be less extensive. However, they are prominent in the left auricle. As in the right pump, blood flows passively from the left atrium into

the left ventricle, in this case, through the two cusps of the **left atrioventricular** or **bicuspid valve**. A **medial** and a **lateral cusp** are attached to those respective walls [Figure 8–6]. In a manner similar to the construction of the tricuspid valve, chordae tendineae extend between the margins of the cusps to papillary muscles protruding from the muscular walls of the ventricle. The final filling of the ventricle is accomplished by contraction of the left atrium.

As the atrium relaxes and the ventricle contracts, the pressure of the engorged ventricle supercedes that of the atrium and blood backwash is again prevented when the cusps of the bicuspid valve slam shut. Contraction of the papillary muscles resulting in a pull on the edges of the cusps prevents eversion of the cusps into the left atrium.

The obviously thicker myocardium of the left ventricle is one of its most distinguishing features. Although it cannot be observed readily, an **interventricular septum** is present between the two ventricles, indicated externally by the interventricular grooves. Trabeculae carneae are again a feature of the inner surface of the chamber. Contraction of the left ventricle forces blood past the **aortic semilunar valve** into the aorta [Figure 8–6]. The morphology of this semilunar valve is identical to the pulmonary semilunar valve. As the ventricle relaxes, the blood pressure in the aorta exceeds that of the ventricle and blood backwashes toward the ventricle, filling the membranous pockets causing them to slam shut.

Continuous pumping of the heart throughout the life of a mammal demands a constant supply of highly oxygenated blood to this hard working muscular organ. This requirement is met by delivery of the most highly oxygenated blood by way of the **left** and **right coronary arteries** that originate immediately above the aortic semilunar valve. Examine the medial and lateral walls of the aorta where you will observe the openings of these two vessels [Figure 8–6]. You may observe a number of small openings that represent coronary blood vessels.

With the exception of the moderator band, the anatomy of the human heart is very similar to the sheep.

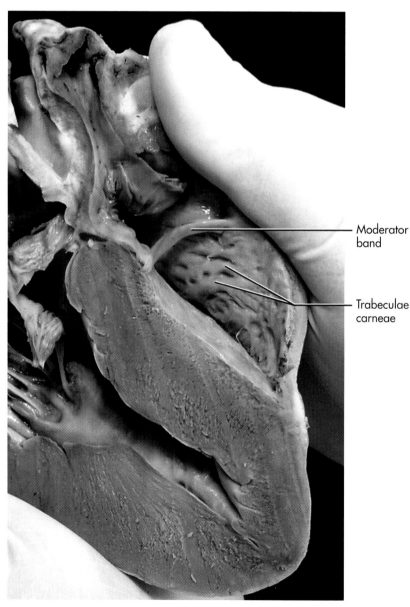

Moderator band

Trabeculae carneae

*Figure 8–5*   Right ventricle: moderator band.

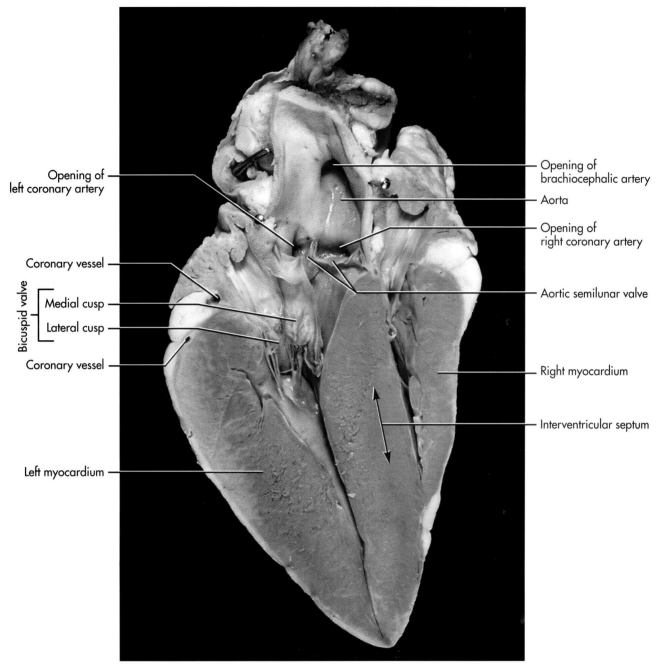

**Figure 8-G**   Left atrioventricular valve.

# Blood Vessels ━━━━━

The arteries, veins, arterioles, and venules that are generally connected by capillary beds are the circulatory channels through which blood moves. In this section, you will be dissecting the major blood vessels.

    When you were in grade school, you learned about the primary colors, red, blue, and yellow. In a triply injected specimen, these same colors appear as injected latex in the vessels. Arteries are red, veins are blue, and the hepatic portal system consisting of the

veins of most of the abdominal organs have been injected with yellow latex.

## Pulmonary Circulation

This circuit includes arterial vessels carrying oxygen poor blood to the lungs and venous vessels carrying oxygen rich blood back to the heart. Take note that these vessels follow the anatomical rules where blood is carried back to the heart by veins and away from the heart by arteries. However, in contrast to the blood vessels of the rest of the body of an adult, the oxygen level of the blood is low in the pulmonary arteries and high in the pulmonary veins.

In order to observe these vessels, it is necessary to cut the pericardial sac with a pair of scissors. Identify the **pulmonary trunk** of the cat exiting from the right ventricle. Dorsal to the heart the pulmonary trunk bifurcates into a **right** and **left pulmonary artery** [Figure 8–7]. Trace these vessels into the root of their respective lungs where they further branch, supplying the

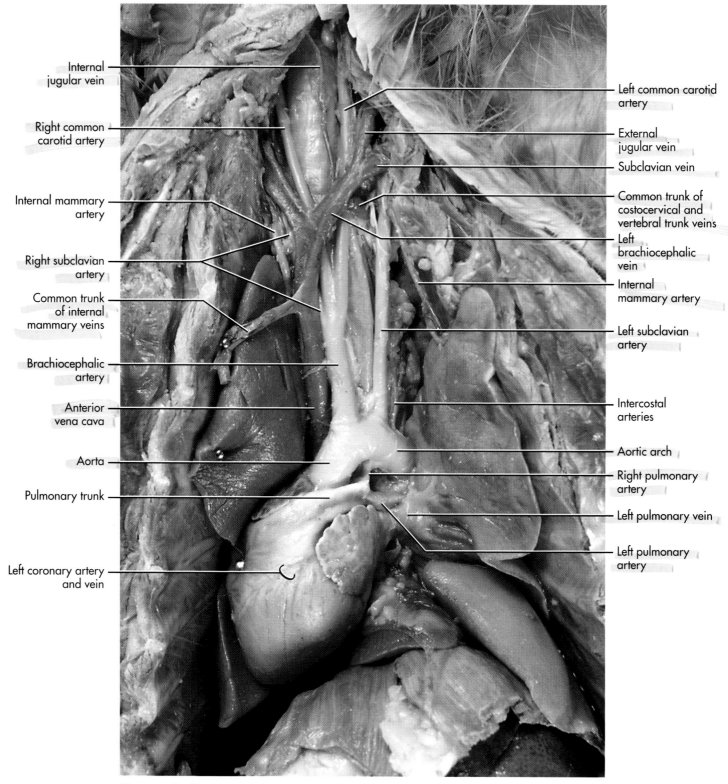

Internal jugular vein
Right common carotid artery
Internal mammary artery
Right subclavian artery
Common trunk of internal mammary veins
Brachiocephalic artery
Anterior vena cava
Aorta
Pulmonary trunk
Left coronary artery and vein

Left common carotid artery
External jugular vein
Subclavian vein
Common trunk of costocervical and vertebral trunk veins
Left brachiocephalic vein
Internal mammary artery
Left subclavian artery
Intercostal arteries
Aortic arch
Right pulmonary artery
Left pulmonary vein
Left pulmonary artery

*Figure 8–7*  Vessels of the thoracic area.

lobes of the lungs. In the root, identify the **pulmonary veins** as they leave the lungs and enter the left atrium [Figure 8–7]. Notice that the pulmonary veins contain red latex. The pulmonary circulation in humans is very similar.

## Systemic Circulation

The architecture of the circulatory system exhibits a consistent pattern of divergence or branching in the arterial portion to supply the tissues of the body and convergence or confluence in the venous portion of the system to drain those tissues. Another common theme is that arteries and veins are paired when organs supplied or drained by them are paired, e.g., each kidney is supplied by an artery and a vein. You will also notice that a vessel that is continuous from its origin to its destination may carry different names as it passes from one area to another, e.g., the subclavian becomes the axillary as it enters the armpit but then is called the brachial as it enters the arm, and so on. This is quite common in the terminology of the circulatory system. In order to identify blood vessels correctly, it is necessary to trace them to or from the tissues that they supply.

This circuit carries oxygen rich blood from the heart to the body in arteries and returns oxygen poor blood back to the heart in veins. To appreciate the enormity and complexity of the circulatory system, we will begin our exploration of the arterial component of this circuit by identifying the **aorta** as it leaves the left ventricle ventrally and curves dorsally to the left as the **aortic arch** [Figure 8–7]. The aorta then continues posteriorly, passing through the diaphragm into the peritoneal cavity, generally following the mid-dorsal line of the body. The portion of the aorta in the thoracic region may be identified as the **thoracic aorta** and that part in the peritoneal area may be identified as the **abdominal aorta.**

As the aorta begins to curve dorsally, identify a **brachiocephalic artery** followed by the **left subclavian artery** branching from the arch, supplying the neck and head and the forelimbs [Figure 8–7]. The brachiocephalic a., at about the level of the second rib, subdivides into the **right subclavian artery**, the **right common carotid artery**, and the **left common carotid artery** [Figure 8–7].

Four small arteries branch from the right subclavian a. before it emerges from the body wall. In general, dissection of this portion of the circulatory system is minimal and consists mainly of picking connective tissue and fat from the surface of the vessels and nerves. *As usual, this activity is to be done very carefully. Please take note that nerves often accompany the blood vessels and appear as shiny cream colored strands of tissue. These can be destroyed easily — be careful!* The first or **internal mammary artery** leaves ventrally and enters the ventral thoracic body wall. As it courses posteriorly it gives off branches to nearby muscles, pericardium, mediastinum, and diaphragm and then anastomoses with the caudal epigastric arteries (described later). The next, the **vertebral artery**, arises as a dorsal artery, continues cranially and dorsally, enters the transverse foramen of the sixth vertebra, giving off branches to nearby neck muscles and spinal cord segments as it passes through the transverse foramina of the cervical vertebrae. As it nears the foramen magnum, it joins with the left vertebral artery to form the basilar artery that courses along the mid-ventral aspect of the medulla oblongata. The **costocervical artery** also emerges from the dorsal surface of the subclavian a., curves dorsally, and subdivides to send branches to neighboring neck, back, and intercostal muscles. The last of the subclavian a. branches, the **thyrocervical artery** leaves the anterior aspect of that vessel, travels anteriorly and laterally and as it approaches the shoulder becomes known as the **transverse scapular artery**. These vessels supply blood to adjacent muscles of the region, particularly the shoulder [Figure 8–8].

As the subclavian artery curves around the first rib and enters the axilla it becomes known as the **axillary artery**. From this artery, several others branch. The **ventral thoracic artery** emerges from the ventral surface of the axillary a. and courses posteriorly to supply pectoral muscles. Notice that the anterior ventral thoracic nerve of the brachial plexus accompanies this artery. A short distance laterally, the **long thoracic artery** branches and with the posterior ventral thoracic nerve of the brachial plexus supplies the pectoral muscles, thoracic mammary glands, and the latissimus dorsi muscle. The relatively large **subscapular artery** leaves the axillary as it nears the shoulder. The **posterior humeral circumflex artery** usually branches from the subscapular and accompanied by the axillary nerve of the brachial plexus, travels beneath the biceps brachii muscle carrying blood to several muscles of the medial aspect of the scapula, the shoulder, and triceps brachii muscle. A second branch of the subscapular a., the **thoracodorsal artery**, arises dorsal to the brachial plexus, giving off branches to the teres major and latissimus dorsi muscles [Figure 8–8]. The subscapular a. continues deep to supply dorsal shoulder muscles.

Beyond this point, the axillary a. becomes known as the **brachial artery** as it passes into the arm. The **anterior humeral circumflex artery** arises almost immediately as a branch of the brachial a. to bring blood to the biceps brachii muscle. At about the midpoint of the biceps brachii, the **deep brachial artery** originates and with the radial nerve of the brachial plexus passes under the belly of that muscle to supply blood to the triceps brachii, latissimus dorsi, and other muscles in the area. Occasionally, the deep brachial a. originates from the subscapular a. A number of muscular branches emerge from the brachial a. as it runs parallel

with the median nerve of the brachial plexus until it nears the elbow where a pair of arteries, the **radial collateral** and **ulnar collateral**, are given off. The radial collateral artery turns laterally and supplies the arm extensor muscles while the ulnar collateral artery turns medially and supplies blood to the muscles of the elbow [Figure 8–8]. With the median nerve the brachial a. passes through the supracondyloid foramen. Below this point it subdivides into an ulnar, a radial, and an interosseus artery.

The common carotid artery can be seen closely associated with the internal jugular vein which may not be well injected, the vagus nerve and sympathetic trunk and is bound to them by a fibrous sheath. Follow the common carotid cranially to the level of the thyroid gland and find a medial branch, the **cranial**

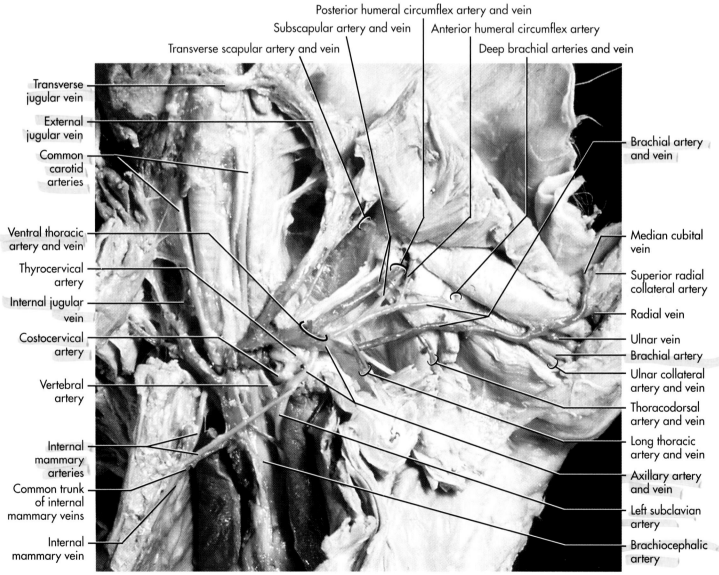

**Figure 8–8** Vessels of the thoracic and brachial area.

**thyroid artery,** supplying the thyroid gland, parathyroid glands and neck muscles and directly opposite it, find the **muscular branch** passing laterally carrying blood to deep neck muscles. The next branch is the **laryngeal artery** that arises medially, supplying muscles in the laryngeal area. A variable number of branches may originate from the lateral side carrying blood to muscles and lymph nodes in the area. To view the cranial branches of the common carotid a., cut the sternomastoid and cleidomastoid muscles at the sternal end and reflect them. The hypoglossal nerve runs across the surface of the common carotid just anterior to the next pair of vessels that branch from it and serves as a landmark for the **occipital** and **internal carotid arteries** [Figure 8–9]. These vessels are generally very small, hairlike branches and may leave the dorsal part of the common carotid individually or may leave as a common stem that subsequently branches into two arteries. Great care must be exercised when probing for them because there is a great

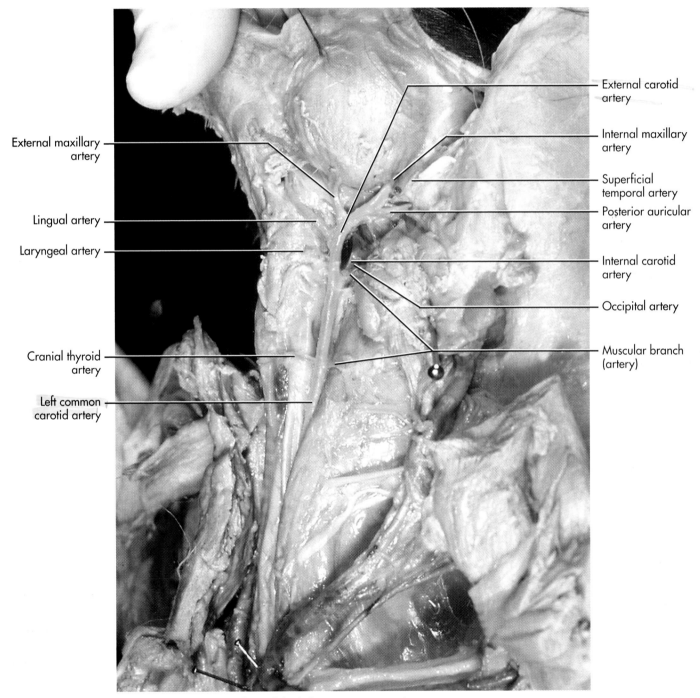

External maxillary artery

Lingual artery

Laryngeal artery

Cranial thyroid artery

Left common carotid artery

External carotid artery

Internal maxillary artery

Superficial temporal artery

Posterior auricular artery

Internal carotid artery

Occipital artery

Muscular branch (artery)

**Figure 8–9**   Branches of the left common carotid artery.

deal of connective tissue in the area and they are often not much more than 2–3 mm apart. The occipital a. originates first (more posteriorly) and passes caudal to the tympanic bulla carrying blood to the neck and occipital region. The internal carotid a. passes cranial to the tympanic bulla and transports blood to the base of the diencephalon, and along with several other arteries contributes to the major arterial blood supply of the brain in the form of the Circle of Willis.

The common carotid now continues as the **external carotid artery** following the branching of the internal carotid a. A large branch, the **lingual artery**, leaves the external carotid and carries blood to muscles of the hyoid and pharynx while continuing into the tongue as its major supply. The more dorsal **external maxillary artery** branches from the external carotid and carries blood to the outer facial region. As the external carotid nears the posterior boundary of the masseter muscle, the **posterior auricular artery** emerges and supplies the outer ear area [Figure 8–9]. The external carotid a. continues along the margin of the masseter, gives off the **superficial temporal artery** that delivers blood to the masseter and outer ear and continues deep to the masseter as the **internal maxillary artery** that supplies internal structures and tissues associated with the upper and lower jaw, nose, eyes, and surrounding regions [Figure 8–9]. In order to expose these vessels it will be necessary to carefully dissect some of the surrounding tissues.

Although we have just described the circulation of the right subclavian artery and the right common carotid artery, the branches of the left common carotid artery and the left subclavian artery are very similar in pattern.

In the human, the branching pattern of the aortic arch is different. The first vessel, the brachiocephalic artery gives rise to the right common carotid and right subclavian arteries. The left common carotid and left subclavian arteries arise independently from the arch. The internal carotid artery is considerably more robust approaching the size of the external carotid in the human with several branches and serving as a major blood supply to the brain and regional organs. The arterial branches of the rest of this region are similar to the cat.

For the most part, arteries and veins lie in close proximity and as an artery is identified, the corresponding vein, often with the same name should be identified. In general, the venous system parallels the arterial system in this portion of the body with the

following exceptions. Tributaries draining the brain, auricular, labial, lingual, palatal, and dental regions of the head form **anterior** and **posterior facial veins** that coalesce to form the **external jugular vein**. In the hyoid region, a **transverse jugular vein** draining that area connects the anterior facial veins. As the external jugular v. approaches the heart, it is joined by the **transverse scapular vein** draining the shoulder region. The brain and surrounding tissues are drained by tributaries of the **internal jugular vein** joining the external jugular [Figure 8–7, Figure 8–8, and Figure 8–10]. Notice that this vein lies close to the trachea and it may not be well injected.

Drainage of the forelimb involves deep and superficial vessels. The superficial veins include the **cephalic vein** that drains the lateral aspect of the forelimb and is connected to the **brachial vein** by the **median cubital vein** [Figure 8–11]. The cephalic v. continues superficially to join with the posterior humeral circumflex v. and the transverse scapular v. The deep veins of the forelimb parallel the arterial circulation.

The brachial-axillary-subclavian vein joins the external jugular v. to form the **brachiocephalic vein**. In contrast to the arterial supply, there are two brachiocephalic veins. The **costocervical** and **vertebral veins** merge to form a common trunk that empties into the brachiocephalic vein. Note that there is no thyrocervical vein. The left and right brachiocephalic veins join to form the **anterior vena cava**. The **left** and **right mammary veins** merge to form a common trunk and join the ventral surface of the anterior vena cava [Figure 8–7]. Although the pattern of the venous and arterial circulation differs somewhat, the regions served are similar.

Venous drainage of the head and neck region in the human is similar with these exceptions: the internal jugular vein is larger than the external jugular vein with many interconnecting channels between them. In contrast to the cat, the brachiocephalic veins are formed by the confluence of the internal jugular and the subclavian veins. The vertebral and external jugular veins join the subclavian independently.

Examine the inner thoracic wall and observe the segmental **intercostal arteries** and **veins** that are associated with the blood supply to the tissues between the ribs. The fairly large **azygous vein** runs along the right side of the aorta in the thoracic region and receives blood from most of the intercostal veins on both sides [Figure 8–12]. It empties into the dorsal region of the anterior vena cava. The origin of the azygous v. is actually in the dorsal abdominal area but it is best seen in the thoracic region and therefore is discussed here.

In humans, not only is there an azygous vein on the right side but also a hemizygous vein on the left side with a number of interconnecting vessels. An accessory hemizygous vein also exists.

As the aorta travels through the abdominopelvic area, it gives rise to an almost universal distribution of three unpaired major arterial branches, the **coeliac artery**, the **cranial mesenteric artery** and the **caudal** mesenteric artery, to visceral organs of the region in most vertebrates and in all mammals [Figure 8–13]. To observe the complex sub-branching of the coeliac a., carefully cut through the diaphragm to the esophagus, avoiding vessels associated with the diaphragm. Free the esophagus from connective tissue anchoring it in place and cut across the esophagus at a point about 2 cm anterior to the stomach. Pull the stomach ventromedially. To begin the dissection of the coeliac and its branches, first locate the coelic a., then

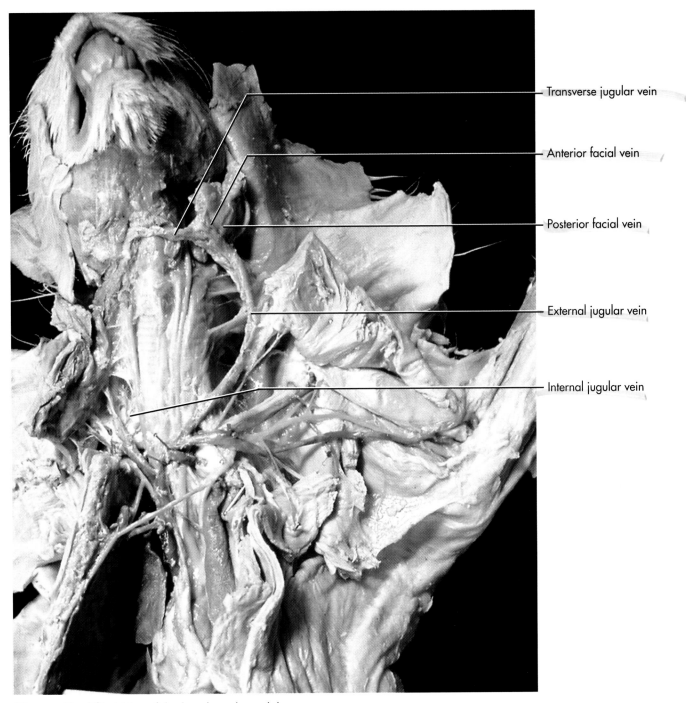

Transverse jugular vein

Anterior facial vein

Posterior facial vein

External jugular vein

Internal jugular vein

*Figure 8–10*   Veins of the head, neck, and thorax.

carefully pick away the connective tissue to expose its three major branches. The **left gastric artery** leaves the coeliac a. carrying blood to the lesser curvature of the stomach. Continue to pick away the connective tissue to completely expose the many smaller branches to the stomach. The **hepatic artery** branches from the coeliac a. and ascends toward the liver where it subdivides into several hepatic branches that supply the

lobes of the liver and the **cystic artery** lying on the surface of the cystic duct. Use great care in exposing these delicate branches. As the hepatic artery travels toward the liver, observe a short **gastroduodenal artery** curving posteriorly and almost immediately giving off 1–3 delicate **pyloric artery** (ies) that supplies blood to the pyloric region of the stomach continuing along the lesser curvature of the stomach and anastomosing

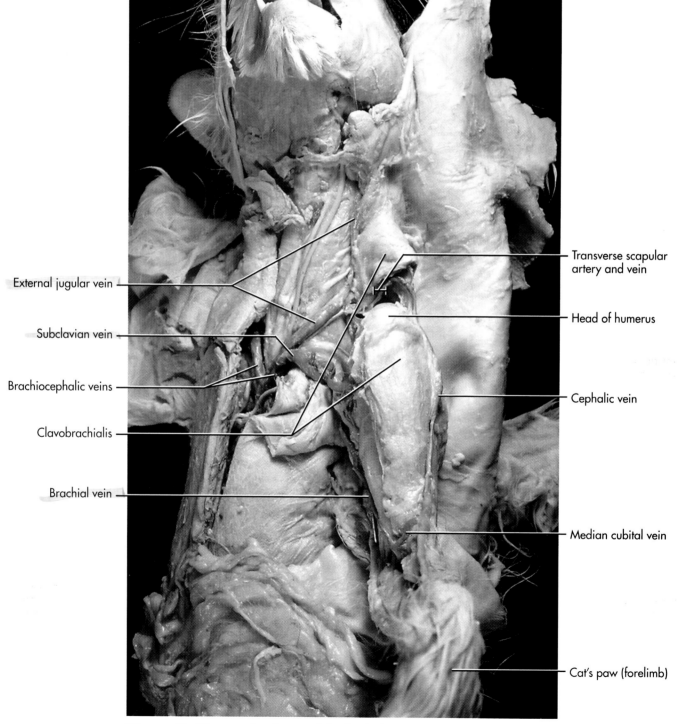

*Figure 8–11*   Superficial veins of the forelimb.

with the left gastric a. A few millimeters from the pyloric a., the gastroduodenal a. bifurcates into the **right gastroepiploic artery** supplying the greater curvature of the stomach and greater omentum and the **anterior pancreaticoduodenal artery** supplying the head of the pancreas and the duodenum [Figure 8–14b]. These arteries are generally more robust than the pyloric a., but you must still exercise great care in exposing them. The largest and most obvious branch of the coeliac, is the **splenic artery** leading toward the spleen. Notice the numerous small branches supplying the tail of the pancreas and the body of the stomach. The main portion of the artery travels along the length of the spleen giving off an **anterior splenic artery** and continuing as the **posterior splenic artery** [Figure 8–14a and Figure 8–14b]. A continuation of the posterior splenic a., the **left gastroepiploic artery** follows along the greater curvature of the stomach and anastomoses with the right gastroepiploic a. [Figure 8–16].

Although the description of the coeliac a. and its branches is applicable to most mammals, including the human, there may be variations in the pattern with additional small branches occurring.

The second unpaired somewhat larger major abdominal artery is the **cranial mesenteric artery**, extending a greater distance than the coeliac a. before supplying blood to the intestines and pancreas. The first branch is the **posterior pancreaticoduodenal artery** supplying the pancreas and duodenum and anastomosing with the anterior pancreaticoduodenal a. [Figure 8–15]. Carefully expose this artery by picking away the connective and pancreatic tissue along the duodenal border. Follow the cranial mesenteric artery as it subdivides into numerous **intestinal arteries**, supplying the jejunum and ileum [Figure 8–15]. The next branch, the **ileocolic artery**, supplies the terminal portion of the ileum, the cecum, the ascending colon, and proximal portions of the transverse colon. Occasionally, a separate **right colic artery**, branching from the cranial mesenteric a., supplies the ascending and proximal portions of the transverse colon. The last branch of the cranial mesenteric a. is the **middle**

*Figure 8–12* Azygous vein.

**colic artery** supplying the transverse and descending colon [Figure 8–15]. Continuity among these colic vessels is the result of anastomoses. Again, the branching pattern of the cranial mesenteric artery of the cat and human is very similar.

The third major abdominal artery, the **caudal mesenteric artery,** is the smallest and least complexly branched. This vessel can be masked by the mesentery and generally must be exposed by picking away this tissue. The branches of the caudal mesenteric include the **left colic artery** supplying blood to the distal portion of the descending colon, and the **cranial hemorrhoidal artery** supplying the proximal portion of the rectum [Figure 8–13]. Notice the anastomosis that may occur between the left and middle colic arteries. The human vessel architecture in this area is similar to the cat.

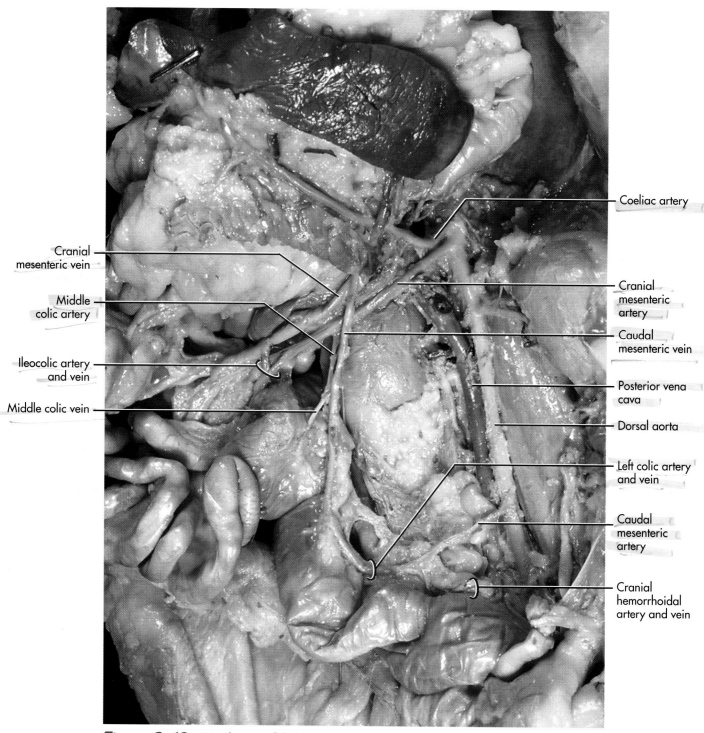

**Figure 8–13** Distribution of the three abdominal arteries.

Drainage of the viscera, including the intestines, stomach, and spleen is accomplished by a venous architecture consisting of a specialized pattern of veins called the hepatic portal system. A portal system is different from the common venous drainage because blood flows from a capillary bed in one organ to another capillary bed in another organ, whereas in normal venous circulation, blood is taken from the capillaries in an organ and eventually delivered to the heart. In the case of the hepatic portal system, carbohydrates and amino acids, vitamins, minerals, ions, toxins, etc. are transported from the digestive system to the liver where an astounding number of metabolic activities occur.

Since the hepatic portal system has capillaries on either end it requires a special injection of yellow latex directly into the system in order to dissect and identify the vessels described here. As with all vessels studied

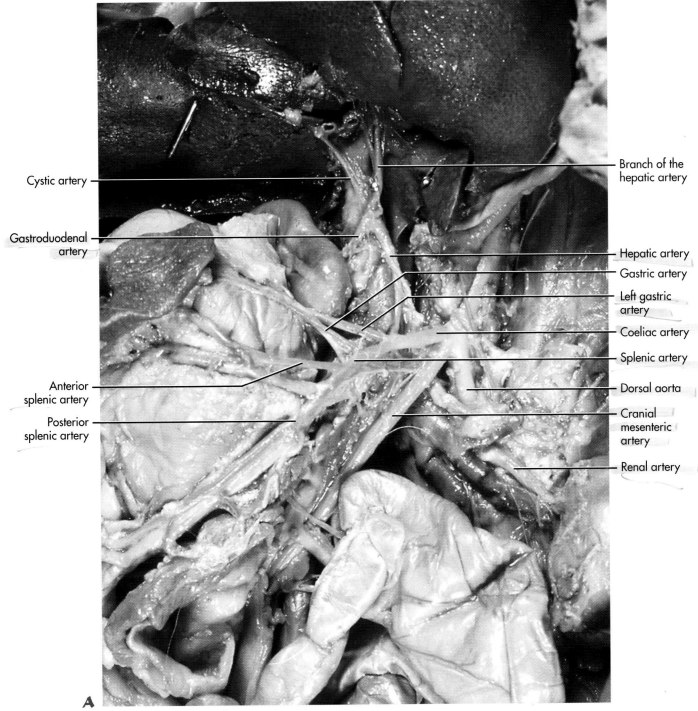

Cystic artery

Gastroduodenal artery

Anterior splenic artery

Posterior splenic artery

Branch of the hepatic artery

Hepatic artery

Gastric artery

Left gastric artery

Coeliac artery

Splenic artery

Dorsal aorta

Cranial mesenteric artery

Renal artery

A

*Figure 8–14*   Coeliac artery.

and to be studied, you must carefully remove associated tissue to expose this system. Be careful not to destroy nearby vessels.

Blood is drained from the large intestine by the **caudal mesenteric vein**. That portion of the caudal mesenteric that drains the rectum and distal descending colon is the **cranial hemorrhoidal vein** while the proximal portion of the descending colon is drained by the **left colic vein**. The **cranial mesenteric vein** drains the transverse and ascending colon, cecum, small intestine and the head of the pancreas. The **middle colic vein** drains the transverse and often the distal portion of the ascending colon. If your cat has a right colic artery, it more than likely will also possess

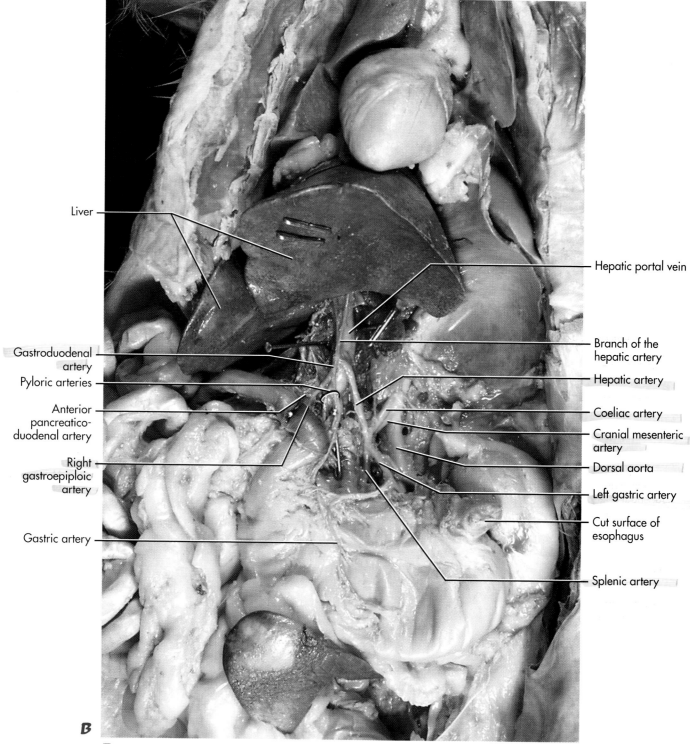

Liver

Gastroduodenal artery

Pyloric arteries

Anterior pancreatico-duodenal artery

Right gastroepiploic artery

Gastric artery

Hepatic portal vein

Branch of the hepatic artery

Hepatic artery

Coeliac artery

Cranial mesenteric artery

Dorsal aorta

Left gastric artery

Cut surface of esophagus

Splenic artery

**B**

*Figure 8–14*   Coeliac artery.

a **right colic vein**, draining the ascending colon. Drainage of the cecum and ileum is by way of the **ileocolic vein**. Numerous **intestinal veins** drain the coils of the small intestine. The **posterior pancreaticoduodenal vein** drains blood from the head of the pancreas and the distal portion of the duodenum. Note that the caudal mesenteric vein joins the cranial mesenteric vein [Figure 8–13 and Figure 8–15].

The stomach, the spleen and the pancreas are drained by the **gastrosplenic vein**. Locate the **anterior splenic** and **posterior splenic veins** draining their respective regions of the spleen. Find the **left gastro-epiploic vein**, paralleling the artery of the same name, draining the greater curvature of the stomach and greater omentum and joining the posterior splenic vein. A variable number of **gastric veins** drains the

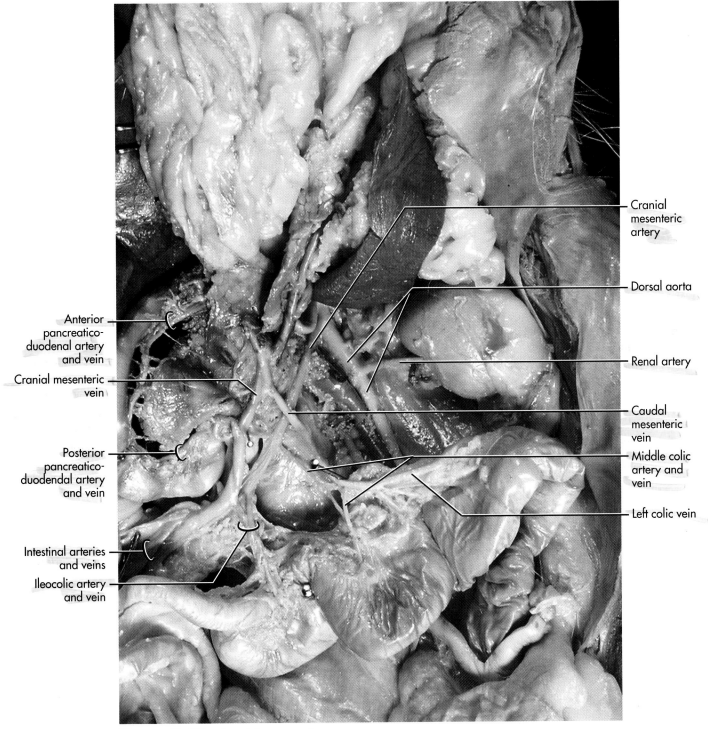

**Figure 8–15** Cranial mesenteric artery.

body of the stomach and also join the posterior splenic vein. The **pancreatic vein(s)** empty into the gastrosplenic v. proximal to the junction of the cranial mesenteric v. to form the **hepatic portal vein**. The **coronary vein** draining the lesser curvature of the stomach, the **right gastroepiploic vein** draining the right end of the greater curvature of the stomach and **anterior pancreaticoduodenal vein** draining the tail of the pancreas and the proximal portion of the duodenum may join the hepatic portal v., independently, shortly after its formation. In most cats, the **gastroduodenal vein**, formed by the juncture of the right gastroepiploic and anterior pancreaticoduodenal veins, joins the hepatic portal vein shortly after its formation. A very small **pyloric vein** draining the pyloric portion of the stomach and emptying into the

gastroduodenal v. may also be present. Follow the hepatic portal vein into the liver [Figure 8–16].

The hepatic portal system in humans is generally similar to that of the cat with the following exceptions. Unlike cats, the hepatic portal vein is formed by the convergence of the superior mesenteric vein (cranial mesenteric of the cat) and the splenic vein (gastrosplenic of the cat). Right and left gastric veins and a small cystic vein empty into the hepatic portal vein independently. In addition, the inferior mesenteric vein (caudal mesenteric vein of the cat), the pancreatic veins and left gastroepiploic vein merge with the splenic vein. The right gastroepiploic vein and the pancreaticoduodenal veins join the superior mesenteric vein.

To reiterate, the general structural plan of the circulatory system is based on vessels that deliver blood

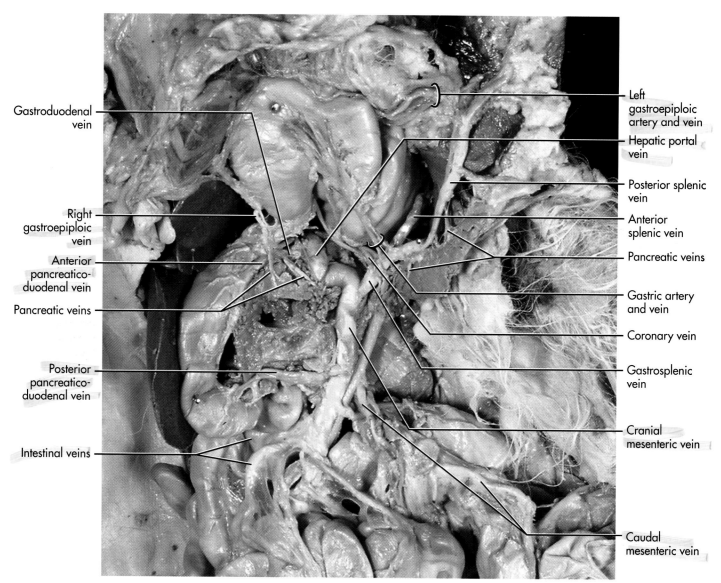

*Figure 8–16*   Hepatic portal system: cranial portion.

to an area (arteries) and vessels that take blood away from an area (veins). For that reason, veins of the same name almost invariably lie in close proximity to the following arteries discussed, including those arteries of both the abdominal and hindlimb regions. As you find the arteries, make sure that you find the corresponding veins at the same time.

In addition to the unpaired arteries, there are several paired vessels that typically occur at various levels along the length of the abdominal aorta. **Adrenolumbar arteries** arise on either side of the body a few centimeters posterior to the diaphragm and just posterior to the cranial mesenteric artery [Figure 8–17]. Their name stems from the destination of their branches. A **posterior phrenic artery** services the diaphragm, while an **adrenal artery** takes blood to the adrenal gland. The adrenolumbar a. then continues laterally to supply the dorsal body wall. The origin of both of these branches

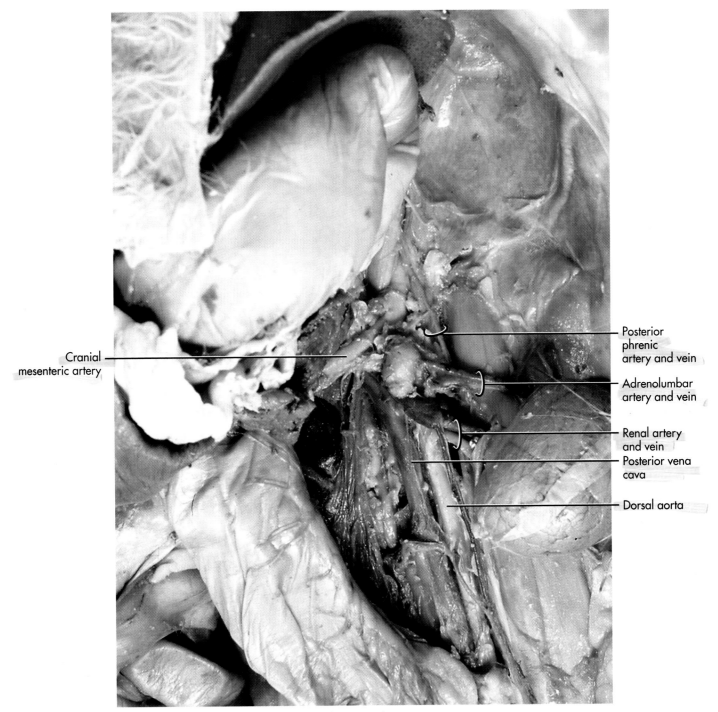

Cranial mesenteric artery

Posterior phrenic artery and vein

Adrenolumbar artery and vein

Renal artery and vein

Posterior vena cava

Dorsal aorta

*Figure 8–17*    Renal and adrenolumbar vessels.

is variable, so it is possible for a number of variants to occur. Find the complementary veins, usually lying in close proximity to the artery [Figure 8–17].

A pair of **renal arteries** emanates from the aorta at the level of the kidneys and since the right kidney is somewhat anterior to the left, its renal artery is also slightly anterior to the left. Identify the renal veins that run parallel to the renal arteries [Figure 8–17].

As we proceed to follow the aorta caudally, the next paired arteries that are given off supply the primary sex organs of the cat. In the male, small diameter **internal spermatic arteries** leave the aorta and extend toward the internal inguinal ring where they accompany the vas deferens, nerves, lymphatic vessels, and **spermatic veins** all of which are wrapped in connective tissue known as the spermatic cord and lead to the testes [Figure 8–18]. There may be some variation in the configuration of these vessels in males. Not only may the right artery originate more posteriorly, but also the left may originate from the left renal a. The **ovarian arteries** are of a larger diameter, usually originating closer to the level of the position of the ovary and then extending laterally and supplying blood to the ovary, uterine tube or oviduct and uterine horns [Figure 8–19]. An anastomosis between the branches of the uterine horns and the uterine branch of the middle hemorrhoidal artery is common.

Several pairs of **lumbar arteries** originate from the aorta in the lower back region, supplying blood to the dorsal muscles.

The final conspicuous pair of abdominal vessels originating from the aorta just caudal to the caudal mesenteric artery is the **deep ilial circumflex arteries.** Each extends laterally across the iliopsoas muscles taking blood to the dorsal body wall [Figure 8–20].

At about the level of the sacrum, the aorta gives off a large **external iliac artery** that extends toward the hindlimb on either side of the body. In contrast to the matching arterial and venous pattern of the pelvic and hindlimb region, a major exception should be noted: there is no common iliac artery, but there is a common iliac vein. Just before the external iliac artery emerges through the body wall from the body cavity, it gives off a **deep femoral artery.** Generally, three branches emanate from the deep femoral a., the **caudal epigastric artery** that extends along the abdominal surface of the rectus abdominis muscle and anastomoses with a branch of the internal mammary artery (sometimes called the cranial epigastric artery), the **external pudendal artery**, embedded in inguinal fat and carrying blood

to the bladder and external genitalia and the third, a deep vessel, the **medial femoral circumflex artery,** carrying blood to the "hamstring" muscles (the biceps femoris, the semitendinosus, and the semimembranosus), as well as the adductor femoris and tenuissimus muscles. You may notice a small branch, the **external spermatic artery,** joining the spermatic cord as it makes its journey to the scrotum in the male [Figure 8–21].

When the external iliac a. appears outside the body wall on the medial surface of the leg, it is now called the **femoral artery.** The first of several branches, the **lateral femoral circumflex artery,** emerges laterally and carries blood to the quadriceps complex (the rectus femoris, vastus lateralis, vastus medialis, and vastus intermedius) as well as the sartorius and tensor fascia latae muscles. A somewhat more distal medial branch, the **muscular artery,** supplies blood to the adductors, gracilis, and semimembranosus muscles. As the femoral a. approaches the knee, it gives off the **articular artery** that transports blood to the gracilis, semimembranosus, and vastus lateralis muscles. At this point, or slightly distal, the superficial **saphenous artery** originates from the femoral and courses over the medial surface of the thigh and shank. In the region of the knee, the femoral a. continues between the vastus medialis and semimembranosus becoming the **popliteal artery.** A number of branches of this artery supply blood to muscles of the shank, foot, and thigh [Figure 8–21].

Now return to the point at which the external iliac arteries originated and note that the aorta persists as a smaller version of its abdominal self and dives deeply into the dorsal portion of the pelvic cavity and is obscured by fat and connective tissue. When you dissected the reproductive system and separated the two os coxae, you undoubtedly observed some of the distal branches of this vessel. After reading the text and checking [Figure 8–21 and Figure 8–22], to observe these vessels, you will have to perform your usual careful job of slowly picking away the fat and connective tissue. When you have done so, you will see that almost immediately a pair of **internal iliac arteries** is given off and then the aorta persists as the small **median sacral artery** continuing along the dorsal aspect of the pelvic cavity and then along the ventral region of the tail as the **caudal artery.** The first branch of the internal iliac a. branching almost immediately is the **umbilical artery** extending laterally, entering the fat of the lateral vesical ligament of the bladder and supplying blood to the urinary bladder. This artery represents

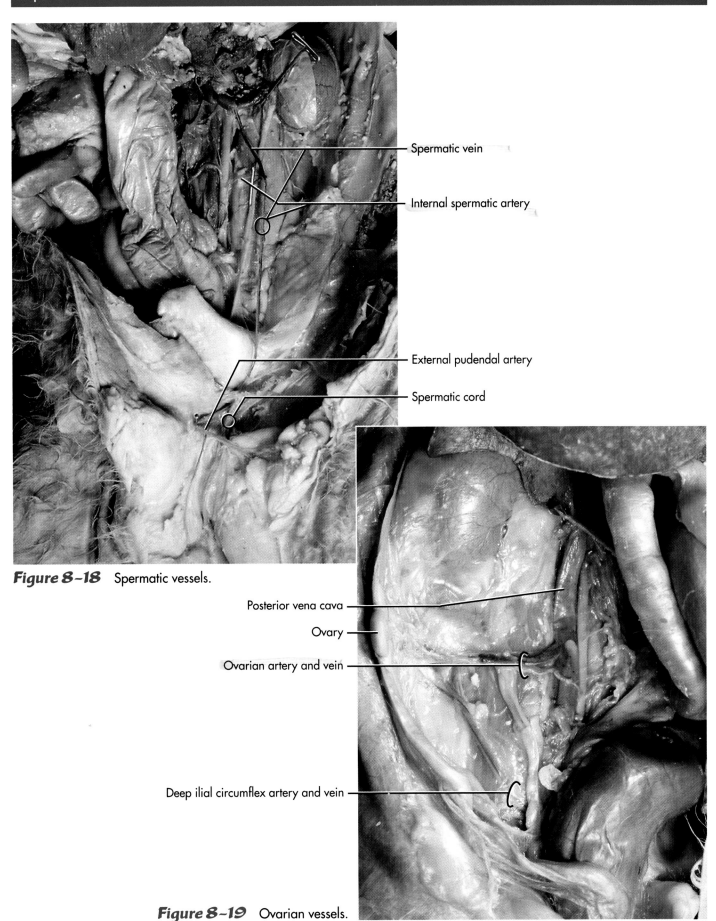

Spermatic vein

Internal spermatic artery

External pudendal artery

Spermatic cord

**Figure 8-18**   Spermatic vessels.

Posterior vena cava

Ovary

Ovarian artery and vein

Deep ilial circumflex artery and vein

**Figure 8-19**   Ovarian vessels.

the remnant of the umbilical arteries that carry blood to the placenta during fetal development. The next branch is the **cranial gluteal artery** that turns lateral and caudal taking blood to hip muscles such as the gluteals, pyriformis, and some thigh muscles. The next vessel, the **middle hemorrhoidal artery**, extends medially toward various structures of the reproductive system, urinary bladder, and rectum. In females, particularly those who were pregnant or had recently been pregnant, a very conspicuous sub-branch, the **uterine artery**, extends cranially along the uterus and anastomoses with uterine branches of the ovarian artery. Finally, the **caudal gluteal artery** represents the end of the iliac artery. It supplies blood to gluteal and pyriformis muscles as well as the region at the base of the tail [Figure 8–22].

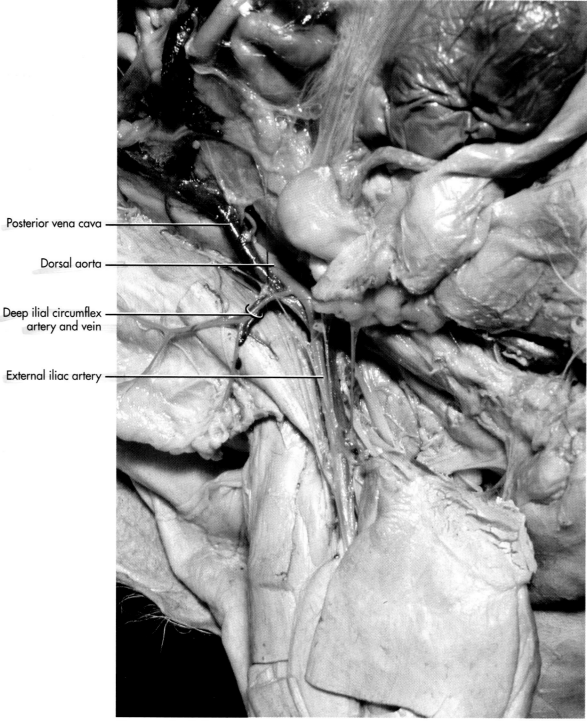

Posterior vena cava

Dorsal aorta

Deep ilial circumflex artery and vein

External iliac artery

*Figure 8–20*  Deep iliocircumflex artery.

In the human, a similar pattern exists with minor modifications. A major difference is the presence of a common iliac artery that branches into the external and internal iliac arteries.

As you recall, arteries deliver blood to tissues and veins drain those same tissues and return it back to the heart. Trace this drainage by the branches of the external and internal iliac veins and observe that they merge into the common iliac vein. The two common iliac veins join to form the posterior vena cava [Figure 8–22]. As the posterior vena cava progresses cranially, note that the veins draining adjacent organs and tissues merge with it, adding their blood to its volume. These veins should already have been identified along

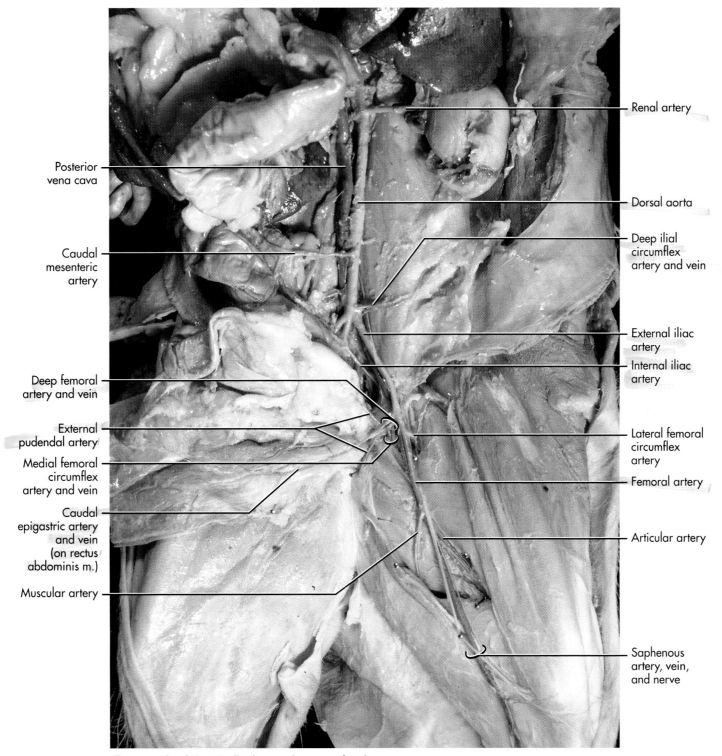

**Figure 8–21**   Hindlimb vessels: superficial.

with the arteries of the same name. In its passage dorsal to the liver it is joined by a pair of **hepatic veins** draining the liver and contributing blood from the abdominal viscera that was carried by the hepatic portal vein to the liver [Figure 8–23]. To observe the hepatic

veins, it is necessary to carefully scrape tissue from the cranial surface of the liver. Follow the posterior vena cava into the right atrium. The human condition is very similar.

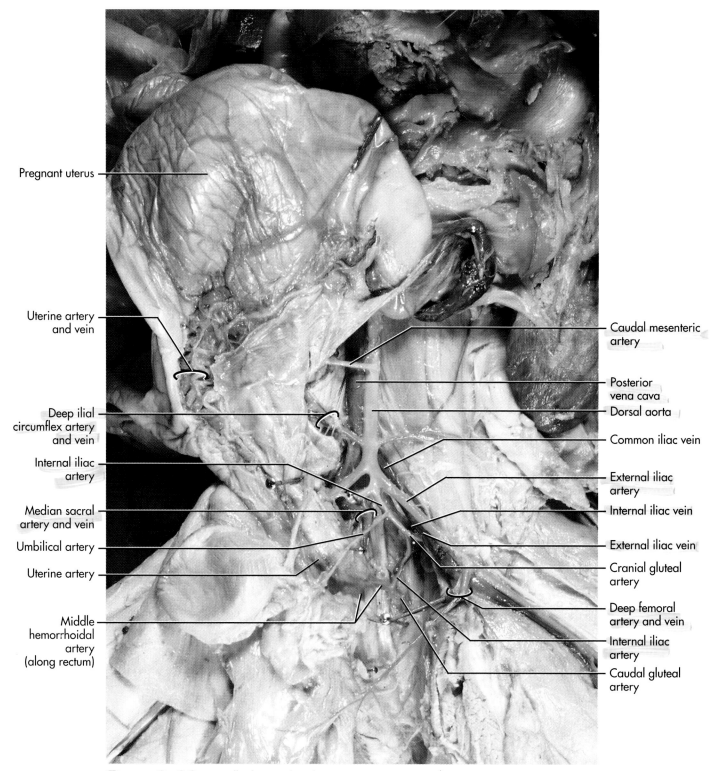

Pregnant uterus

Uterine artery and vein

Deep ilial circumflex artery and vein

Internal iliac artery

Median sacral artery and vein

Umbilical artery

Uterine artery

Middle hemorrhoidal artery (along rectum)

Caudal mesenteric artery

Posterior vena cava

Dorsal aorta

Common iliac vein

External iliac artery

Internal iliac vein

External iliac vein

Cranial gluteal artery

Deep femoral artery and vein

Internal iliac artery

Caudal gluteal artery

**Figure 8–22**   Hindlimb vessels:  deep.

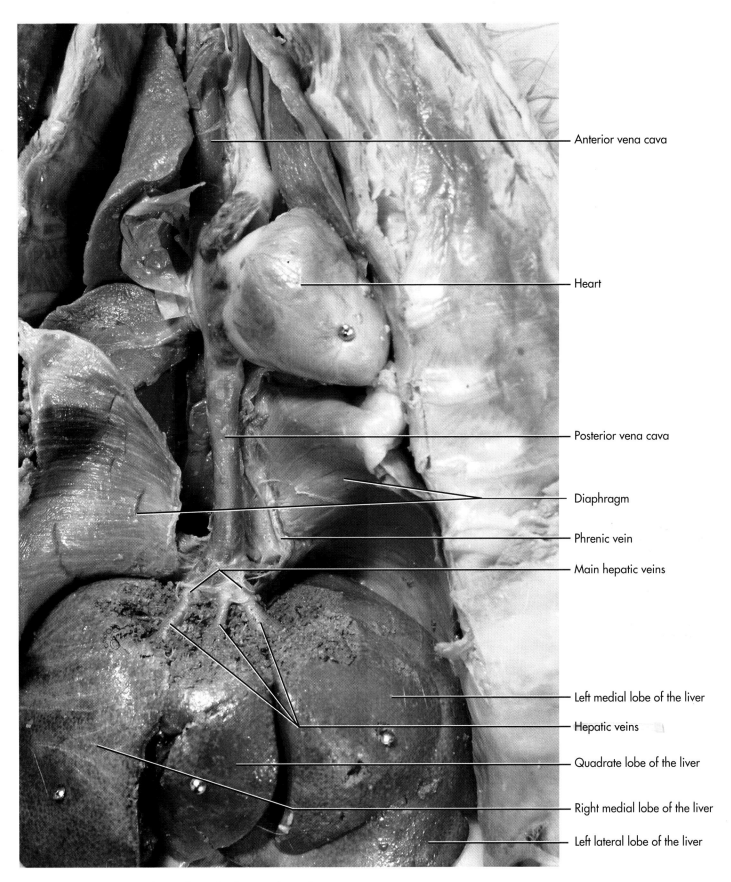

Anterior vena cava

Heart

Posterior vena cava

Diaphragm

Phrenic vein

Main hepatic veins

Left medial lobe of the liver

Hepatic veins

Quadrate lobe of the liver

Right medial lobe of the liver

Left lateral lobe of the liver

*Figure 8-23*    Circulation from the liver to the right atrium.

# Lymphatic Circulation ━━━━━

Since it is difficult to obtain specimens with injected lymphatic vessels, the treatment of this system will be confined to a discussion. However, lymphatic nodes, glands, and organs can be identified.

The architecture of the lymphatic system consists of a network of thin walled, highly permeable vessels located throughout the body. Small fingerlike capillaries called lacteals project into the villi of the small intestine and are involved in fat absorption. The lymphatic fluid is returned to the circulatory system by way of a number of smaller vessels that coalesce into the larger thoracic duct opening into the venous system near the left subclavian vein. A large number of small organs, lymph nodes, embedded in connective tissue and often not easily identified, are clustered along the vessels. Larger lymph nodes that are more noticeable, are identifiable in the cervical, intestinal, and groin regions. As a matter of fact, the cervical nodes are often misidentified as salivary glands by students. Those found in the mesenteries of the intestines are particularly obvious and readily identified.

Large prominent lymphoid organs that may have been previously identified during the study of other systems include the palatine tonsils, the thymus gland, and the spleen. In humans, a similar architecture exists with some modifications such as Peyer's patches, a cluster of lymph nodules associated with the intestines.

The function of this system is several-fold. At the capillary-tissue level in the body, fluid pressure differences at the arteriole end cause fluids to move from the vessels into the tissues. Most of the fluid diffuses back into the circulatory system at the venule end again due to pressure differences, but a small volume remains in the tissues and is returned to the circulatory system by way of lymphatic vessels. Following fat absorption through the lacteals, these lipid molecules are transported to the blood in lymphatic vessels.

Lymph nodes and nodules are part of the internal "body sanitation and defense department." They are responsible for filtration and destruction of foreign proteins and particles such as viruses and bacteria. These are also the sites of lymphocyte production involved in the immune response to foreign matter.

Of the lymphoid organs, the tonsils function in a similar manner to the lymph nodes, eliminating possible foreign invaders. The thymus gland whose size is influenced by age in mammals, that is, young mammals have much larger thymuses than adults, is the site of production of lymphocytes that migrate to lymph nodes providing immune defense functions.

The largest of the lymphoid organs, the spleen is the site of immune surveillance and production of leukocytes. It is the site of aged erythrocyte destruction with release of the components into the circulatory system for production of new blood cells. A number of other organs also play an important role in the life cycle of erythrocytes. In the fetus it is a major site of erythrocyte production that generally ceases after birth, but can be reactivated in adults under conditions of erythrocyte decimation. Further, the spleen serves as a reservoir of blood platelets.

# Nervous System

The nervous system is one of the most complex and least understood of any of the systems in animals. The complexity of this system is reflected not only in the anatomy but also in its physiology. Consider that this system, often in conjunction with portions of the endocrine system, is the controlling center for the homeostatic well-being of the body. These systems initiate, moderate, and coordinate all body activities.

Characteristic of the most complex of any known animal nervous system, that of vertebrates, is a dorsal hollow nerve cord with a greatly elaborated anterior end known as a brain. Invertebrate animals are often said to possess a brain but it consists of a mass of nervous tissue called ganglia and is generally capable of behavior associated with stereotypic activities.

Originating from the vertebrate brain are 10–12 pairs of cranial nerves that generally innervate glands, muscles, and organs at the anterior end of the animal, with the exception of the vagus nerve that innervates most of the visceral organs. Cranial nerves are associated with various regions of the brain and pass through specific foramina of the vertebrate skull.

The dorsal hollow nerve cord, mentioned above, is more often referred to as the spinal cord. It extends from the brain, passes through the foramen magnum, and continues through the vertebral foramen of the spinal column made up of vertebrae. Paired spinal nerves, associated with the innervation of skin and its structures and muscles of individual body segments, emerge between individual vertebrae.

Among tetrapods, with their more sophisticated appendage movement, a more complex arrangement of the simple primitive segmental spinal nerve pattern is encountered in the forelimb and hindlimb region of the spinal cord. In the forelimb region, this arrangement is known as the brachial plexus while in the hindlimb region the arrangement is called the lumbosacral plexus.

Classically, the brain and spinal cord are grouped together as the central nervous system while the cranial nerves, spinal nerves, and autonomic nerves are known as the peripheral nervous system.

## The Brain

The mammalian brain, in many ways, is unique among vertebrates. The most prominent portions are the cerebrum and cerebellum, both of which have evolved in a similar fashion to accommodate the immense increase in neurons and supporting cells of this part of the central nervous system. The surfaces of both exhibit numerous convolutions (gyri) and crevices (sulci) as a means to substantially increase the surface area of the cerebrum and cerebellum with the result that many more cells can be fit into these areas while still conserving space in the cranium. In many instances in the cerebrum, the gyri and the sulci each have a specific name. More than likely, mammal heads would be even larger than they are without this design. Further, in contrast to nonmammalian vertebrates, the cerebrum and cerebellum of mammals possess a thin outer layer of gray matter, the cortex, consisting mainly of nerve cell bodies and unmyelinated nerve fibers overlying the main mass of white matter consisting primarily of myelinated nerve fibers. The prominent paired optic lobes of the mesencephalon, the major integration and coordination center of nonmammalian vertebrates, appear in mammals as two paired lobes, the corpora quadrigemina, now a center for the regulation of auditory, visual and other reflex activities since the original functions now reside in the cerebrum and cerebellum.

Three primitive embryological divisions of the brain are recognized — the anterior prosencephalon, or forebrain, and the posterior rhombencephalon, or hindbrain, separated by the mesencephalon or midbrain.

As differentiation occurs, the mesencephalon remains intact but the prosencephalon subdivides into the telencephalon and the diencephalon while the rhombencephalon divides into the metencephalon and myelencephalon, yielding a five-part brain. Later events lead to the development of the olfactory bulbs and cerebrum from the telencephalon, the corpora quadrigemina from the roof of the mesencephalon, the cerebellum and pons from the metencephalon, and the medulla oblongata from the myelencephalon.

Since accessing the intact brain of the cat is most difficult and often results in a poor specimen, we suggest using a sheep brain as representational of the typical mammalian pattern of anatomy. We have found that brains with intact cranial nerves and pituitary glands and with the meninges removed are the best dissection specimens. We also recommend that your instructor, using a sharp kitchen knife, cut each brain into two equal halves so that the internal sagittal anatomy can be studied.

## The Meninges and Ventricles of the Brain

The central nervous system is isolated from the rest of the body by three protective layers known as meninges. The innermost layer, the pia mater, remains in intimate contact with the brain surface and can be recognized by its abundant vascularity. The outermost whitish, tough fibrous layer, the dura mater, often remains adherent to the area surrounding the pituitary gland (hypophysis) even after removal of the meninges. The middle layer, the arachnoid membrane, is delicate, web-like and extends between the pia and dura maters.

Since the brain represents a phenomenal specialization of the anterior portion of the dorsal hollow nerve cord, it should not be surprising to learn that the brain possesses cavities known as ventricles. Ventricles I and II lie in the left and right cerebral hemispheres, respectively. They are each connected by a small canal to ventricle III that occurs in the diencephalon which is, in turn, connected by a canal called the cerebral aqueduct in the mesencephalon to ventricle IV, lying in a V-shaped space of the medulla oblongata. Each of these ventricles is roofed by a complex of tissues called a choroid plexus. A choroid plexus consists of the inner lining of the brain, the ependyma, and a highly vascularized portion of the pia mater. This is the site of the "blood-brain barrier"

that is effective in preventing the contamination of the central nervous system by such potentially damaging invaders such as bacteria, viruses, etc. A specialized secretion, the cerebrospinal fluid, is produced by the choroid plexi. Cerebrospinal fluid circulates within the ventricles of the brain, the central canal of the spinal cord and in the subarachnoid space between the pia mater and arachnoid membrane in mammals. It functions as a lubricant, prevents damage from mechanical shock, and also acts as a buoyant fluid, allowing the brain to float and be perceived as a fraction of its actual weight.

## External Anatomy

### The Telencephalon

From the dorsal view, observe the cerebrum consisting of paired **cerebral hemispheres** separated from each other by the deep **longitudinal cerebral fissure**. Notice the numerous **gyri**, elevations, and **sulci**, shallow depressions, sculpting the surface [Figure 9–1]. On the ventromedial aspect of the cerebrum lie the **olfactory bulbs**. The bulbs lie above the cribriform plate of the ethmoid bone and receive fibers from neurons in the olfactory epithelia lining the nasal cavity. Those fibers represent part of the **olfactory nerve** (I) that carry sensory information to the cerebrum. Two flat bands, the more conspicuous **lateral olfactory band** and the **medial olfactory band** lead from the olfactory bulbs toward the olfactory portion of the brain, **the pyriform lobe**, that is separated from the rest of the cerebrum by a somewhat indistinct **rhinal sulcus**. A triangular area between the two bands is often recognized as the **olfactory trigone** [Figure 9–2].

With two exceptions, the human cerebrum is very similar. In addition to being considerably larger, the human brain is more complexly folded and subdivided into recognizable lobes and the olfactory bulbs are smaller.

### The Diencephalon

Since the cerebrum has developed to such an extraordinary degree in mammals and has attained a size that brings it into contact with the second largest portion of the brain, the cerebellum, a great deal of the **diencephalon** can be best seen in the sagittal section and in the dissection of the brainstem to be done later. Three areas, the floor or **hypothalamus**, the sides or **thalamus**, and the thin roof, the **epithalamus**, enclose the **third ventricle** of the diencephalon. A

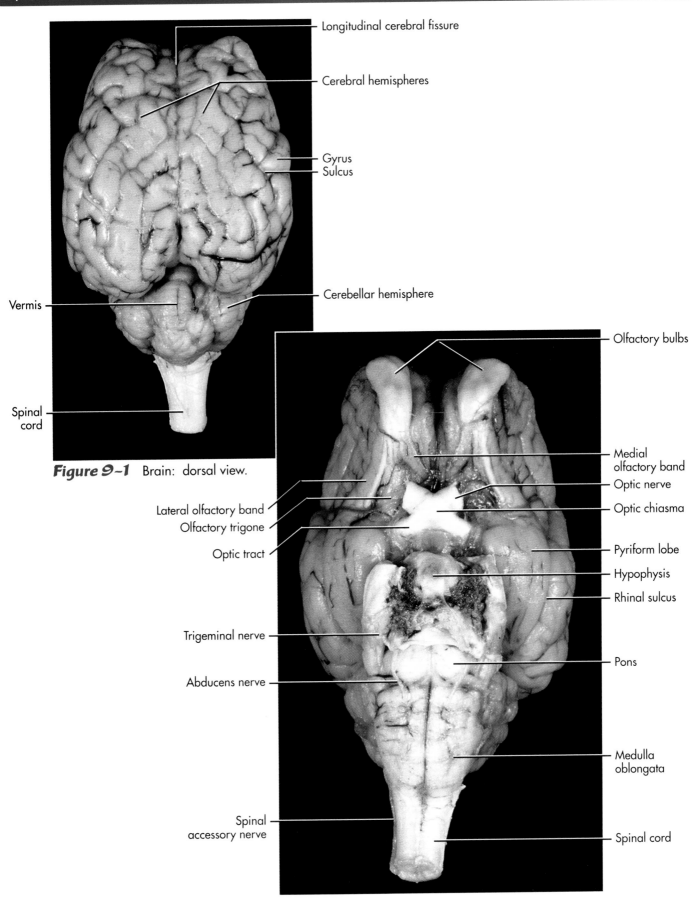

Longitudinal cerebral fissure

Cerebral hemispheres

Gyrus
Sulcus

Cerebellar hemisphere

Vermis

Spinal cord

**Figure 9-1** Brain: dorsal view.

Olfactory bulbs

Medial olfactory band

Optic nerve

Optic chiasma

Pyriform lobe

Hypophysis

Rhinal sulcus

Lateral olfactory band

Olfactory trigone

Optic tract

Trigeminal nerve

Abducens nerve

Pons

Medulla oblongata

Spinal accessory nerve

Spinal cord

**Figure 9-2** Brain: ventral view.

major landmark, the **optic chiasma**, an X-shaped structure, demarcates the cranial end of the hypothalamus on the ventral surface of the brain. The two stout bands of tissue at the cranial end of the chiasma are the **optic nerves** (II) that consist of nerve fibers carrying sensory information from the eyes. At the chiasma, some fibers from each eye cross over to the opposite side while others pass straight through, carried via **optic tracts** to their respective sides [Figure 9–2, Figure 9–3a, and Figure 9–3b]. This circuitry allows mammals to see life three dimensionally. A delicate slender tube, the **infundibulum**, extends from the hypothalamus to the **pituitary gland** (hypophysis). The slightly convex area of the hypothalamus just posterior to the infundibulum is the **tuber cinereum**. Just caudal to the tuber cinereum are the paired

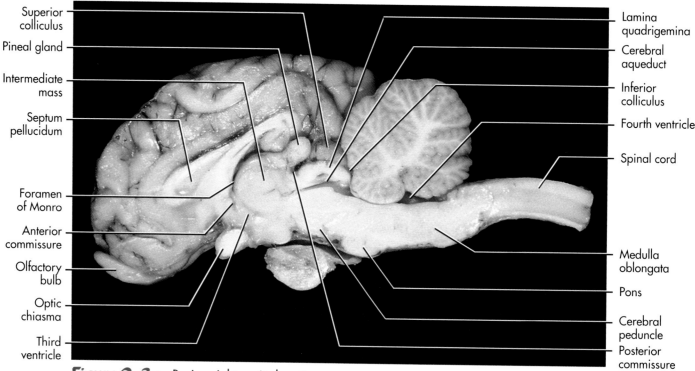

Superior colliculus
Pineal gland
Intermediate mass
Septum pellucidum
Foramen of Monro
Anterior commissure
Olfactory bulb
Optic chiasma
Third ventricle

Lamina quadrigemina
Cerebral aqueduct
Inferior colliculus
Fourth ventricle
Spinal cord
Medulla oblongata
Pons
Cerebral peduncle
Posterior commissure

**Figure 9–3a** Brain: right sagittal section.

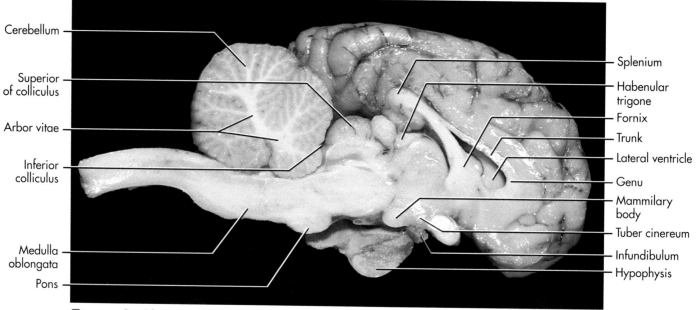

Cerebellum
Superior of colliculus
Arbor vitae
Inferior colliculus
Medulla oblongata
Pons

Splenium
Habenular trigone
Fornix
Trunk
Lateral ventricle
Genu
Mammilary body
Tuber cinereum
Infundibulum
Hypophysis

**Figure 9–3b** Brain: left sagittal section.

mammilary bodies, marking the caudal end of the hypothalamus [Figure 9–3a and Figure 9–3b].

### The Mesencephalon

While gently spreading the cerebrum and cerebellum apart, observe the bulges representing the **corpora quadrigemina**. These bodies consist of a larger, more prominent, pair of **superior colliculi** resting on a smaller less conspicuous pair of **inferior colliculi**. On the ventral surface observe elongated paired longitudinal **cerebral peduncles** representing bundles of nerve fibers extending between anterior and posterior areas of the brain [Figure 9–3a and Figure 9–3b]. The yellowish flat bands emanating from the ventral surface of the cerebral peduncles and often adhering to the dura mater attached in the region of the hypophysis are the **oculomotor nerves** (III). The **trochlear nerve** (IV) is unique because it is the only cranial nerve to emerge from the dorsal surface of the brain, the mesencephalon just anterior to the pons [Figure 9–4].

### The Metencephalon

This region of the brain consists of a ventral bulging band of transverse fibers, the **pons**, located just posterior to the cerebral peduncles. The largest and most conspicuous of the cranial nerves, the **trigeminal** (V), emanates from the most posterior region of the pons. By far, the larger portion of the metencephalon consists of the dorsal **cerebellum**. Notice the medial **vermis**, flanked by paired **cerebellar hemispheres** [Figure 9–1, Figure 9–2, and Figure 9–3b].

### The Myelencephalon

The **medulla oblongata** contains fiber tracts permitting communication between the brain and the spinal cord [Figure 9–2, Figure 9–3a, and Figure 9–3b]. Cranial nerves VI, the **abducens**, VII, the **facial**, VIII, the **acoustic**, IX, the **glossopharyngeal**, X, the **vagus**, XI, the **spinal accessory**, and XII, the **hypoglossal**, are all associated with the medulla oblongata. The spinal accessory, as its name implies, also receives fibers from the anterior end of the spinal cord [Figure 9–5].

## Table of Cranial Nerves

| Name | Number | Sensory | Motor | Distribution |
|---|---|---|---|---|
| Olfactory | I | X | | Neurosensory cells of nasal epithelium. |
| Optic | II | X | | Sensory fibers of the retina. |
| Oculomotor | III | X | X | Innervates dorsal rectus, ventral rectus, medial rectus, and ventral oblique muscles. Innervates retractor bulbi, levator palpebrae superioris, and intrinsic ciliary muscles. |
| Trochlear | IV | X | X | Innervates dorsal oblique muscle. |
| Trigeminal | V | X | X | This nerve consists of three branches, all associated with the facial and jaw regions. **Ophthalmic branch:** innervates the skin in region of eye and nose, upper eyelid, eyeball, and lacrimal glands. **Maxillary branch:** innervates the palate, upper lip, upper teeth, vibrissae, skin of upper jaw, and vicinity. **Mandibular branch:** innervates the lower lip, lower teeth, pinna, skin of lower jaw and cheek; muscles of mastication — masseter, temporal, and pterygoid. |
| Abducens | VI | X | X | Innervates the lateral rectus. |
| Facial | VII | X | X | Innervates facial and digastric muscles; sensory innervation of the tastebuds of anterior two-thirds of tongue; mandibular, sublingual, and lacrimal glands. |
| Vestibulocochlear (Acoustic) | VIII | X | | Two branches: **Vestibular branch** innervates organs of equilibrium, saccule, utricle, and semicircular canals. **Cochlear branch** innervates the acoustic organs, organs of Corti, in cochlea. |
| Glossopharyngeal | IX | X | X | Innervates pharyngeal muscles; sensory innervation of pharynx and tastebuds of posterior one-third of tongue; parotid gland. |
| Vagus | X | X | X | Innervates pharynx, larynx, esophagus, lungs, heart, abdominal viscera. |
| Accessory | XI | X | X | Innervates the cleidomastoid, sternomastoid, trapezius muscles. |
| Hypoglossal | XII | X | X | Innervates the styloglossus, hyoglossus, genioglossus, and intrinsic muscles of the tongue. |

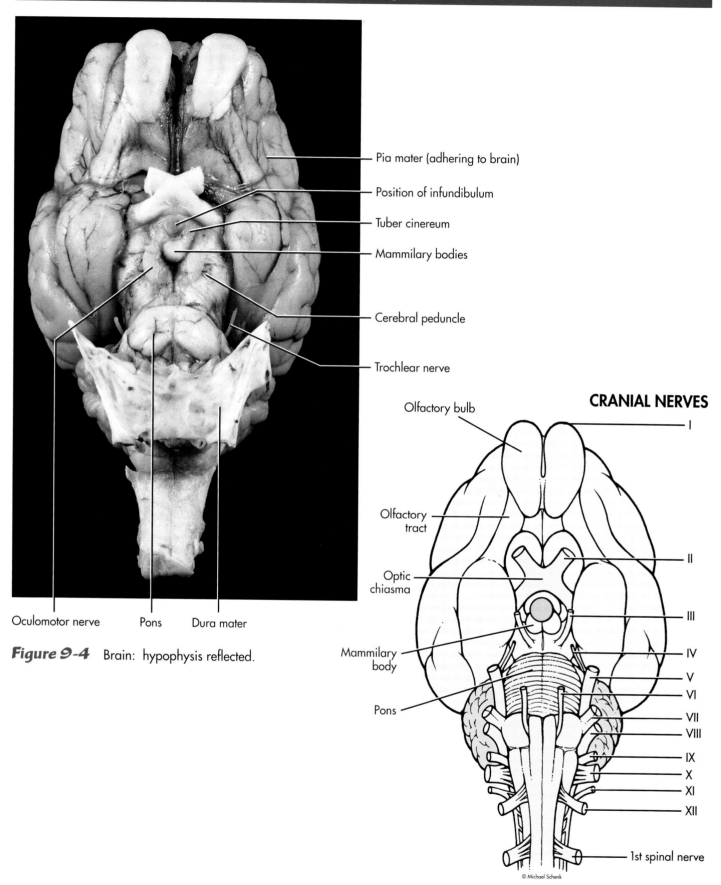

Pia mater (adhering to brain)

Position of infundibulum

Tuber cinereum

Mammilary bodies

Cerebral peduncle

Trochlear nerve

Oculomotor nerve    Pons    Dura mater

**Figure 9-4** Brain: hypophysis reflected.

**CRANIAL NERVES**

Olfactory bulb

Olfactory tract

Optic chiasma

Mammilary body

Pons

I

II

III

IV

V

VI

VII

VIII

IX

X

XI

XII

1st spinal nerve

© Michael Schenk

**Figure 9-5** Brain: ventral view, cranial nerves.

In the human brain, the most obvious difference is size and less obvious is its shape. The brain is larger and less elongate with the cerebellum and medulla tucked under the immense cerebrum. Have you ever wondered why your sense of smell is not as good as your dog or cat? There are two reasons: the area of human olfactory epithelium is a fraction of that of other mammals and the olfactory bulbs are greatly reduced.

## Internal Anatomy —
## Sagittal Section of the Brain

A careful sagittal section usually results in two halves that are very similar. External features just discussed, in many cases, will be seen in this dissection, sometimes in greater detail. It is easier to see the relationship of the cerebrum to the diencephalon and mesencephalon. The thin layer of gray matter (actually tan in preserved specimens) on the outer surface of the cerebrum and cerebellum is very obvious in this section. In the following discussion, refer to Figure 9–3a, Figure 9–3b, and Figure 9–6].

Within the three groups of mammals living today, the monotremes or egg-laying mammals, the marsupials, and the placental mammals, it is only among the placental mammals that a **corpus callosum** has evolved. It consists of transverse nerve fibers that permit transmission of nervous impulses between the cerebral hemispheres. The cranial curve of the corpus callosum is known as the **genu** and the caudal end is called the **splenium**, with the **trunk** extending between them. Another paired bundle of fibers, the **fornix**, more extensive than seen in this section, appears ventral to the corpus callosum. Connecting the corpus callosum and the fornix is the thin wall of tissue called the **septum pellucidum**. It consists of a double sheet of gray and white matter that separates the two lateral ventricles of the cerebrum. Very often, the sagittal cut will have left the septum entirely in one of the brain halves. If that is true, it will be easy for you to observe one of the lateral ventricles, on the side devoid of the septum.

Now, direct your attention to the area almost directly ventral to the regions just discussed. If the

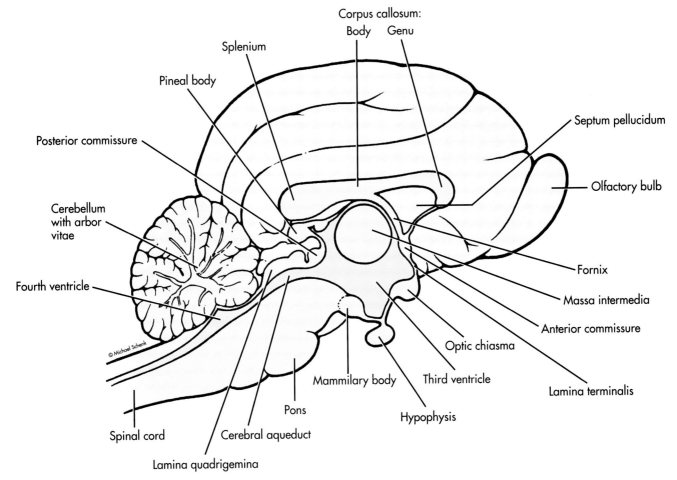

*Figure 9–6*  Brain: sagittal section.

sagittal cut was successful in approximating the mid-sagittal plane, a rather prominent circular mass, the **intermediate mass**, will be distinguishable residing within a shallow irregular space, the **third ventricle** and **cerebral aqueduct**. Each of the cerebral hemispheres contains a **lateral ventricle** that communicates with the third ventricle by way of the **foramen of Monro**. Recall that the third ventricle is enclosed within the walls of the diencephalon and the aqueduct sits within the confines of the mesencephalon leading to the **fourth ventricle** resting within the medulla oblongata. The intermediate mass is a central connective bridge between the left and **right thalamus** that make up the two lateral walls of the diencephalon. Actually, all of the tissue lateral to the third ventricle in this section, with the exception of the single layered ependymal lining the ventricle, is thalamus. The floor and ventral walls of the diencephalon consists of the **hypothalamus**. Observe the relationships of the **optic chiasma, infundibulum, hypophysis,** and **mammilary bodies**, all associated with the hypothalamus and seen in external view. The thin **lamina terminalis** forms the cranial wall of the diencephalon. Notice the small thickening, the **anterior commissure**, in the dorsal portion of the lamina terminalis. The **epithalamus** is the very thin roof of the diencephalon. The most prominent structure here is the **pineal gland** or **body** projecting from its surface. Just cranial to it is the **habenular trigone** and ventral to it is the **posterior commissure**.

Features of the mesencephalon include the dorsally located **corpora quadrigemina**, consisting of a pair of **superior colliculi**, controlling visual reflexes, and a pair of **inferior colliculi**, controlling auditory reflexes and resting on the **lamina quadrigemina**. The thick floor consists of the **cerebral peduncles**, bundles of nerve fibers extending between the cerebrum and other brain areas. The usually narrow space enclosed in the mesencephalon is the **cerebral aqueduct** connecting the third and fourth ventricles.

The rounded protuberance posterior to the cerebral peduncles is the **pons** and the somewhat elongated, flattened region just caudal to the pons is the **medulla oblongata**. Caudal to the medulla oblongata the central nervous system continues as the **spinal cord** whose cavity is the **central canal**.

The large, deeply grooved body lying dorsally over the fourth ventricle and pons and medulla oblongata is the **cerebellum**. Note the similarity in tissue arrangement between the cerebrum and cerebellum,

with the outer layer of gray matter lying over the white matter. In sagittal section, this relationship of the tissues of the cerebellum suggested a tree-like construction to early anatomists and they named this arrangement of white matter in the cerebellum the **arbor vitae** (tree of life).

## The Brainstem

The brainstem of mammals consists of the mesencephalon, pons, and medulla oblongata. It is the site of a number of relay and vital reflex centers. The specimen in Figure 9–7a includes portions of the diencephalon, as well. To produce a dissection similar to Figure 9–7a grasp the cerebrum of one of your sagittal sections and carefully separate it from the rest of the section. Now slice through the thalamus of the diencephalon to create a specimen similar to Figure 9–7a. Carefully lift up the cerebellum and remove it from the brainstem using a sharp knife or scalpel, while watching its connection to the underlying tissue so that tears do not occur in the area. After removal, if necessary, use a sharp scalpel to make a smooth slice through the anterior, middle, and posterior cerebellar peduncles similar to Figure 9–7a.

Beginning with structures associated with the diencephalon, not part of the brainstem, locate the **thalamus, intermediate mass,** the **habenular trigone,** and **pineal gland**. Notice the two subtle bulges on the lateral wall of the thalamus. The more anterior and less obvious of these diencephalic structures, the **lateral geniculate body**, associated with the **superior colliculus**, part of the mesencephalon and anterior portion of the brainstem, is involved in visual function, while the posterior and more obvious **medial geniculate body**, associated with the **inferior colliculus**, also part of the brainstem, serves as a relay of auditory impulses [Figure 9–7a and Figure 9–7b].

Locate the **anterior, middle,** and **posterior cerebellar peduncles**, representing bundles of fibers connecting the cerebellum to the brainstem. The space existing between the Y-shaped halves of the medulla oblongata is the **fourth ventricle**. This Y-shaped configuration consists of fiber tracts transmitting sensory impulses between the spinal cord and the medulla oblongata. Note the shallow central dorsal groove, the **dorsal median sulcus**. The two halves of the Y consist of the **fasciculus gracilis**. Lateral to the fasciculus gracilis, locate the **fasciculus cuneatus** and the **tuberculum cuneatum** [Figure 9–7a].

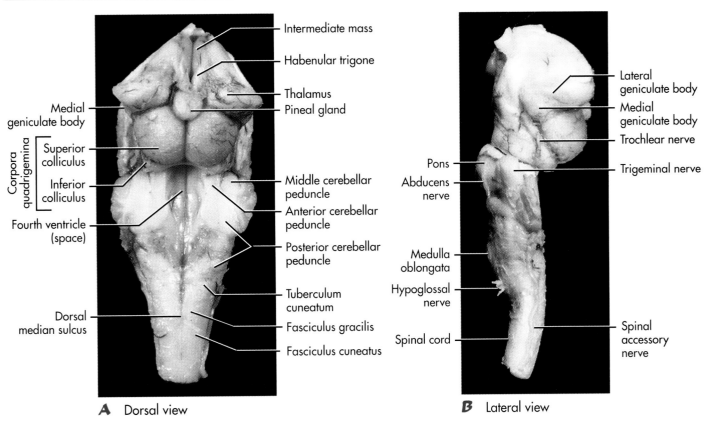

Intermediate mass
Habenular trigone
Thalamus
Pineal gland
Medial geniculate body
Corpora quadrigemina
Superior colliculus
Inferior colliculus
Fourth ventricle (space)
Dorsal median sulcus
Middle cerebellar peduncle
Anterior cerebellar peduncle
Posterior cerebellar peduncle
Tuberculum cuneatum
Fasciculus gracilis
Fasciculus cuneatus

**A** Dorsal view

Lateral geniculate body
Medial geniculate body
Trochlear nerve
Pons
Abducens nerve
Trigeminal nerve
Medulla oblongata
Hypoglossal nerve
Spinal cord
Spinal accessory nerve

**B** Lateral view

**Figure 9-7** Brainstem.

## Spinal Cord

Note that the more or less cylindrical spinal cord is continuous with and posterior to the medulla oblongata. Like the brainstem, the white matter in the spinal cord surrounds the gray matter, in contrast to the arrangement in the cerebrum and cerebellum. This portion of the central nervous system is the site of interconnecting synapses between sensory, association, and motor neurons involved in various reflex actions. Recall that the nerve cord in vertebrates is defined as dorsal and hollow. Examine the cut end of the spinal cord of the brain specimen and note the small central canal that constitutes the "hollow" part of the definition. The central canal is continuous with the fourth ventricle therefore the cerebrospinal fluid not only circulates within the brain ventricles, but also within the central canal of the spinal cord. Passage of the fluid through foramina in the fourth ventricle into the subarachnoid space allows circulation of the cerebrospinal fluid, thereby bathing the outer surface of the central nervous system.

In the body, the spinal cord lies within the vertebral canal formed by the articulated vertebrae. The spinal cord is not uniform in diameter, but exhibits two conspicuous enlargements, the anterior cervical that supplies nerves to the forelimb and the posterior lumbosacral that supplies nerves to the hind limb. It continues posteriorly, ending in the tail as a slender thread of tissue called the filum terminalis. The human condition is very similar.

## Spinal Nerves

There are 38–39 pairs of spinal nerves in the cat, 8 cervical, 13 thoracic, 7 lumbar, 3 sacral, and 7 or 8 caudal nerves. Unlike the cat, the human possesses 31 pairs of spinal nerves, 8 cervical, 12 thoracic, 5 lumbar, 5 sacral, and 1 caudal (coccygeal). Each spinal nerve generally carries both sensory and motor fibers. Spinal nerves are constructed at their spinal cord ends with a dorsal root carrying the sensory neurons and a ventral root carrying the motor neurons. They combine to form the spinal nerve, emerge between adjacent vertebrae as paired structures, and then subdivide into dorsal and ventral rami (branches) supplying their respective body segments.

Complex interrelationships of the ventral rami in certain body regions are identified as a plexus.

Commonly, three of these, the cervical in the neck region, the brachial in the shoulder and forelimb region, and the lumbosacral in the hip and region of the hind limb are discussed. In our treatment, the cervical and brachial are combined and discussed as the brachial plexus. In other treatments, spinal nerves 1–5 (cervical nerves 1–5) are referred to as the cervical plexus. Cervical nerves 6–8 along with the first thoracic nerve are referred to as the brachial plexus.

## Brachial Plexus

During the dissection of the muscular and circulatory systems, many of the nerves of this plexus were exposed. To do an orderly dissection of this complex, you will begin at its anterior end and work posteriorly. For the following dissection and discussion, see Figure 9–8. As reference points, locate the **hypoglossal nerve** (XII) which overlies the hyoglossus muscle previously discussed during the dissection of the neck muscles and the **spinal accessory nerve** (XI). To expose the spinal accessory nerve, carefully cut the sternomastoid and cleidomastoid muscles at their insertion ends. Since these are muscles innervated by this nerve, exercise great caution. Find a pair of swellings, the **superior cervical** and **nodose ganglia**, which occur just ventral to the hypoglossal nerve. Find the **vagus nerve** (X) extending posteriorly from the nodose ganglion and running along the common carotid artery in a sheath closely applied to the trachea. Although the vagus, spinal accessory, and hypoglossal are cranial nerves, they are important as references to a complete and orderly dissection. The nerves of the brachial plexus often have more than one point of origin, e.g., the first subscapular nerve arises from the sixth and seventh cervical nerves. In a plexus, interconnecting nerves carry fibers of the ventral rami from one spinal nerve to another, thereby contributing to the multiple origin of certain nerves in these complexes.

The **first cervical nerve**, quite small and difficult to recognize because of copious amounts of connective tissue in the area, passes medially over the ventral surface of the longus coli m. to supply ventral muscles of the neck.

Locate the **second, third, fourth,** and **fifth cervical nerves**, somewhat obscured by connective tissue and supplying the tissues of the shoulder and neck area.

Fibers of the fifth and sixth cervical nerves contribute to the formation of the **phrenic nerve** that travels lateral to and in close association with the vagus nerve through the thoracic region and innervates the diaphragm.

The **sixth cervical nerve** extends to the area of the shoulder joint where the prominent **suprascapular nerve** originates and passes with the transverse blood vessels between the supraspinatus and subscapularis muscles, supplying the supraspinatus and infraspinatus muscles. Notice that a small branch to the skin of the shoulder originates at the same point as the suprascapular nerve.

The **sixth** and **seventh cervical nerves** give rise to the **first subscapular nerve** that innervates the subscapularis muscle and travels with the subscapular vessels. The **axillary nerve** originates from these two cervical nerves and travels with the posterior humeral circumflex vessels beneath the posterior edge of the biceps brachii m. to innervate lateral shoulder muscles such as the teres major, teres minor, deltoids, and cleidobrachialis. Likewise, the **musculocutaneous nerve** originates from the sixth and seventh cervical nerves and branches near the biceps brachii, innervating the biceps brachii, brachialis and coracobrachialis muscles as well as the skin of the forelimb.

The **second subscapular nerve** originates from the seventh cervical nerve and innervates the teres major muscle.

The **anterior ventral thoracic** nerve arises from the seventh cervical nerve, travels with the ventral thoracic vessels, and innervates the pectoral muscles.

The largest nerve in the plexus is the **radial** that originates from cervical nerves six, seven, eight and the first thoracic nerve, travels with the deep brachial vessels, and innervates the triceps brachii, epitroclearis, and extensor muscles of the forelimb.

The **median nerve** arises from cervical nerves seven, eight, and the first thoracic nerve, and travels with the brachial artery passing through the supracondyloid foramen to innervate some of the flexor muscles of the forelimb.

The **posterior ventral thoracic nerve** originates from the eighth cervical and first thoracic nerves, travels with the long thoracic blood vessels, and innervates the pectoral muscles.

The **ulnar nerve** arises from the eighth cervical and first thoracic nerves, travels parallel with the median nerve, crosses the medial epicondyle of the humerus, and innervates flexor muscles of the forelimb.

The **medial cutaneous nerve** originates from the first thoracic nerve and innervates the skin of the forelimb.

The **third subscapular nerve** originates from cervical nerves seven and eight, travels with the thoracodorsal vessels, and innervates the latissimus dorsi muscle.

The **long thoracic nerve**, lying along the lateral surface of and supplying the serratus ventralis m., originates from the seventh cervical nerve.

With the exception of the first thoracic nerve, the remainder of the thoracic nerves are referred to as the intercostal nerves, supplying intercostal muscles, lateral thoracic muscles, some abdominal muscles, back muscles, and skin.

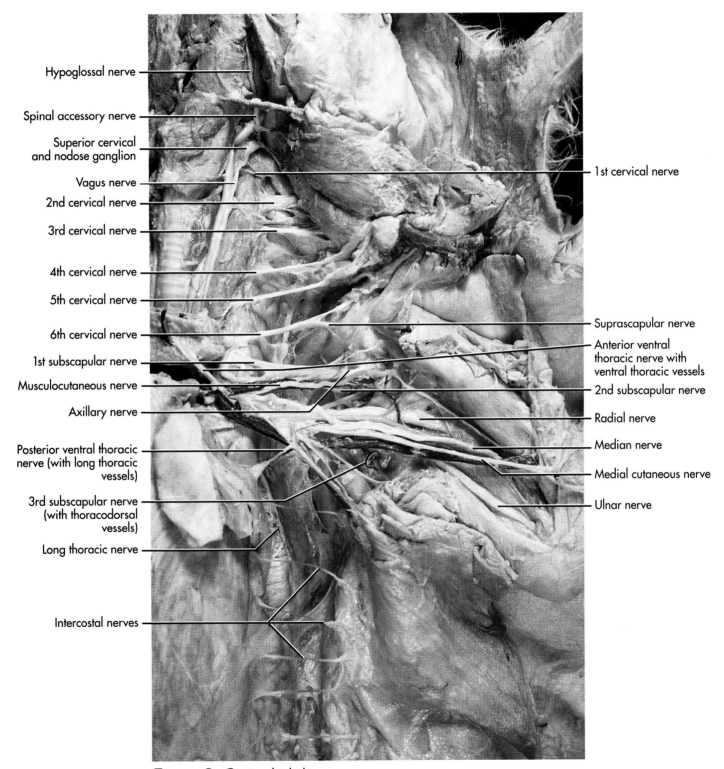

**Figure 9-8** Brachial plexus.

# Lumbosacral Plexus (Ventral View)

The nerves that supply the lumbar and sacral regions and the hind limb consist of a series of paired nerves, seven lumbar and three sacral, passing between adjacent lumbar and sacral vertebrae. Not surprisingly, the basic construction of nerves in this area mirror those in the brachial region, in that they possess dorsal and ventral rami. The dorsal rami supply dorsal muscles and structures of the skin. The anatomical architecture of the ventral rami of the first three lumbar nerves consists of a medial and lateral branch that innervate muscles and structures in this region. The basic structural plan of the lumbosacral plexus consists of the ventral rami of lumbar nerves 4–7, sacral nerves 1–3, and communicating branches between these regions.

To study the architecture of the neural anatomy of these areas, we will begin by finding the medial branch of the **third lumbar nerve** as it emerges from beneath the illiopsoas muscle and passes lateral to it. Trace it anteriorly to its source by carefully removing the anterior portion of the illiopsoas muscle. Care must be exercised in its removal since other lumbar nerves lie beneath it. Find the lateral branch of the third lumbar nerve. By removing the illiopsoas muscle, you should be able to find the **second** and **first lumbar nerves** with their medial and lateral branches [Figure 9–9a and Figure 9–9b].

The remainder of the dissection involves the **lumbosacral plexus**. One of the distinctive, but delicate and fragile nerves of this complex is the **genitofemoral nerve** that originates as the medial branch of the fourth lumbar nerve. An inconspicuous lateral branch of the fourth joins the fifth lumbar nerve. First, locate the genitofemoral nerve on the surface of the external iliac blood vessels [Figure 9–9a and Figure 9–9b]. Follow it anteriorly as it passes beneath the dorsal aorta and posterior vena cava to its source. In good dissections, particularly in males, you should be able to distinguish a genital branch innervating structures in the pelvic region.

The **lateral femoral cutaneous nerve** originates primarily from the fifth with minor contributions from the fourth lumbar nerve [Figure 9–9a and Figure 9–9b]. It emerges from beneath the psoas minor m., passes over the illiopsoas m., travels with the deep ilial circumflex vessels, and supplies the lateral surfaces of the hip and thigh regions.

The majority of fibers of lumbar nerve six, in company with a branch of the fifth, form the prominent **femoral nerve** [Figure 9–9a and Figure 9–9b]. This nerve passes between the illiopsoas and psoas minor muscles, penetrating the abdominal wall, subdivides into three branches, one of which is the **saphenous** running parallel with the femoral vessels and distally the saphenous vessels. One of the other branches innervates the quadriceps muscle complex and the third innervates the sartorius m.

The **obturator nerve** originates from the sixth nerve with contributions from the fifth and seventh lumbar nerves [Figure 9–9a and Figure 9–9b]. It passes into the pelvic region through the obturator foramen where it branches to supply the thigh adductors, pectineus, gracilis, and obturator externus muscles.

The **lumbosacral cord** or **trunk** appears medial to the obturator nerve and is formed by fibers of the sixth and seventh lumbar nerves. As the cord passes caudally, it receives fibers from the sacral nerves. Carefully expose the cord and the three **sacral nerves** and note their interconnections [Figure 9–9a and Figure 9–9b].

Although the **sympathetic trunks** are present from the head to the tail, it is in this region that they may be best viewed. They appear as two very delicate strands of nervous tissue medial to the lumbar and sacral nerves, appearing to lie almost on the ventral surface of the vertebral column. In each body segment, paired **ganglia** appear in the trunks with connecting rami to the spinal nerves [Figure 9–9a and Figure 9–9b].

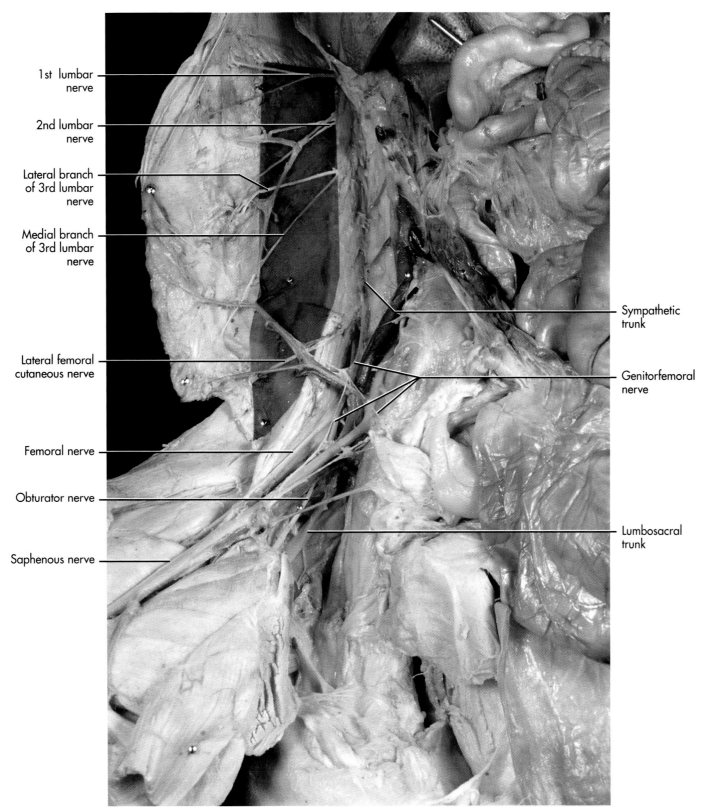

1st lumbar nerve

2nd lumbar nerve

Lateral branch of 3rd lumbar nerve

Medial branch of 3rd lumbar nerve

Lateral femoral cutaneous nerve

Femoral nerve

Obturator nerve

Saphenous nerve

Sympathetic trunk

Genitorfemoral nerve

Lumbosacral trunk

**Figure 9-9A** Lumbosacral plexus: ventral view — enhanced to demonstrate the lumbar nerves.

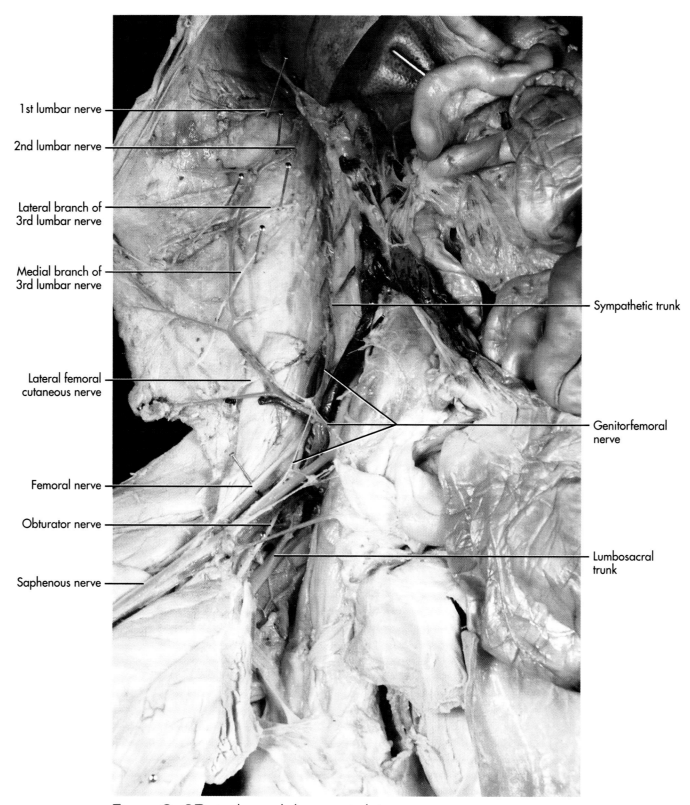

1st lumbar nerve

2nd lumbar nerve

Lateral branch of
3rd lumbar nerve

Medial branch of
3rd lumbar nerve

Lateral femoral
cutaneous nerve

Femoral nerve

Obturator nerve

Saphenous nerve

Sympathetic trunk

Genitorfemoral
nerve

Lumbosacral
trunk

*Figure 9-9B* Lumbosacral plexus: ventral view.

# Lumbosacral Plexus (Dorsal View)

The following dissection will expose the nerves of the lumbosacral plexus, nerves originating from the lumbosacral cord, and branches of the sacral nerves and appear in Figure 9–10. During the dissection of the deep hip muscles, many of these nerves were partially exposed.

The largest and most readily observed of these nerves is the **ischiatic nerve** (sciatic) that extends from the lumbosacral cord. It courses over the lateral muscles of the thigh, giving off a **muscular branch** that divides to supply the biceps femoris, the semi-membranosus, semitendinosus, tenuissimus, and other thigh flexor muscles. As it continues distally, the ischiatic gives off a delicate **sural nerve** that passes across the gastrocnemius m. to the ankle. As it nears the knee, the ischiatic nerve divides into the **common peroneal** and **tibial nerves** [Figure 9–10]. The common peroneal nerve pierces the lateral head of the gastrocnemius m. to supply the peroneal muscles, the tibialis anterior and extensor digitorum longus muscles, eventually innervating muscles of the digits. The tibial nerve extends between the heads of the gastrocnemius m. and innervates the gastrocnemius, plantaris, soleus,

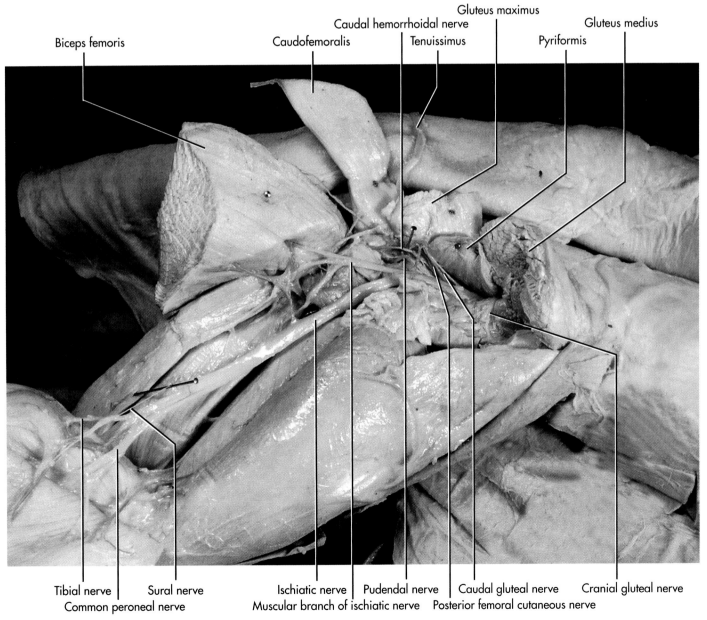

**Figure 9-10** Lumbosacral plexus: dorsal view.

and other muscles associated with extension and flexion of the foot.

The **cranial gluteal nerve**, a branch originating from the lumbosacral cord, passes over the dorsal aspect of the ilium and beneath the gluteus minimus m., innervating the gluteus minimus, gluteus medius, gemellus cranialis, and tensor fasciae latae muscles [Figure 9–10]. The **caudal gluteal nerve** also originating from the lumbosacral cord passes posteriorly to innervate the caudofemoralis and the gluteus maximus muscles [Figure 9–10 and Figure 9–11]. The **posterior femoral cutaneous nerve** arises from the second and third sacral nerves and travels with the caudal gluteal blood vessels. It arches over to the biceps

femoris muscle and extends over the surface of that muscle innervating the skin at the base of the tail and over the biceps femoris m. [Figure 9–10 and Figure 9–11]. The **pudendal nerve** arises from the second and third sacral nerves, appearing as a forked nerve that innervates the anus and genital structures in both sexes [Figure 9–10 and Figure 9–11]. The **caudal hemorrhoidal nerve**, the deepest of these hip nerves, originates from sacral nerves two and three, passes deep, supplying the rectum and the urinary bladder [Figure 9–10 and Figure 9–11]. Generally, this nerve is difficult to find since it lies in connective tissue that must be carefully removed.

**Figure 9–11** Closeup of deep nerves of the hip.

# Sense Organs

In mammals, the major organs associated with detection of environmental stimuli — the eyes, ears, nose, and tongue — are concentrated in the head. Imbedded in these organs are cells of the nervous system specialized for sensing changes in external conditions. The sensory information is transmitted to the appropriate areas of the brain where interpretation occurs, allowing sophisticated perception and appropriate action.

## Tongue

The tongue in most mammals actually is employed in a variety of activities — feeding, drinking, grooming, as well as gustation (tasting). The receptors associated with gustation are located within papillae scattered over the surface of the tongue. Recall that the various papillae and their distribution were discussed in the digestive system.

## Nose

The nose functions during respiration and olfaction (smelling). The sense receptors involved with detection of odoriferous stimuli are located within the epithelium of the mucous membranes lining the nasal cavities.

## Ear

The ear of mammals is very difficult to dissect since it is imbedded within heavy bone of the skull. The ear consists of the external, middle, and inner regions. The external ear, also known as the pinna, is easily identifiable in most mammals and functions as a collecting funnel for sound waves. This sound energy passes through the external acoustic meatus and causes the tympanic membrane (eardrum) to vibrate. The vibration is transmitted sequentially to the inner ear through a series of three ear ossicles — the malleus, the incus, and the stapes — located in the tympanic cavity of the middle ear. The footplate of the stapes fits into the oval window, transmitting vibrations to the fluid filled cochlea. The membranous labyrinth consists of a blind tube (the cochlear duct), shaped like a snail shell, that is continuous with the organ of equilibrium consisting of the saccule, utricle, and three semicircular canals. These organs rest in the bony labyrinth of the petromastoid portion of the skull. Within the membranous labyrinth circulates the endolymph while within the bony labyrinth circulates the perilymph. Located within the cochlear duct is the organ of Corti. Waves of fluid within the cochlea cause bending of the microvilli of the hair cells of the organ of Corti and produce nerve impulses that are transmitted by way of cochlear nerves to the brain for sound interpretation. The saccule, utricle, and semicircular canals are involved with equilibrium.

## Eye

### External Structures

The eyeball of the cat is also difficult to dissect because one must remove it from the head, but an excellent substitute, a cow or sheep eye, is readily available. It is advantageous to dissect two eyes, one to study the extrinsic eye muscles that position the eyeball within the orbit and the other to view the internal eye structures.

To facilitate the study of the eye muscles, carefully remove the white connective tissue and fat, avoiding removal of any pink, tan or gray structures which may be muscles or glands from the eyeball. The optic nerve, which is white and located on the back and near the center of the eyeball, must be conserved [Figure 10-1a]. All mammals possess six extrinsic eye

Lacrimal gland    Levator palpebrae superioris    Dorsal rectus        Dorsal oblique

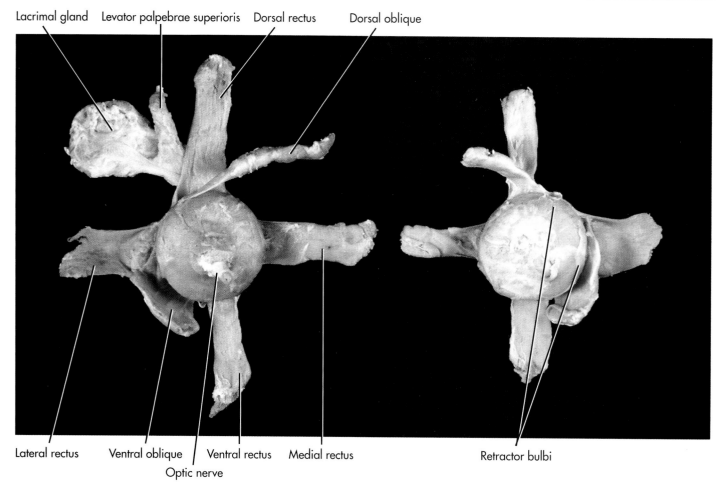

Lateral rectus      Ventral oblique    Ventral rectus    Medial rectus                    Retractor bulbi
                         Optic nerve

***Figure 10–1a***  Extrinsic eye muscles; left eye and right eye.

muscles — a ventral oblique, a dorsal oblique, a medial rectus, a lateral rectus, a dorsal rectus, and a ventral rectus. In order to identify these muscles correctly, it is imperative to determine whether the eyeball is left or right. The key to this determination is identification of the **ventral oblique muscle**. This muscle is found on the bottom of the eyeball and is the only muscle that naturally wraps around the circumference of the eyeball. Its insertion is on the lateral aspect of the eyeball very near the insertion of the **lateral rectus muscle**. The cut end of the ventral oblique muscle represents the medial aspect of the eyeball [Figure 10–1a]. You now should be able to identify the dorsal, ventral, medial, and lateral aspects of the eyeball. Identify the **ventral rectus muscle** over which the ventral oblique muscle lies. Next identify the **medial rectus muscle** appearing approximately opposite the lateral rectus muscle. Continue around the eyeball dorsally and identify the **dorsal rectus muscle** that inserts approximately opposite the ventral rectus muscle. Finally, identify the **dorsal oblique muscle**

whose insertion and muscle direction is as its name implies, somewhat oblique, and opposes the ventral oblique muscle [Figure 10–1a].

In the cat, but not the human, on the posterior surface of the eyeball and surrounding the projecting optic nerve, is a four-part muscle, the **retractor bulbi** [Figure 10–1a]. This muscle retracts the eyeball. Another muscle, the **levator palpebrae superioris**, attached to the upper eyelid and found on the anteriodorsal surface of the eyeball, lifts the eyelid. You may see yet another muscle, the **orbicularis oculi**, that is arranged in a circular sphincter-like pattern in and around the eyelids. It functions during forced closure of the eyelids, e.g., when the cat is being disciplined. If the eyelids are missing, these muscles will not be observed.

Eyeball moisture for most terrestrial vertebrates affords a well lubricated surface to assure that the surface remains clean and can function as part of the lens system. To provide this moisture, three glands are present. A **lacrimal gland**, also present in humans, located on the dorsolateral aspect of the eyeball, secretes a solution known as tears [Figure 10–1a]. This secretion moves across the eyeball, keeping it moist, and then draining into the nasolacrimal duct and eventually into the nasopharynx. A small salivary gland, the **infraorbital gland**, not found in humans, is located in the orbit beneath the eye. It drains into the mouth. Within a transparent fold, the **nictitating membrane** [Figure 10–1b], located in the medial angle of the eye, the small **harderian gland** may be identifiable. Its secretions, like that of the lacrimal gland, bathe the eyeball. This gland is not present in humans. The nictitating membrane acts as a protective mechanism in many mammals, but is vestigial in humans.

## Internal Structures

If you received two eyeballs, dissect the one not used for external structures. When only one eyeball is available, use caution during the following dissection so that you preserve muscles, etc., previously identified.

To prepare a specimen that is superior for the study of internal structures, insert the tip of a sharp scalpel into the eyeball approximately one centimeter from the posterior edge of the cornea and continue to cut around the circumference of the eyeball to separate it into anterior and posterior parts. Store the

anterior and posterior parts of the eyeball in the open air at room temperature for 24–48 hours or until the jelly-like substance has dried out. This gelatinous substance, the **vitreous humor**, occurs between the lens and the retina and functions in holding the retina and lens in place and serves as a refractive medium as part of the lens system of the eye. Between the cornea and the ciliary body is the **aqueous humor**, a fluid continuously secreted by the ciliary body into this space. The aqueous humor is also continuously removed through a venous sinus surrounding the eye, therefore under normal conditions its volume remains constant. It functions in keeping the structures of the eye in position as well as serving as part of the lens system of the eye. Further, it supplies the structures in this area with nutrients and oxygen while removing metabolites.

Three distinct concentric tunics or layers form the eyeball. In the posterior end of your preparation, identify the three layers. The outer layer is a tough white, fibrous coat, the opaque **sclera**. Over the anterior surface of the eyeball the sclera is modified as a transparent window called the **cornea** [Figure 10–2]. The middle layer, the **choroid**, is heavily pigmented and appears black. The **retina**, the innermost tunic, consists of an outer pigmented layer abutting the choroid and an inner neural layer abutting the vitreous humor. The neural layer will appear creamy, folded and displaced from its normal position due to preservation while the pigmented layer generally associates with the choroid. Because of this displacement,

**Figure 10–1b** Nictitating membrane.

Nictitating membrane

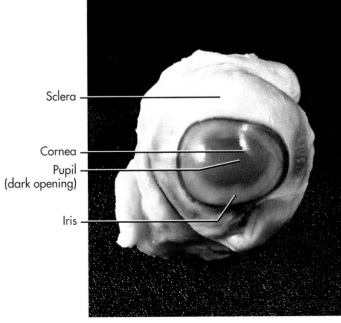

Sclera

Cornea

Pupil
(dark opening)

Iris

**Figure 10–2** Anterior eyeball: exterior.

an iridescent bluish-green area, the **tapetum lucidum,** is obvious [Figure 10–3]. This is common in vertebrates that are active in subdued light. Have you noticed that cat eyes when suddenly illuminated by incidental light in the dark appear yellow or green? It is light reflecting from the surface of their tapetum lucidum. Gently move the retina to one side to see its point of attachment at the back of the eyeball. This point of attachment is the **optic disk** [Figure 10–3]. Through this area, pass the neurons of the optic nerve and nutrient blood vessels. The optic disk is the area known as the blind spot since there are no photoreceptors, rods, and cones, located there.

Anteriorly, the choroid is modified as the **iris.** It consists of smooth muscle arranged radially and circularly around an opening known as the **pupil** and regulates its diameter dependent upon incident light [Figure 10–2 and Figure 10–4]. Pigment of the iris influences eye color. The iris is continuous with a second modification of the choroid, the **ciliary body.** The ciliary body consists of **ciliary muscles** and the **ciliary process.** The delicate **zonule fibers** of the suspensory ligament extend from the ciliary body

to the lens. The ciliary muscles are smooth muscles that regulate lens shape. The folded ciliary process secretes the aqueous humor. The scalloped junction along the posterior aspect of the ciliary body is known as the **ora serrata** [Figure 10–4]. It marks the anterior margin of the neural portion of the retina.

The **lens** is a biconvex transparent structure that is responsible for fine focusing the ocular system [Figure 10–5]. In your specimen, the lens will appear opaque, due to the preservation process.

The anatomy of the human eye is virtually identical to that of the cat.

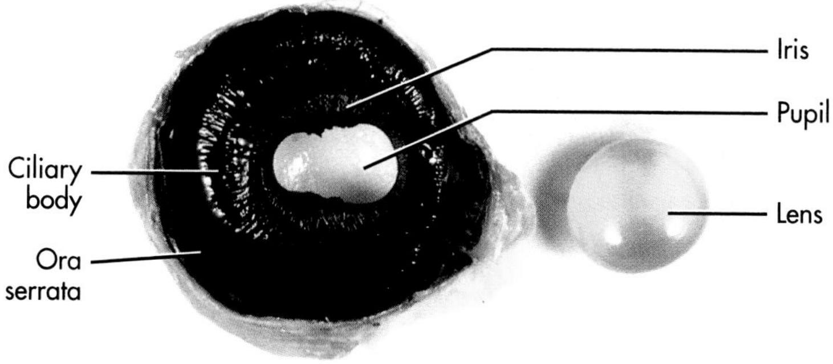

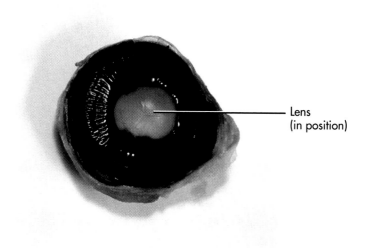

***Figure 10–4***  Internal anatomy of the eye.

***Figure 10–3***  Tunics of the eyeball.

***Figure 10–5***  Lens in natural position.

# Glossary

**Abdominopelvic cavity** Caudal subdivision of the coelom created by the diaphragm. It can be arbitrarily subdivided into the abdominal and pelvic spaces.

**Abduct** Muscle action that pulls a body part away from the midline of the body.

**Adduct** Muscle action that pulls a body part toward the midline of the body.

**Alimentary canal** The digestive system extending from the cranial mouth to the caudal anus.

**Amphiarthrosis** A joint in which there is slight movement, e.g., between vertebrae.

**Anterior** Directional term meaning ahead or before.

**Aorta** Major artery that carries blood from the left ventricle.

**Appendicular division** Portion of the skeleton that includes the bones of the anterior limb, pectoral girdle, posterior limb, and pelvic girdle.

**Artery** Blood vessel that carries blood away from the heart.

**Atlas** First cervical vertebra modified to allow nodding motion between it and the occipital condyles of the skull.

**Auricle** Ear-like flaps attached to the atria that increase their volume somewhat.

**Axial division** Portion of the skeleton that includes the skull, mandible, hyoid, sternum, ribs, and vertebral column.

**Axis** Second cervical vertebra modified to allow rotary motion between it and the atlas.

**Bolus** A mass of chewed food, saliva, and enzymes produced in the oral cavity.

**Brainstem** The mesencephalon, pons, and medulla oblongata, collectively, where reflex centers control such activities as vomiting, breathing, heart functions, etc. reside.

**Bronchi** Subdivisions of the trachea that increase the surface area of the respiratory system in the lungs.

**Canal** Usually tube-like passage with rounded or oval opening in bones through which nerves and blood vessels may pass.

**Capitulum or head** Proximal end of rib that articulates with demi-facets between adjacent vertebral bodies.

**Caudal** Directional term meaning toward the butt or tail of an animal.

**Cervix** The distal portion of the uterine body that projects into the vagina.

**Clitoris** Erectile female sex organ, part of which is homologous with the penis. It is found in a depression in the ventral wall of the urogenital sinus.

**Coelom** Body cavity that is further divisible into compartments, e.g., thoracic, pericardial, abdominopelvic. The outer wall of the coelom is lined by a parietal serous membrane that is continuous with a visceral serous layer covering all organs that project into the cavity. Mesenteries are double layers of membrane that suspend the organs.

**Condyle** Smooth, rounded projection occurring at the end of articulating bones, e.g., the medial and lateral condyles of the femur.

**Coronary sinus** Main venous space of the heart carrying coronary venous blood to the right ventricle. It opens into the right ventricle.

**Cranial** Directional term meaning toward the head of an animal.

**Cremasteric pouch** The internal sac derived from peritoneal tissues that suspends the testis within the scrotum.

**Demi-facet** Smooth articulating surface on the body of two adjacent vertebrae where the capitulum of a rib articulates.

**Diaphragm** The muscular partition between the thoracic and abdominopelvic cavities of mammals. The diaphragm is an integral and essential component of the respiratory system.

**Diarthrosis** a joint in which there is free movement, e.g., between the femur and os coxa.

**Distal** Some distance from the point of attachment or origin.

**Dorsal** Directional term meaning toward the back of an animal.

**Endocrine gland** A ductless gland that secretes and/or releases chemical compounds (hormones) into the circulatory system. These chemicals affect target tissues throughout the body to control metabolism, secretion, growth, etc.

**Epicondyle** Projection above or dorsal to a condyle, e.g., lateral epicondyle of humerus. Muscles originate from these projections.

**Epididymis** Convoluted tubules occurring on the dorsal surface of the testis, but connected to the seminiferous tubules of the testes, where sperm maturation occurs.

**Extension** Muscle action causing an increase in the angle of a joint and movement of a distal body part away from a proximal one, e.g., extension of the forearm away from the upper arm by the Triceps brachii.

**Facet** Smooth, concave surface on lateral surface of vertebral transverse process that articulates with the tuberculum of a rib.

**False vocal cords** Anterior pair of folds at the cranial end of the larynx. Not involved in sound production.

**Fimbria(e)** Movable finger-like projections around the edge of the infundibulum that sweep the surface of the ovary, making it likely that oocytes released from the ovary will move into the oviduct.

**Fissure** Often-elongated opening with jagged edges in bones through which nerves and blood vessels may pass.

**Flexion** Muscle action causing reduction of the angle at a joint and movement of a distal body part toward a proximal one, e.g., flexion of the forearm toward the upper arm by the Biceps brachii.

**Foramen** Short, smooth, usually round or oval opening in bones through which nerves and blood vessels may pass.

**Fossa ovalis** A depression in the interatrial septum, best seen in the right atrial wall. It marks the position of a fetal opening between the right and left atrium allowing oxygenated blood returning from the placenta to be shunted into the "left heart" to be pumped to the anterior portion of the fetal body.

**Fossa** A depression in an organ in which another organ may sit, e.g., the cerebellar fossa of the skull that houses the cerebellum of the brain.

**Frontal Section** A section parallel to the horizontal plane of the body or organ.

**Glottis** A slit between the true vocal cords that leads into the trachea.

**Gustation** Term for the sense of taste.

**Gyrus** Convolution of the surface of the brain.

**Hormone** Chemical compound secreted by tissues or organs that regulate functions and growth in their own or other tissues and organs.

**Infundibulum** Hood-like funnel attached to the proximal end of the oviduct that envelopes the ovary and receives oocytes as they are released from the ovary, thereby conveying them to the oviduct.

**Insertion** Generally the more movable end of a muscle, causing movement of a body part.

**Larynx** The "voicebox" or "Adam's apple" a sound-producing organ whose wall is reinforced by a number of cartilages.

**Lateral** Directional term meaning toward the side.

**Ligamentum arteriosum** Ligamentous band between the pulmonary trunk and the aortic arch in mammals. In the fetus, it is the ductus arteriosus, a short vessel that allows most "right heart" blood to be shunted into the lower body circulation away from the lungs which are nonfunctional in the fetus.

**Linea alba** White line of connective tissue that extends down the midline of the belly.

**Meatus** A passageway, e.g., the external auditory meatus leading to the eardrum or tympanic membrane.

**Medial** Directional term meaning toward the midline.

**Mediastinum:** a potential space in the central part of the chest occupied by the pericardial cavity and its contents, trachea, esophagus, nerves, and blood vessels. Connective tissue occurs in the mediastinum that is important in securing these structures in this area.

**Meninges** Investing membranes associated with the brain and spinal cord.

**Midline** An imaginary line that runs down the middle of the back or belly.

**Mid-sagittal section** A section exists that passes through the exact midline of the body or organ. There is only one of these.

**Myocardium** Muscular wall of the heart.

**Nares** The **external nares** are synonymous with the nostrils that open into the nasal cavity. **Internal nares** open into the nasopharynx at the anterior edge of the soft palate.

**Olfaction** Term for the sense of smell.

**Omentum** Specialized mesenteries occurring in the abdominal cavity. The greater omentum is a double layered apron-like organ that hangs over the viscera. The lesser omentum extends between the liver and the stomach.

**Optic chiasma** X-shaped area of the optic neural circuit on the ventral aspect of the diencephalon. Some optic fibers pass straight through while others cross over as they course to the respective sides of the brain.

**Origin** Generally the more stable and less movable end of a muscle.

**Ostium tubae** The opening of the infundibulum of the oviduct.

**Ovary** The primary reproductive organ in the female from which primary oocytes are released and in which important hormones controlling reproductive functions and influencing secondary sex characteristics are synthesized and secreted.

**Oviduct** Reproductive tube leading from the peritoneal cavity to the uterine horns. Fertilization in mammals occurs here. Also known as uterine tubes.

**Palate** The hard palate delimits the roof of the mouth and consists of the palatine processes of the premaxilla and maxilla, as well as the palatines. The soft palate extends from the posterior rim of the hard palate.

**Penis** The erectile copulatory organ in the male that functions as an avenue to transfer sperm to the female reproductive tract and also to allow elimination of urine.

**Pericardial cavity** Space in which the heart lies.

**Pericardium** Serous membrane associated with the pericardial cavity; parietal layer lines the pericardial sac and the visceral layer covers the heart and is synonymous with the epicardium of the heart.

**Peritoneum** Serous membrane associated with the abdominopelvic cavity; parietal layer lines the cavity and visceral layer covers organs that project into the cavity.

**Pleura** Serous membranes associated with the lungs; parietal layer delimits the pleural cavity and visceral layer covers the lungs that project into the pleural cavity.

**Pleural cavity** Subdivision of the thoracic cavity that houses the lungs.

**Posterior** Directional term meaning after or behind.

**Postzygapophysis or posterior zygapophysis** Posterior projection of neural arch of vertebra whose articulating surface points ventrally and which articulates with a prezygapophysis of the adjacent vertebra posterior to it.

**Prepuce** Fold of skin that envelopes the tip (glans) of the penis. Sometimes referred to as the foreskin.

**Prezygapophysis or anterior zygapophysis** Anterior projection of neural arch of vertebra whose articulating surface points dorsally and which articulates with a postzygapophysis of the adjacent vertebra anterior to it. This arrangement permits adjacent vertebrae to support each other.

**Process** Projection of a bone usually distinct from the main body of the bone.

**Pronation** Muscle action that results in the palm of the hand pointing ventrally.

**Protraction** Muscle action that advances a body part anteriorly in a direction parallel to the longitudinal axis, e.g., as the leg swings forward, it is protracted.

**Proximal** Nearest the point of attachment or origin.

**Raphe** A line of connective tissue indicating the junction of two muscles, e.g., between the two halves of the mylohyoid.

**Retraction** Muscle action that pulls a body part posteriorly in a direction parallel to the longitudinal axis, e.g., as the leg swings backward, it is retracted.

**Retroperitoneal** Term describing an organ that is situated beneath or behind the parietal peritoneum, e.g., the kidney, ureter.

**Sagittal section** A section parallel to the midline of an animal or organ. There are an infinite number of sagittal sections.

**Sinus** Irregular space in an organ, e.g., frontal sinus in the frontal bone.

**Sulcus** Groove in the surface of the brain.

**Supination** Muscle action that results in the palm of the hand pointing dorsally.

**Symphysis** Type of amphiarthrotic joint between bones, e.g., the vertebrae or the two pubes or ischia.

**Synarthrosis** A joint in which there is little or no movement, e.g., between skull bones.

**Testis(es)** The primary reproductive organ of the male where sperm are produced and hormones involved in controlling reproductive activities and influencing secondary sex characteristics are synthesized and secreted.

**Thoracic cavity** Cranial subdivision of the coelom created by the diaphragm. It is compartmentalized into the pleural and pericardial cavities.

**Transverse or cross section** a section that passes perpendicular to the longitudinal axis of the body or organ. There are an infinite number of transverse sections.

**True vocal cords** Pair of folds posterior to the false vocal cords at the cranial end of the larynx. Involved in sound production.

**Tuberculum** Smooth, concave projection distal to the capitulum of rib that articulates with the transverse process of a vertebra.

**Tuberosity** Roughened projection on the bone surface where muscles insert.

**Urogenital sinus** Space in the female reproductive tract distal to the vagina where the vagina (vaginal orifice) and the urethra (urethral orifice) open. It continues to the outside where it opens by way of the urogenital aperature.

**Uterine horns** Enlarged distal portions of the oviduct where developing fetuses are carried.

**Uterus** Fused uterine horns result in the body of the uterus. During birth, kittens pass through the uterus.

**Vagina** Portion of the female reproductive tract that receives the penis of the male during copulation.

**Vas deferens** Tube leading from the epididymis and conveying sperm to the urethra.

**Vein** Blood vessel that carries blood toward the heart.

**Vena cava** Major veins that delivers blood directly to the right atrium.

**Ventral** Directional term meaning toward the belly of an animal.

# References

Clemente, Carmine D. 1985. *Gray's Anatomy of the Human Body.* Philadelphia, Lea and Febiger.

Gilbert, Stephen G. 1987. *Pictorial Anatomy of the Cat.* 2nd ed. Seattle, University of Washington Press.

O'Brien, Stephen J. 1997. *The Family Line (The Human–Cat Connection).* National Geographic, 191(6): 77-85.

Reighard, Jacob and H. S. Jennings. 1935. *Anatomy of the Cat.* 3rd ed., revised by R. Elliot. New York, Holt, Rinehart and Winston.

Tortora, Gerard J. and Sandra R. Grabowski. 1996. *Principles of Anatomy and Physiology.* 8th ed. New York, Harpers Collins College Publishers.

Ulmer, Martin J, Robert E. Haupt, and Ellis A Hicks. 1971. *Anatomy of the Cat: Atlas and Dissection Guide).* New York, Harper and Row, Publishers.

Walker, Warren F. and Dominique Homberger. 1993. *A Study of the Cat (with reference to human beings).* 5th ed. Orlando, Saunders College Publishing.

Weichert, Charles K. 1951. *Anatomy of the Chordates.* New York, McGraw Hill Book Company, Inc.

# Index